Dr James Napier

CCEA | A2

BIOLOGY

2nd Edition

COLOURPOINT
EDUCATIONAL

Print ISBN: 978 1 78073 100 1

eBook ISBN: 978 1 78073 294 7

Second Edition
Fifth Impression, 2022

Layout and design: April Sky Design
Printed by GPS Colour Graphics Ltd, Belfast

COLOURPOINT
EDUCATIONAL

Colourpoint Educational
An imprint of Colourpoint Creative Ltd
Colourpoint House
Jubilee Business Park
21 Jubilee Road
Newtownards
County Down
Northern Ireland
BT23 4YH

Tel: 028 9182 0505
E-mail: sales@colourpoint.co.uk
Web site: www.colourpointeducational.com

The Author

Dr James Napier is a former teacher in a Northern Ireland grammar school. He has written and co-written a number of Biology and Science textbooks supporting the work of students and teachers. He has also published a range of popular Science books in the areas of Genetics and Evolution. His 'non-science' charity books have raised significant amounts of money for cancer and mental health charities.

Acknowledgements

The author would like to thank Wesley and Rachel and all their colleagues at Colourpoint. A special thanks to Dr Terence Henry for his invaluable feedback, advice and diligence.

Thanks also to Dr Catherine Napier and Dr Kelly Moffitt for providing their cutting-edge knowledge and expertise in the fields of immunity and gene technology.

Thanks to Jacqueline Gray, Neal McKnight and Ronnie Irvine for their ideas and photographs.

Publisher's Note: This book has been written to help students preparing for the A2 Level Biology specification from CCEA. While Colourpoint Educational and the author have taken every care in its production, we are not able to guarantee that the book is completely error-free. Additionally, while the book has been written to closely match the CCEA specification, it is the responsibility of each candidate to satisfy themselves that they have fully met the requirements of the CCEA specification prior to sitting an exam set by that body. For this reason, and because specifications change with time, we strongly advise every candidate to avail of a qualified teacher and to check the contents of the most recent specification for themselves prior to the exam. Colourpoint Creative Ltd therefore cannot be held responsible for any errors or omissions in this book or any consequences thereof.

Health and Safety: This book describes practical tasks or experiments that are either useful or required for the course. These must only be carried out in a school setting under the supervision of a qualified teacher. It is the responsibility of the school to ensure that students are provided with a safe environment in which to carry out the work.

CONTENTS

A2 1 Physiology, Coordination and Control, and Ecosystems

A2 2 Biochemistry, Genetics and Evolutionary Trends

Unit A2 1:
Physiology, Coordination and Control, and Ecosystems

Chapter 1 – Homeostasis and the Kidney

Homeostasis

Mammalian tissue is essentially made up of a collection of cells bathed in a fluid medium or 'extracellular' fluid (tissue fluid). The composition of this fluid (and consequentially the **blood** due to the permeable nature of the capillary walls) must be kept **constant** in terms of factors such as water and ion content, temperature, pH and oxygen levels, **irrespective of the external conditions** outside the body.

Homeostasis is the maintenance of constant or steady state conditions within the body. Most homeostatic responses have three basic features:

- A **control system** with **sensors (receptors)** which provides information allowing the **monitoring** of the factor being controlled. The receptors can be in the brain or localised throughout the body. However, the monitor (control centre) is usually in the brain.

- If the receptors show a departure from normal levels (the **set point**) for the factor being controlled, for example temperature, then a **corrective mechanism** brings about the changes required to return the factor to its normal level. For example, if mammals overheat, the corrective measures can include sweating and the vasodilation of capillaries in the skin.

- The corrective mechanism involves a **negative feedback** system. *Negative* feedback occurs as the return of the factor being controlled to its normal level (set point) causes the corrective measures to be turned off. This prevents over-correction. In our example of temperature regulation, the stimulation of the sweat glands and the degree of vasodilation of blood capillaries is reduced as blood (body) temperature returns to normal.

Communication between the sensors/receptors and the monitor (and between the monitor and the effectors that bring about the corrective response) can be by **nervous** or **hormonal** control. The control of temperature, as described on page 5, is primarily under nervous control, whereas control of blood glucose levels is under hormonal control.

Homeostatic control of mammalian body systems is essential for many reasons including:

- providing the optimum conditions for enzyme reactions in terms of pH and temperature.
- avoiding osmotic problems in cells and in body fluids.

While mammals have complex and effective homeostatic controls, many other animals have simpler controls that are less able to keep the internal environment constant, for example, the body temperature of insects usually varies with the external environment. Consequently, many species of less complex animals avoid large swings in body conditions by living in an environment where the external environment is relatively constant, such as the sea.

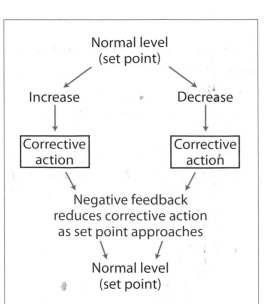

The general principles of homeostatic control

The kidney

A major homeostatic organ in mammals is the kidney. The kidney has two very important functions:

Excretion is the removal of the toxic waste of metabolism. The main toxic waste product excreted by the kidneys is **urea**, a nitrogenous waste produced during the breakdown of excess amino acids (and nucleic acids) in the liver. Other toxic products are also excreted by the kidneys, for example creatinine, a waste product produced from the breakdown of creatine phosphate (a molecule important in ATP synthesis) in muscles.

Osmoregulation is the control of the water potential of body fluids. The kidney helps regulate the water potential of the blood through controlling both the volume and concentration of urine produced.

The structure of the urinary (excretory) system

Note: Traditionally the body system including the kidneys, ureters, bladder and urethra has been called the excretory system. However, this is perhaps not the best term as excretion is also carried out by other parts of the body (for example, CO_2 is excreted from the lungs); consequently, many textbooks now refer to it as the urinary system.

The following figure shows the urinary (excretory) system. Blood travelling through the aorta and renal artery reaches the kidney at the high pressures required for filtration. In essence, the kidney operates as a complex filter, keeping useful products in the blood and eliminating excretory products and excess water.

Filtered blood leaves the kidney via the renal vein whereas the excretory products and excess water pass into the ureter as urine, which takes it to the bladder for storage. Sphincter muscles in the base of the bladder control the release of the urine, which exits the body through the urethra.

Kidney structure

A section through a kidney shows that it contains two main zones (regions) of tissue:

- The **cortex** is the outer dark region immediately under the thin covering layer (capsule). — middle
- The **medulla** is the inner lighter region. The medulla is subdivided into a number of pyramids whose apices extend down into a large central cavity called the **pelvis**.

The **functional unit** of the kidney is the **nephron**. There are over one million nephrons in each kidney – each operating as an individual filter. As seen in the diagram below, the nephron originates and ends in the cortex, with a long central region (the loop of Henlé) extending down into the medulla. Many nephrons join with a collecting duct, which also extends down through the medulla.

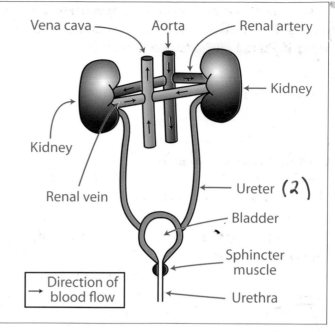

The urinary (excretory) system

The structure of the nephron

The nephron originates as a cup-shaped **Bowman's capsule** (also called the **renal capsule**). Each Bowman's capsule is supplied with blood from an **afferent arteriole**

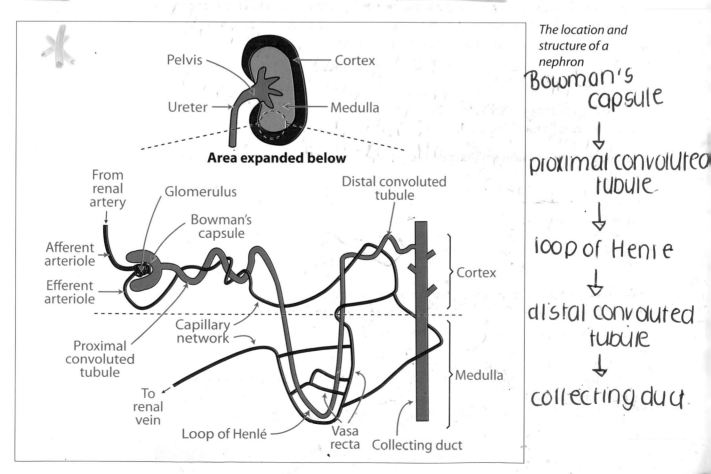

The location and structure of a nephron

Bowman's capsule
↓
proximal convoluted tubule
↓
loop of Henle
↓
distal convoluted tubule
↓
collecting duct

(a branch of the renal artery) and the blood leaves through an **efferent arteriole**. Within the 'cup' of the capsule, the arteriole branches to form a tightly coiled knot of capillaries called the **glomerulus** – capillaries which subsequently unite before forming the efferent arteriole.

After leaving the Bowman's capsule, the efferent arteriole branches to form a capillary network (the **vasa recta**) that remains closely associated with the rest of the nephron.

In the nephron itself, the Bowman's capsule extends into a coiled tube called the **proximal convoluted tubule** (proximal = first; convoluted = coiled). The proximal convoluted tubule extends into the **loop of Henlé** which dips down into the medulla of the kidney. The descending part of the loop is, unsurprisingly, called the descending limb. The loop of Henlé then bends sharply and returns back up through the medulla (the ascending limb) to reach the cortex again. At this stage it becomes the **distal convoluted tubule**. The distal convoluted tubule (and the distal convoluted tubules from many other nephrons) joins a **collecting duct**. The collecting ducts converge at the base of the pelvis and empty their contents (now called urine) into the ureter which takes the urine to the bladder.

Kidney function 1 (excretion – producing urine)

Kidney (and nephron) function involves two main processes:

- **Ultrafiltration** – The filtration of plasma and substances below a certain size into the Bowman's capsule (nephron).
- **Reabsorption** – As ultrafiltration is based purely on molecular size (and not whether products are useful or not), it is essential that filtered useful products are selectively reabsorbed back into the bloodstream from the nephron.

Ultrafiltration

Blood entering the glomerulus has a **high hydrostatic pressure** for a number of reasons: *why?*

- The **short distance** from the heart that the blood travels down the aorta and into the renal artery before branching into the kidney arterioles.
- The fact that the afferent arteriole of each glomerulus is **wider** than its efferent arteriole.
- The **coiling of the capillaries** in the glomerulus further restricts blood flow therefore increasing pressure.

The high hydrostatic pressure produced forces the smaller components in the blood (glucose, amino acids, salts, water and urea) out of the capillaries and into the Bowman's capsule. However, the larger components of the blood, including blood cells and plasma proteins, are too large to pass through into the nephron.

The process of ultrafiltration is aided by the structure of the capillary walls of the glomerulus and the lining of the Bowman's capsule itself.

As seen in the following diagram, the single layer of **squamous** (flattened) **endothelial cells** that form the walls of glomerular capillaries contain small **pores** and the Bowman's capsule is lined with specialised cells known as **podocytes**. Podocytes have extensions in two planes that allow the filtered material to pass through easily. It is the **basement membrane** (separating the capillary and podocytes) that is the **effective filter** and determines which components of the blood enter the Bowman's capsule – it is the basement membrane that prevents the blood cells and plasma proteins from leaving the blood.

Note: The basement membrane is an extracellular matrix (gel) formed of many different substances including proteins. It is effectively a molecular sieve.

In effect, each of the **three layers** separating the blood in the capillary and the inside of the Bowman's capsule is specialised through either being porous (capillary endothelial cells and podocytes) or through acting as a filter (basement membrane).

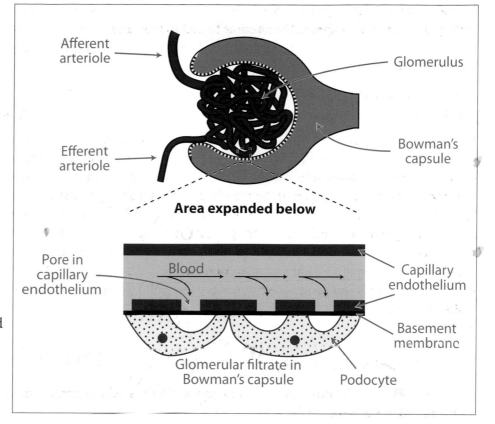

The site of ultrafiltration

The **glomerular filtrate** (the substances that pass through the basement membrane and enter the Bowman's capsule) is similar to blood (except for the plasma proteins and blood cells that are too large to penetrate the membrane).

Note: Apart from the podocytes lining the Bowman's capsule, the remaining epithelial cells lining the nephron (and the collecting duct) are cuboidal (cube-shaped) epithelial cells.

The filtration force – Ultrafiltration is a necessary process in kidney function. However, the hydrostatic pressure forcing through water and small molecules is not the only force involved. In terms of water potential, it is important to compare the forces on each side of the membrane. For filtration to occur, the water potential within the glomerular capillaries (blood plasma) must exceed the water potential within the Bowman's capsule (glomerular filtrate), ie the glomerular filtrate must have a more negative water potential. How is this difference in water potential produced?

Remember that water potential has two components – pressure potential and solute potential. The hydrostatic pressure (**pressure potential**) of the blood is much greater than the hydrostatic pressure (back pressure) created by the filtrate in the nephron for reasons listed above.

The **solute potential** is represented by the plasma proteins, as there are plasma proteins in the blood in the glomerular capillaries but not in the filtrate. The filtrate has a less negative solute potential than the blood in the glomerulus. Therefore, although the difference in solute potential **opposes** filtration, this effect is insignificant when compared to the differences in hydrostatic pressure across the basement membrane;

a difference that very strongly promotes filtration. Consequently, the **net filtration pressure** causes fluid to move from the glomerular capillaries into the Bowman's capsule.

Worked example

In this example the water potential of the blood plasma in the glomerulus is higher, ie more positive or less negative (2.0 kPa) compared to the water potential of the glomerular filtrate in the Bowman's capsule (0.7 kPa), therefore producing the net filtration force or pressure (+ 1.3 kPa) that forces liquids and small molecules through the basement membrane.

Blood plasma (in glomerulus)	Glomerular filtrate (in Bowman's capsule)
$\psi_s = -3.5$ kPa (due to presence of plasma proteins) $\psi_p = 5.5$ kPa (high hydrostatic pressure)	$\psi_s = -0.7$ kPa (less negative due to absence of plasma proteins) $\psi_p = 1.4$ kPa (low hydrostatic pressure)
$\psi_{plasma} = 2.0$ kPa	$\psi_{filtrate} = 0.7$ kPa
Net filtration force = +1.3 kPa	

Reabsorption

Useful blood products temporarily lost to the glomerular filtrate are reabsorbed back into the blood, mainly as the filtrate passes along the **proximal convoluted tubule**. **Glucose** and **amino acids** – small enough to pass through the basement membrane but too valuable to be lost in the urine – are **selectively reabsorbed** by **facilitated diffusion** and **active transport**.

Note: The term selectively reabsorbed is used as toxic substances such as urea are not actively reabsorbed but (mainly) remain in the filtrate.

As glucose, amino acids and some salts are actively reabsorbed into the blood the osmotic effect created causes over **70%** of the **water** in the filtrate to re-enter the blood capillaries passively by **osmosis**. **Small plasma proteins** which may have passed through the basement membrane in the glomerular filtrate are reabsorbed by **pinocytosis**.

Note: The reabsorption of glucose, amino acids and salts reduces the solute potential in both the (reabsorbing) epithelial cells of the tubule and the blood in the capillaries, thus creating the osmotic gradient required for the reabsorption of water.

The table below shows relative values of some of the substances filtered into the nephron and subsequently reabsorbed in the proximal tubule.

Substance	Amount in blood plasma / %	Amount filtered into glomerular filtrate / %	Amount reabsorbed back into blood in proximal convoluted tubule / %
Large plasma proteins	100	0	N/A
Glucose	100	100	100
Amino acids	100	100	100
Urea	100	100	< 50 (by diffusion)

Note 1: Although urea (being a toxic metabolic waste) is not selectively reabsorbed, some urea passes from the nephron back into the blood by diffusion. Theoretically up to 50% can diffuse back into the blood.

Note 2: The glucose and amino acids can be absorbed by **facilitated diffusion** as long as the concentration gradient permits. **Active transport** is necessary to ensure that all the glucose is reabsorbed from the nephron back into the capillary network.

The epithelial cells of the proximal convoluted tubule have high levels of metabolic activity and continually carry out energy-demanding processes such as active transport. Consequently, they are highly adapted for this role as seen in the diagram below.

By the time the filtrate reaches the end of the proximal tubule, it will have no glucose or amino acids present as they all will have been reabsorbed. Although some urea diffuses back into the blood by diffusion along the length of the proximal convoluted tubule, as noted in the table, the **concentration of urea** in the filtrate increases along its length due to the reabsorption of water. At the end of the proximal convoluted tubule, the filtrate is **isotonic** with the blood plasma.

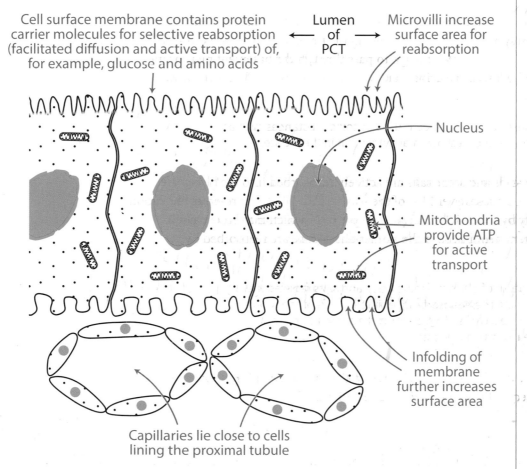

Cell surface membrane contains protein carrier molecules for selective reabsorption (facilitated diffusion and active transport) of, for example, glucose and amino acids

Lumen of PCT

Microvilli increase surface area for reabsorption

Nucleus

Mitochondria provide ATP for active transport

Infolding of membrane further increases surface area

Capillaries lie close to cells lining the proximal tubule

Adaptations of the epithelial cells lining the proximal tubule

Further regulation of blood composition takes place in the **distal convoluted tubule**. The pH and ionic composition of the blood in the capillaries surrounding the tubule are adjusted and some toxic substances, for example, creatinine (a byproduct from muscle metabolism), are secreted from the blood into the filtrate for disposal.

Kidney function 2 (osmoregulation)

Osmoregulation is a homeostatic process that controls water balance in the body. It does this through controlling water balance in the blood; consequently the water content of the tissue fluid and the cells is also controlled.

The collecting duct is where the water regulation takes place. Although **most water** is reabsorbed in the proximal convoluted tubule (and some from the descending limb of the loop of Henlé – see page opposite), the process is passive and the exact amount of water reabsorbed back into the blood cannot be controlled. However, reabsorption in the collecting ducts can be controlled by varying the permeability of the collecting duct walls – this is where the fine control of water balance takes place. The **antidiuretic hormone (ADH)** is crucial in this process as it can control the degree of permeability of the collecting duct walls.

The role of the antidiuretic (ADH) hormone

ADH is *produced* in the **hypothalamus** (part of the brain just above the junction with the spinal cord) and then secreted into the **posterior lobe** of the **pituitary body** where it is *stored*. The solute potential of the blood is monitored by **osmoreceptors** (specialised cells) in the **hypothalamus**.

↳ found in brain

What happens if the blood becomes too concentrated? Blood can become too concentrated, ie a more negative solute potential, for many reasons. For example, sweating after exercise or on a hot day, not drinking enough water or eating a very salty meal. If this happens:

- the solute potential of the blood becomes *more* **negative** and this is detected by the osmoreceptors in the hypothalamus.
- the posterior lobe of the pituitary body releases *more* **ADH** into the blood.
- this causes the walls of the distal convoluted tubules and the collecting ducts to become *more* **permeable** – special channel proteins (aquaporins) open which helps make the walls of the collecting ducts more permeable.
- therefore *more* **water is reabsorbed** from the collecting ducts back into the blood.
- the net result is that the solute potential of the blood returns to normal (becomes less negative) and a smaller volume of *more* **concentrated (hypertonic) urine** is produced.
- this process exemplifies **negative feedback**. As the blood concentration changes it sets in train a process (as described above) that returns the solute potential back to normal; as the blood concentration returns to normal the release of ADH reduces, returning to normal levels.

What if the blood is too dilute? This is most likely to happen when drinking (hypotonic) liquid. In this situation the opposite happens: the blood develops a higher solute potential (becomes less concentrated) and this is detected by the osmoreceptors in the hypothalamus, *less* ADH is released, the walls of the collecting ducts become *less* permeable and *less* water is reabsorbed back into the blood (large quantities of **dilute (hypotonic) urine** are produced).

The role of the loop of Henlé

The loop of Henlé is the part of the nephron that enables mammals to produce a **hypertonic urine** and plays a significant role in water reabsorption from the collecting ducts.

Structure of the loop of Henlé – The walls of the **descending limb** are thin and permeable to water. The **ascending limb** walls are much thicker and impermeable to water.

> **Note:** The descending limb is the part of the loop of Henlé that drops down from the cortex and extends down into the medulla. The ascending limb is the section that extends back up into the cortex again.

Function of the loop of Henlé *couter current multiplier effect !*

The **ascending limb** secretes Na^+ ions and Cl^- ions into the medulla. This process involves active transport of these ions. Consequently, sodium chloride (salt) builds up in the interstitial fluid in the medulla, creating a very negative solute potential. As a result of the ions leaving the ascending limb, the filtrate in it becomes progressively more dilute and is **hypotonic** by the time it reaches the top of the ascending limb.

The net result of the very negative water potential in the medulla, caused by the high concentration of sodium chloride, and the permeability of the **descending limb** walls, is that water is osmotically removed along the length of the descending limb. Therefore, the filtrate in the descending limb becomes progressively more concentrated with distance down the limb (aided by sodium and chloride ions entering the descending limb by diffusion) until at the very bottom it is **hypertonic** to the blood.

thin permeable D. ↓   A ↑ *thick impermeable cuboidal epithelial cells.*

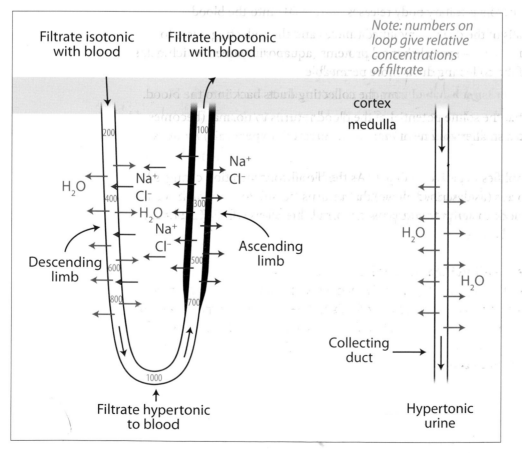

The role of the loop of Henlé

The main function of the loop of Henlé is to create the very concentrated interstitial fluid in the medulla, a feature which facilitates the osmotic removal of water from the collecting ducts (which also pass through the medulla.)

Note 1: The cuboidal epithelial cells in the ascending limb are rich in mitochondria. The mitochondria provide the ATP necessary to pump the sodium and chloride ions into the medulla.

Note 2: Water that leaves the descending limb by osmosis enters the capillary network (vasa recta) and is removed from the medulla, therefore having little effect on the solute potential of the interstitial fluid.

Note 3: The osmotic differences between the descending and ascending limbs at any one level are small but the cumulative effect over the length of the limbs (depth of medulla) is significant. This, together with the filtrates in the limbs travelling in opposite directions, is why the process is described as the **countercurrent multiplier** effect.

Note 4: There is a positive correlation between the length of the loop of Henlé and the ability to reabsorb water and concentrate the liquid in the collecting duct (liquid that will become urine) and conserve water in a species. The longer the loop of Henlé, the more water that can be reabsorbed. This is largely because a longer loop allows the medulla to have an even more negative water potential.

The kidneys are a very effective filter but are equally effective in osmoregulation. All the blood in the circulatory system passes through the kidneys every five minutes with over 99% of the water filtered being reabsorbed with less than 1% ending up as urine.

Exam questions

1. The diagram below shows the site of ultrafiltration in a kidney. Make a copy of the diagram.

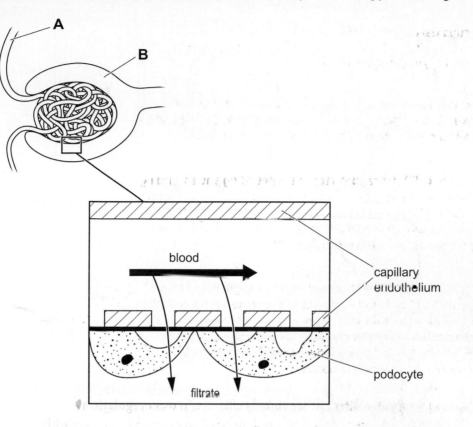

(a) (i) Identify structures A and B shown on the diagram. [2]

    (ii) On your copy of the diagram, label and name the structure which is the effective filter in ultrafiltration. [1]

(b) The table below shows the value of water potential components in both the blood plasma and the renal filtrate (in the nephron) at the site of ultrafiltration. The pressure potential, Ψ_p, is a measure of hydrostatic pressure. All units are in kPa.

Blood plasma	Renal filtrate
$\Psi_s = -3.5$	$\Psi_s = -0.5$
$\Psi_p = 6.5$	$\Psi_p = 1.2$
$\Psi_{plasma} =$	$\Psi_{filtrate} =$

Using the information provided, calculate the net filtration force. (Show your working out.) [2]

(c) In healthy individuals, protein does not normally appear in the urine.

One indicator of high blood pressure is the presence of protein in the urine. Explain the presence of protein in the urine in someone with high blood pressure. [1]

Question taken from CCEA's Biology Assessment Unit A2 1, Physiology and Ecosystems, January 2013, © CCEA 2017

2. The diagram below is of a mammalian nephron and associated structures.

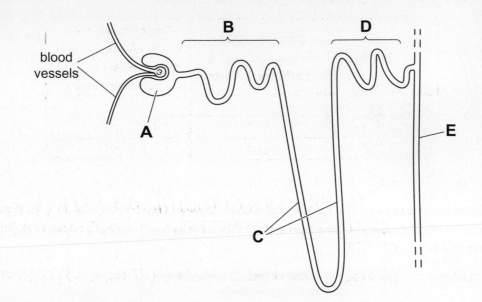

(a) (i) Identify the parts labelled D and E. [2]

Reabsorption of substances takes place along the regions labelled B–E.

(ii) Which two letters correspond to the regions in which most water is absorbed? [1]

(b) The proximal tubule is the main site of reabsorption of solutes. The diagram below represents the cells lining the proximal convoluted tubule.

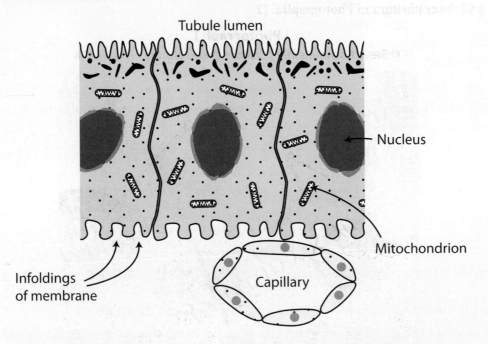

For copyright reasons this diagram has replaced the diagram in the CCEA past paper.

(i) Describe and explain two distinct ways in which the cells of the proximal tubule are adapted for the function of selective reabsorption. [2]

The table below summarises differences in the concentration of some substances in the blood plasma and the renal filtrate at the end of the proximal convoluted tubule.

Substance	Concentration in blood plasma / arbitrary units	Concentration in renal filtrate at end of proximal tubule / arbitrary units
Large proteins	12	0
Glucose	0.15	0
Urea	0.04	0.09

(ii) Explain these results. [3]

(c) In mammals, there is a strong positive correlation between the length of the loop of Henlé and the degree of aridity (dryness) of the environment that a mammal, such as the desert rat, inhabits. Explain this relationship. [2]

Question adapted from CCEA's Biology Assessment Unit A2 1, Physiology and Ecosystems, May 2013, © CCEA 2016

3. (a) Photograph I is an electron micrograph of a section through the wall of a proximal convoluted tubule in the kidney.

   (i) Identify the structures labelled A and B.

   (ii) Explain precisely the role of the structures labelled A in the proximal convoluted tubule. [2]

(b) (i) Name the type of epithelial cells shown in the electron micrograph. [1]

   (ii) Give two differences in structure between the endothelium lining the glomerular capillaries and the epithelium in Photograph I. [2]

Photograph I
© Steve Gschmeissner / Science Photo Library / P550/0208

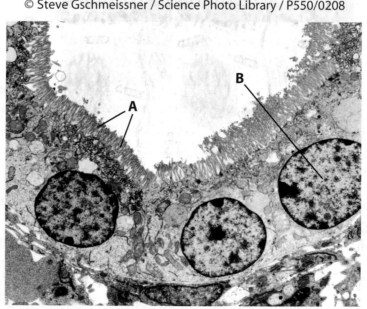

Question taken from CCEA's Biology Assessment Unit A2 1, Physiology and Ecosystems, May 2015, © CCEA 2017

6. *Quality of written communication is awarded a maximum of 2 marks in this section.*

   The kidney is a homeostatic organ important in excretion and osmoregulation.

   (a) Describe and explain the processes of ultrafiltration and reabsorption in excretion in the kidney. [11]

   (b) Using osmoregulation in the kidney as an example, explain the term homeostasis and outline the essential components of homeostatic mechanisms. [5]

   Quality of written communication. [2]

Question taken from CCEA's Biology Assessment Unit A2 1, Physiology and Ecosystems, January 2014, © CCEA 2017

Chapter 2 – Immunity

Pathogens and immunity

Most microorganisms are harmless or even beneficial (for example, the many types of bacteria and fungi involved in decay and decomposition are essential for life on Earth). However, a small percentage of microorganisms, including some bacteria, fungi, protoctists and viruses (although technically viruses are not classified as living organisms) can cause disease or be **pathogenic**.

If a **pathogen** gains entry to the body it could cause significant harm or even death, therefore the body's **first line of defence** against pathogens is to try to **prevent entry**.

If pathogens do enter the body, the subsequent defence mechanisms can be grouped into two types:

- **Non-specific** – These defence mechanisms are not specific to individual types of pathogens. **Phagocytosis** is an example of a non-specific defence mechanism.
- **Specific immune response** – This type of response does distinguish between individual pathogens and the response is tailored to the pathogen involved. Specific immune responses take **longer to work** but tend to provide **long term immunity**. Specific immune responses involve **lymphocytes**, a specialised type of white blood cell.

Natural barriers to pathogen entry

Barriers preventing the entry of pathogens in humans include:

- **an outer protective covering (skin)** – The skin provides a tough physical barrier that most pathogens cannot penetrate. The skin only ceases to be an effective barrier to most pathogens if it is punctured, for example, a wound or cut, or if it is not in its normal healthy condition.

- the enzyme **lysozyme** – is contained in many body secretions including **tears**, **saliva** and **sweat**. Lysozyme is anti-bacterial as it is able to digest (hydrolyse) bacteria cell walls. Tears can also wash away debris and pathogens from the front of the eye, which is delicate and easily damaged.

- **epithelial lining** covered in **mucus**, such as in the respiratory tract – The mucus traps pathogens (and other foreign particles) and prevents them penetrating the underlying membranes. **Cilia**, tiny hairs that line the respiratory tract, sweep the mucus and its trapped pathogens, back up the trachea.

- **hydrochloric acid** in the **stomach** – This kills most pathogens that are in the food we eat or the liquids we drink. It is effective as it provides a very low pH that denatures the enzymes of the pathogens.

However, despite these (and other) barriers to pathogen entry, many do invade our body. The next line of defence is **phagocytosis**.

Phagocytosis

Phagocytosis is non-specific but has the advantage of being rapid. Phagocytosis is carried out by a number of types of white blood cell, collectively known as **phagocytes**.

As part of an **inflammatory response** following infection, the capillaries in the area affected become leaky, allowing plasma to seep into the surrounding areas. Inflamed parts of the body tend to become swollen with phagocytes, dead pathogens and cell debris, collectively known as pus. Inflamed areas appear red due to the increased blood flow to that area.

> **Note:** Inflammation also involves the affected part of the body becoming hot (as well as swollen). The raised temperature helps reduce infection by denaturing enzymes in the pathogen.

Phagocytes including **polymorphs** (the most common and first to arrive) and **macrophages** (develop from monocytes in the blood, they are larger but much longer lived than polymorphs) are able to squeeze through the capillary walls and engulf the pathogenic bacteria and surrounding cell debris at the site of the infection. The process of phagocytosis is summarised below:

- The phagocyte moves towards the pathogen, **attracted by the chemicals** it produces.

- As it does so the **phagocyte membrane invaginates** to begin to enclose the pathogen.

Phagocytosis

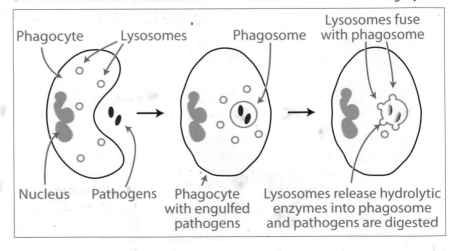

Phagocyte   Lysosomes   Phagosome   Lysosomes fuse with phagosome

Nucleus   Pathogens   Phagocyte with engulfed pathogens   Lysosomes release hydrolytic enzymes into phagosome and pathogens are digested

- As the pathogen is **engulfed**, the invaginated phagocyte membrane forms a vesicle (**phagosome**) around the pathogen.
- Lysosomes move towards the phagosome and fuse with it.
- Hydrolytic **enzymes** within the lysosomes are released into the phagosome, onto the pathogen. These enzymes **hydrolyse** the pathogen.
- The soluble digested products are absorbed into the cytoplasm of the phagocyte.

The specific immune response

Specific immune responses are associated with **lymphocyte** white blood cells. The responses are triggered by the body being able to recognise 'foreign' cells, linked to the concept of self and non-self tissue.

Self and non-self – Foreign (non-self) cells are cells not recognised by the body. If detected they will produce an immune response. In reality, it is specific molecules, or clusters of molecules, that form part of the cell surface membrane that are recognised as foreign. These molecules are often protein, but can be other substances, for example, polysaccharides, glycoprotein and glycolipid, and are collectively referred to as **antigens**. Different pathogens have different antigens, consequently the immune response is specific to these antigens. This specific response is due to the lymphocyte having a receptor on its cell surface membrane that is *complementary* in shape to the antigen. Antigen and lymphocyte fit together like substrate and enzyme in the lock and key model of enzyme action.

> **Note:** Antigens can be defined as chemicals/molecules capable of producing a specific immune response

How do lymphocytes know what is self and non-self? – There are many million different types of lymphocytes, each having receptors with a complementary shape to a potential antigen. In the foetus, these lymphocytes frequently make contact with other foetal (self) cells. Lymphocytes that are complementary in shape with foetal cells are 'switched off' so by the time the baby is born the functional lymphocytes that remain are those that are not complementary to self cells. However, because there are many million functional lymphocytes remaining there are only a few of each type. This is part of the reason why the specific immune response is relatively **slow**.

Types of lymphocyte – There are two types of lymphocyte, each of which has a specific but different type of response. The two types, **B-lymphocytes** (**B-cells**) and **T-lymphocytes** (**T-cells**) are summarised in the following table.

Type of lymphocyte	Where formed	Site of development (maturation)	Name of immune response	Nature of immune response
B-lymphocytes	Formed from stem cells in the bone marrow	Mature in bone marrow	**Antibody-mediated** (humoral) immunity	Produce **antibodies** which respond to antigens found in **body fluids** (for example, blood and tissue fluid). Respond usually to bacterial or viral infection.
T-lymphocytes	Formed from stem cells in the bone marrow	Mature in thymus gland (lymph gland in the neck)	**Cell-mediated** immunity	Respond to antigens attached to **body cells**. Respond usually to body cells affected by viral infection.

Lymphocyte activation – Once infection occurs, a specific immune response requires an antigen to come into contact with its complementary lymphocyte – a process that may take some time due to the small numbers involved. When this happens the lymphocytes become **sensitised** or **activated**. However, the process is different in the two types of lymphocyte.

In **B-lymphocytes**, certain genes are activated to set in motion a process that eventually leads to the production of **antibodies**. In **T-lymphocytes**, a number of types of **T-cell** are produced, each type having different roles in the battle against infection. In both B and T-cells, sensitised lymphocytes are **cloned** (involving division by **mitosis**). The products of the cloned B and T-cells will be investigated in the next two sections covering cell-mediated and antibody-mediated immunity.

Cell-mediated immunity

In an immune response, the production of **T-cells** is stimulated by the body's **own** cells that have been changed due to the presence of non-self material within them. These cells are referred to as **antigen-presenting cells**. Examples include:

- macrophages (phagocytes) that have engulfed and broken down a pathogen and **'present'** some of the pathogen's antigens on their own cell surface membrane.

- any type of **body cell** that has been invaded by a virus – again some of the viral antigens are presented on the cell surface membrane of the body cell (remember, viruses cannot live on their own, they must live inside other cells).

- cancer (tumour) cells, as many types of cancer cells present abnormal antigens on their cell surface membranes.

The **antigen-presenting** cells bring about a response as summarised by the diagram below.

The cloned T-cells produced from this response can develop into:

- **killer T-cells** – Killer (cytotoxic) T-cells destroy infected cells by attaching to the antigens on the cell surface membrane of the infected or abnormal cell and destroying it by direct enzyme action.

- **helper T-cells** – These cells stimulate other cells involved in the immune response, for example, they stimulate B-cells to divide (and produce the plasma cells that produce antibodies – see next section) and promote the process of phagocytosis through their effect on phagocytes.

The development of a range of T-cells in cell-mediated immunity

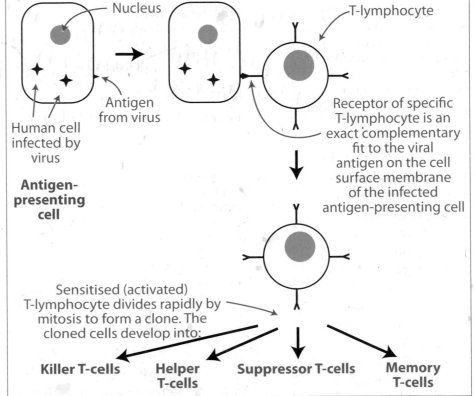

Nucleus

T-lymphocyte

Antigen from virus

Human cell infected by virus

Antigen-presenting cell

Receptor of specific T-lymphocyte is an exact complementary fit to the viral antigen on the cell surface membrane of the infected antigen-presenting cell

Sensitised (activated) T-lymphocyte divides rapidly by mitosis to form a clone. The cloned cells develop into:

Killer T-cells   **Helper T-cells**   **Suppressor T-cells**   **Memory T-cells**

Phagocytosis is a slow process without the activating role of the helper T-cells. They also attach special chemicals (**opsonins**) to the pathogens that mark them out for the attention of phagocytes. Helper T-cells also secrete the protein interferon that helps limit the ability of viruses to replicate.

- **suppressor T-cells** (also known as regulatory T-cells) – These cells 'suppress' the immune response of other immune cells when required. Suppressor T-cells switch off the immune response after invading microbes and infected cells have been destroyed. They are also important in preventing autoimmune responses, the situation where the immune system attacks 'self' cells in the body.

- **memory T-cells** – These cells circulate in body fluids and can respond rapidly to future infection by the same pathogen (presenting the same antigen(s)). If a subsequent infection occurs, as the memory cells are already sensitised, they can very rapidly produce a large clone of T-lymphocytes.

Note 1: Suppressor T-cells deactivate the immune response of both B-and T-cells.

Note 2: It is thought that the onset of Type 1 diabetes, an autoimmune condition, is linked to reduced numbers of a type of suppressor T-cells, resulting in a cell-mediated attack on the insulin-producing cells in the pancreas.

Note: Interferon is a group of proteins referred to as **cytokines** which regulate the immune system through the stimulation or damping of its different components.

Antibody-mediated immunity

This type of response targets microorganisms (usually bacteria or viruses) that are found in the **body fluids** (for example, blood and tissue fluid), rather than in body cells. As its name suggests, antibody-mediated immunity defends the body through the production and action of **antibodies**.

The development of plasma cells and memory cells in antibody-mediated immunity

Note: Antibodies can be defined as globular proteins which are complementary to specific antigens and which can react with the antigens (microbes) leading to their destruction.

Specific antigens sensitise specific **B-lymphocytes** that have receptors that match the pathogen's antigens. Therefore, following infection by a particular pathogen, a particular type (or types) of B-lymphocyte becomes cloned. In common with sensitised T-cells, sensitised B-cells produce different types of cell, in the case of B-cells, plasma cells and memory cells.

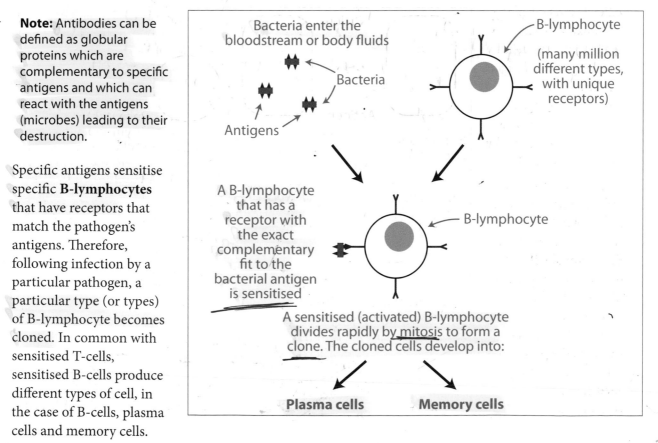

Bacteria enter the bloodstream or body fluids

Bacteria

Antigens

B-lymphocyte
(many million different types, with unique receptors)

A B-lymphocyte that has a receptor with the exact complementary fit to the bacterial antigen is sensitised

B-lymphocyte

A sensitised (activated) B-lymphocyte divides rapidly by mitosis to form a clone. The cloned cells develop into:

Plasma cells   Memory cells

However, most cloned B-cells become plasma cells. **Plasma cells** are short lived (a few days) but each produces very large numbers (many millions) of antibodies. The antibodies neutralise the pathogens as a consequence of **antigen-antibody reactions**.

The action of antibodies – The antibodies produced as a consequence of a specific antibody-mediated response will have a complementary shape to the antigens of the invading bacteria (or other pathogens). The antibodies latch on to the bacterial antigens clumping the bacteria together. Typically, the build up of antibodies in the body fluids will enable a sufficient number to be present to immobilise the bacteria causing their **agglutination** or clumping as an **antigen-antibody complex**. In due course the antigen-antibody complex (clump of bacteria and antibodies) is engulfed by polymorphs and other phagocytes.

The action of antibodies in forming an antigen-antibody complex

Antibodies can defend against infection by other methods as well as the process described in the diagram on the right. Other methods include the destruction of the invading cells directly. Antibodies can also act as opsonins by attaching to pathogens and marking them for phagocytosis.

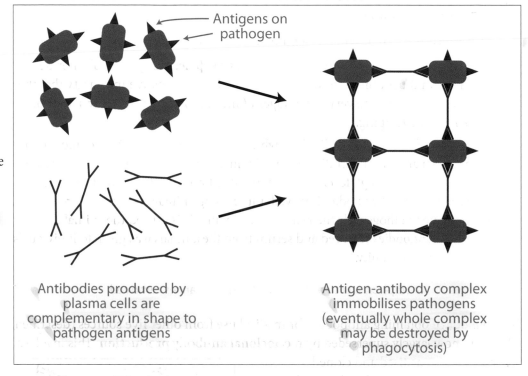

Antibodies produced by plasma cells are complementary in shape to pathogen antigens

Antigen-antibody complex immobilises pathogens (eventually whole complex may be destroyed by phagocytosis)

Note 1: Antibodies are **globular proteins**. Protein is the ideal molecule as small changes in the sequence of amino acids in the primary structure can produce the millions of different three-dimensional shapes required to be **complementary** in shape to the range of antigens that exist.

Note 2: The receptor on the sensitised B-lymphocyte and the part of the antibody that attaches to the antigen are exactly the same shape (and both are complementary in shape to the antigens on the invading pathogen).

The **memory cells** produced by B-cells can live for many years (sometimes for life) in the body fluids. These cells remain inactive unless stimulated by the presence of the same antigen (pathogen) again. If this happens, the memory cells **divide rapidly** (they are already sensitised) and produce **vast numbers** of plasma cells as there are more memory cells than there were 'correct' B-cells at the start of the primary response. The plasma cells produce the antibodies necessary to destroy the pathogen while the memory cells provide a guarantee of further long term protection. This is known as the **secondary immune response**. The **primary immune response** is the initial response of the body to the antigen when meeting it for the first time.

Note 1: Pathogens can contain many different types of antigen. Each antigen can produce an immune response with a different type of B-lymphocyte. Therefore, for any one type of pathogen there may be many different antigen-antibody reactions taking place at the same time.

Note 2: No one individual is immune to all potential pathogens and diseases. However, individuals can be immune to (protected against) specific diseases.

Active and passive immunity

readymade

Immunity can be active or passive. **Passive immunity** is when the individual receives antibodies from another source (ie from outside the body). **Active immunity** is produced when the individual achieves immunity through the production of antibodies by his/her own body.

Passive immunity – can develop by a number of methods. These include:

- antibodies passing from mother to baby across the **placenta** (placental [uterine] transfer) or in the mother's 'first' milk (**colostrum**). The passive immunity that this produces is crucial in the very early stages of life, a time when the baby's immune system is still developing.

- antibodies made in another individual, which are harvested and **injected** into another person as a serum. The antibodies can be obtained from individuals recovering from illness (they will have high levels of the required antibody in their blood). An older method of obtaining antibodies involved immunising animals, for example horses, with attenuated pathogens or their inactivated toxins. This caused the animal to produce the antibodies required and serum from the animals was given to individuals requiring rapid immunity.

Note: Serum is blood plasma with all blood clotting substances removed.

Note: Immunity provided by placental transfer or colostral transfer are examples of **natural** immunity.

The methods of obtaining antibodies for medical use from other live sources (described above) are now largely superseded by **monoclonal antibody production**. This involves the removal of sensitised and cloned B-lymphocytes from a mouse that has been infected with a particular antigen. The mouse B-lymphocytes are hybridised with cancer cells to produce long lived lymphocytes that can produce the required antibodies in a fermenter, conveyer-belt style over a long period.

Monoclonal antibodies have many advantages. Compared to obtaining antibodies from horses or other large mammals they:

- can be produced in large quantities in the laboratory.

- can produce a single type of antibody (antibodies obtained from horses usually come as a range of types, together with other chemicals that can potentially cause allergies).

Monoclonal antibodies

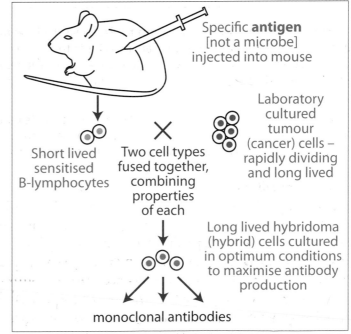

Specific **antigen** [not a microbe] injected into mouse

Short lived sensitised B-lymphocytes

× Two cell types fused together, combining properties of each

Laboratory cultured tumour (cancer) cells – rapidly dividing and long lived

Long lived hybridoma (hybrid) cells cultured in optimum conditions to maximise antibody production

monoclonal antibodies

Passive immunity provides **rapid** immunity as the processes of B-lymphocyte sensitisation and plasma cell production do not need to take place first. It is especially effective if someone becomes infected with a particularly harmful pathogen when it is probable that they have no defence against it (for example, a 'new' disease encountered in a foreign country or when suffering from a snake bite).

However, passive immunity is only **temporary**, as in time the antibodies are broken down (see graph below) and the individual's immune system is not programmed to make more.

Active immunity – This can develop through **having had the disease**. The individual becomes ill but recovers as a consequence of the primary response to the infection. Should a subsequent infection occur, involving the same pathogen, the secondary response is so rapid and strong that the immune system may destroy the pathogen(s) so quickly that individuals may not even be aware that they were infected. In contrast, the primary immune response is **slow** to develop and the individual usually suffers the disease symptoms for a period of time (it may take 4–5 days before antibody levels reach a high enough level to be effective in a primary response, due to the time involved in activating the specific B-lymphocyte and producing plasma cells) but once in place it is **long lasting**.

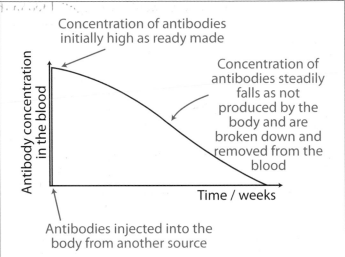

Changes in the concentration of antibodies during passive immunity

The very **strong** and **rapid secondary response** (relative to the primary response) is due to there being many more memory cells than there were specific B-lymphocyte cells at the start of the primary response (strength) and the fact that the memory cells are already sensitised (speed).

> **Note:** Some antibodies can last in the blood for a considerable time. However, the fact that active immunity is long lasting is primarily due to the presence of memory cells and their ability to respond quickly and effectively if a subsequent infection occurs.

Vaccinations also produce active immunity. In the UK, vaccination programmes are in place for many diseases, for example, measles and mumps. Most vaccinations are given early in childhood and their function is to stop individuals being infected by potentially common and harmful infectious diseases. Vaccinations trick the immune system into thinking the body has been infected by a particular pathogen; consequently the primary immune response is triggered and the immune system is equipped to produce a secondary response if required. Due to the speed and strength of the secondary response, vaccinations render the individual immune.

Vaccinations normally contain one of the following:

- Killed or **weakened** (attenuated) **pathogens** – These pathogens contain the antigens required to produce an immune response but they will not cause the disease itself (however, mild symptoms may sometimes appear).
- Modified **toxins** produced by the pathogen – With some pathogens it is their toxins

that can produce the immune response. The toxins must be modified and made harmless but not changed so much they do not produce an immune response.

- Isolated **antigens** separated from the pathogen itself – For some pathogens the antigens can be made by genetic engineering.

Sometimes vaccinations require subsequent **booster** injections. These produce a secondary immune response, similar to the response produced when catching a particular disease for a second time.

The characteristics of active immunity are highlighted in the following graph.

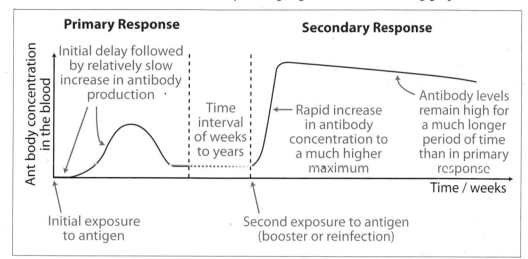

Changes in the concentration of antibodies during active immunity

Note: Immunity provided by cell-mediated action is also active immunity.

The importance of vaccinations to society and the economy

The main benefit of vaccination is obvious – there are fewer sick people and the lives of many people are extended, often considerably, compared with the pre-vaccination world. World child mortality has halved in the last 25 years, largely due to the increasing availability of vaccination programmes.

Society benefits in that fewer people are ill and less care is needed to tend the ill. Healthy children tend, on average, to do better at school.

While setting up vaccination programmes is expensive, the overall benefit to a nation's economy is much greater.

Economies benefit as:

- there are lower treatment costs to treat those who are ill.
- employees do not have to take time off work, therefore productivity increases.
- carers, for example parents, do not have to take time off work to care for the sick.

The vaccination programmes in large developed countries save billions of pounds annually through reducing illness from infectious disease.

Note: The concept of **'herd immunity'** is important in vaccination programmes. This is the concept that if a high enough proportion of the population is vaccinated, those who are not vaccinated are less likely to catch a particular infectious disease (as they are less likely to come in contact with someone who is infectious). This is very important in protecting those who cannot get vaccinated, for example newborns (first NHS immunisation is currently at six weeks) and the very ill. Of course, it also helps protect the small numbers who, against medical advice, choose not to get vaccinated.

The different types of immunity are summarised in the following flow diagram.

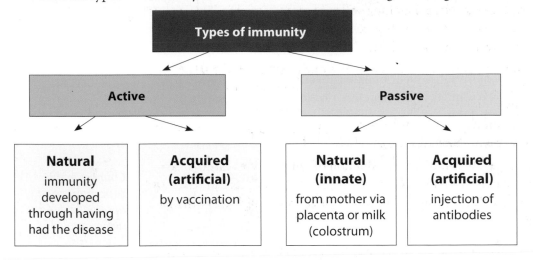

Transplanting tissue

As discussed in the previous section, the body will produce an immune response to the presence of any non-self antigens. Normally this response occurs as a consequence of infection. However, transplanted organs (such as kidneys) or tissue (such as skin grafts) will also produce an immune response, as the transplanted organs/tissue will contain non-self antigens if they come from someone else. Exceptions are if the tissue is transplanted within the same person (as can happen with skin grafts) or if tissues/ organs are transplanted between identical twins (identical twins are genetically identical therefore they have identical antigens).

Transplant rejection – Most organ transplants do not take place between identical twins, therefore the risk of transplant rejection exists. Transplant rejection is the main reason for many organ transplants failing.

The process of rejection involves the following steps:

- **T-lymphocytes** are stimulated (sensitised) by the non-self antigens present in the transplanted tissue.
- These T-cells are cloned by mitosis to produce **killer T-cells** (and the range of other T-cells associated with cell-mediated immunity).
- The killer T-cells destroy the transplanted cells.

Note: Transplant rejection can also involve the action of B-lymphocytes and antibodies. For example, if the blood of a donor and a recipient is different, this can produce an immune response involving antibodies (see next section). Normally, tissue matching is accurate so rejection by B-lymphocytes in this situation is unlikely to occur.

As organ transplants may be a last resort in saving a life or even in providing a better quality of life for a patient, considerable scientific endeavour has gone into devising strategies for reducing transplant rejection.

These include:

- **tissue typing** – This is the term that describes the process of matching the donor and recipient cell surface markers (antigens) so that there is as good a match as possible, ie there is as small a difference as possible between the self and non-self antigens. Generally, the best tissue matching will take place between close relatives. The best possible transplant will be between identical twins, who will have identical antigens therefore the transplant is much less likely to be rejected.

- **immunosuppression techniques** – such as the use of **drugs to inhibit DNA replication** and therefore the cloning of lymphocytes (and the production of killer T-cells) will slow down or stop rejection processes. For many types of transplant, the immunosuppression drugs have to be taken for a very long time (for the life of the transplant and therefore often for life).

- **X-rays** – can also be used to inhibit the production of lymphocytes through the irradiation of bone marrow or lymph tissue. Unpleasant side effects can result and the use of X-rays is usually a backup to immunosuppressant drugs rather than a first course of action.

Immunosuppression (whether by drugs or X-rays) will **compromise the recipient's immune system**. This makes the individual susceptible to infection, as immunosuppression depresses the immune system in general (not just its response to the antigens involved in the transplanted tissue). A number of additional strategies are used to help support the transplant patient against subsequent infections including anti-viral drugs, anti-bacterial mouth rinses and the use of monoclonal antibodies to help target and reduce the effect of the T-cells involved in rejection.

Nonetheless, there is a delicate balance (see diagram below) between reducing the risks of rejection and restricting the side effects that are linked to the use of immunosuppressant technologies.

Blood transfusion

Red blood cells also have **antigens** (markers) on their cell surface membrane. The blood of any one individual will not have antibodies that correspond to the antigens on his/her red blood cells as this would trigger an immune reaction. As with other B-lymphocytes that correspond with self-antigens, the lymphocytes responsible for these blood antibodies are switched off during very early development.

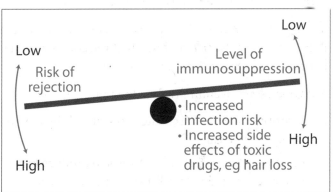

The delicate balancing act between risk of transplant rejection and use of immunosuppressant agents

However, the type of antigens on the red blood cells of different people varies. In the **ABO** system, there are four different types of blood group (A, B, AB and O) and everyone belongs to one of these groups. This is an example of **polymorphism** – a situation where there are several distinct categories or forms.

When giving a **blood transfusion** to an individual (for example, following surgery, an accident or when treating some illnesses), it is important that the transfusion is compatible. Take the following two examples:

- Blood **can** be donated from an individual with blood **group A (the donor)** to another individual with blood **group A (the recipient)**. This is because the recipient has no antibodies (no anti-a antibodies) that correspond to the antigens on the donor's red blood cells.

- Blood **cannot** be donated from a donor with blood **group A** to a recipient with blood **group B**. This is because the recipient has anti-a antibodies in his/her plasma. The presence of both antigen A and anti-a antibodies causes an antigen-antibody reaction. The anti-a antibodies cause the blood, containing red blood cells with antigen A, to **agglutinate** or clump. This agglutination could block capillary networks and lead to organ failure and death.

Note: An individual with blood group B will have anti-a antibodies as they had no A antigens in early development; therefore, A antigens were not identified as self antigens and the lymphocytes responsible for producing antibody-a were not 'switched off'.

The antigens and antibodies of the ABO blood group system are shown in the following table.

Blood group	Antigens on red blood cells	Antibodies in plasma
A	A	anti-b
B	B	anti-a
AB	both A and B	neither anti-a nor anti-b
O	neither A nor B	both anti-a and anti-b

Using the information in the previous table, it is possible to work out which blood can be transfused into which other types(s). Donated blood does not have to be the same type as the recipient but it is important that the donated blood type does not lead to an antigen-antibody reaction and subsequent agglutination.

Safe (no reaction) and unsafe (agglutination occurs) transfusion combinations

Blood group of donor	Blood group of recipient			
	A	B	AB	O
A	no reaction	agglutination	no reaction	agglutination
B	agglutination	no reaction	no reaction	agglutination
AB	agglutination	agglutination	no reaction	agglutination
O	no reaction	no reaction	no reaction	no reaction

As blood of group O does not have either A or B antigens, blood of group O can be transfused into any of the four blood groups. Consequently, blood group O is referred to as the **universal donor**. Blood group AB lacks both anti-a and anti-b antibodies, therefore this is referred to as the **universal recipient**, as people with blood group AB can receive blood from any group.

Note: A key point when working out transfusion compatibility is that donated blood is mainly red blood cells and that the amount of donated plasma is insignificant. The table above indicates that blood group A can be donated to a recipient with blood group AB. This is only because none, or a very insignificant number of, anti-b antibodies in blood group A will be transfused into the recipient with blood group AB.

Why do we have an ABO system? It is thought that the different antigens (groups) evolved as a consequence of mutations. Currently, none of the blood groups appears to give individuals a selective advantage (ie the mutations are neutral). However, it is possible that in our evolutionary past some of the mutations gave selective advantage against specific diseases – this would explain why the different groups have persisted through time. The ABO is only one of a number of many blood group systems in humans, although it is the most important in clinical practice. Another very important blood group system is the **rhesus system**.

The rhesus system – This system is based on the presence or absence of an antigen (the rhesus antigen or antigen D) on the cell surface membranes of the red blood cells. Around 85% of the population have this antigen and are described as **rhesus positive** (Rh^+). **Rhesus negative** (Rh^-) individuals do not have the antigen. Unlike the antibodies for the ABO system, antibodies against the antigen D marker (anti-D antibodies) do not occur naturally in the plasma. An individual who is rhesus positive will not produce anti-D antibodies (relevant B-lymphocytes are 'switched off' when the rhesus positive marker is recognised as self during development).

Rhesus negative individuals do not normally have the antibodies either, **but** can produce anti-D antibodies if their blood becomes contaminated with blood containing antigen D as can happen in the following situations:

- Blood transfusion between a rhesus positive donor and a rhesus negative recipient. In reality, this is unlikely to occur with modern blood matching techniques.

- When a **rhesus negative mother** has a **rhesus positive baby**. The typical sequence of events is explained in the following flow diagram.

> During birth (or late in pregnancy) some foetal red blood cells (rhesus positive so contain antigen D) leak into the mother's circulation.

↓

> This causes the rhesus negative mother's immune system to produce anti-D antibodies. By the time the antibodies are produced in significant numbers by the mother, the baby will have been born therefore there is no threat to the developing foetus.

↓

> However, during subsequent pregnancies, if the foetus is rhesus positive, the relevant B-lymphocytes in the mother are already sensitised and large numbers of anti-D antibodies can be produced immediately if any foetal blood cells enter the maternal circulation. The anti-D antibodies can cross the placenta and cause agglutination of foetal red blood cells, a condition known as haemolytic disease of the newborn.

Foetal death, or serious illness, due to haemolytic disease of the newborn seldom occurs today as rhesus negative mothers are treated during pregnancy (around 30 weeks) by being given an injection of anti-D antibodies. These attach to any antigen D-containing foetal red blood cell fragments that may pass across the placenta and enter the mother's circulation before the mother's B-lymphocytes are stimulated to produce anti-D antibodies. Following birth, if the baby proves to be rhesus positive, another injection of anti-D antibodies is given within 72 hours.

However, if medical screening and intervention is bypassed and the condition does occur, the baby can be treated by blood transfusion.

Antibiotic resistance in bacteria and other factors affecting the spread of disease

Antibiotic resistance in bacteria

Antibiotics are drugs that are developed to kill bacteria. Different antibiotics work in different ways but they usually kill bacteria by one or more of the following methods:

- Disrupt cell wall formation by inhibiting an enzyme involved in the process. The bacteria are killed as the cell bursts, as it cannot resist osmotic pressure due to a weakened cell wall. Penicillin works in this way.
- Inhibit metabolic processes including protein synthesis, for example, erythromycin destroys the ribosomes in prokaryotic cells.

> **Note:** The fact that erythromycin does not affect the larger ribosomes (80S) in eukaryotic cells means it can disrupt protein synthesis in bacteria (70S ribosomes) and not damage the ribosomes in patients taking this antibiotic.

However, in recent decades more and more species of bacteria are becoming antibiotic resistant. Bacteria are **antibiotic resistant** when one, or more, antibiotics no longer have an effect on them. Mutations in the bacterial genome lead to metabolic changes that result in antibiotics no longer being effective. As bacteria can reproduce very rapidly by binary fission (asexually), one resistant bacterium can very rapidly result in a large population of antibiotic resistant bacteria. The diagram below summarises the process of antibiotic resistance.

Antibiotic resistance in bacteria

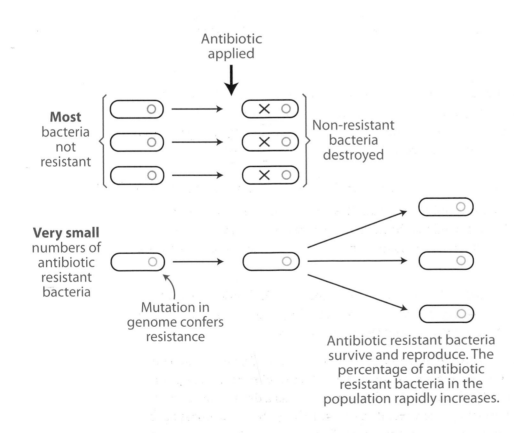

Note: Penicillin-resistant bacteria have evolved a number of methods of resisting the effects of penicillin. These include producing penicillinase to break penicillin down; exporting the active ingredient in penicillin out of the cell before it can work; and alternative metabolic pathways in cell wall formation that render the penicillin ineffective.

Some antibiotic resistant bacteria are resistant to a number of types of antibiotics and the risk is that some strains could become resistant to **all** antibiotics, resulting in a so-called 'antibiotic winter'.

The graph below shows deaths in Northern Ireland where the antibiotic resistant MRSA (Methicillin Resistant *Staphylococcus aureus*) was the underlying cause of death between 2004 and 2014.

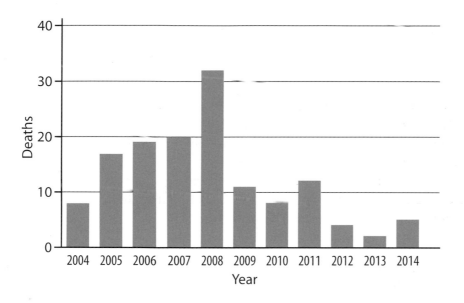

Deaths in Northern Ireland from MRSA between 2004 and 2014

The decrease in deaths in recent years is due to a combination of a more rigorous hygiene culture in hospitals, more effective isolation of MRSA patients, a more judicious approach to antibiotic use and new targeted drug treatments. It doesn't mean that the problem of antibiotic resistance is decreasing!

The importance of discovering new sources of antibiotics to society and the economy

With so many bacteria being antibiotic resistant it is very important that new sources of antibiotics are found. It is hoped that bacteria that are resistant to the current generation of antibiotics will not be resistant to 'new generation' antibiotics that work in different ways.

The benefits to the **individual** and **society** of discovering new antibiotics are similar to the benefits of having vaccination programmes with very high rates of uptake, ie more effective treatment, less treatment costs and less time off work.

Many research programmes are investigating the possibility of finding new sources of antibiotics in natural environments, for example, the soil, an environment where some types of microbe naturally produce antimicrobial substances as a defence mechanism within the soil against competing microbes. Recent research has been investigating the antibiotic properties of some bacteria that are naturally found in the human nasal cavity.

Factors affecting disease spread

How rapidly a disease spreads through a population depends on many factors including how easily it is spread from person to person; how likely someone will fall ill to the disease once infected; and whether there is a vaccination for that disease and the percentage uptake of that vaccination. Bacterial resistance to antibiotics is another factor if the disease in question is caused by a bacterium.

Diseases that spread rapidly through a small region (usually within one country) and affect a higher proportion of the population than normal are called **epidemics**. Diseases affecting many thousands of people or several countries at the same time are referred to as **pandemics**.

Are viruses (rather than bacteria) the major cause of epidemics and pandemics?
Although scientists are very worried that antibiotic resistance in bacteria could lead to the rapid spread of previously controlled bacterial infections, most major epidemics and pandemics are caused by viruses.

There are a number of factors that make **viruses** the more likely causal agents of widespread infections. These include:

- viruses have very small genomes that are **prone to mutation**.
- many disease-causing viruses are **retroviruses** with RNA in the genome. These viruses are much **less stable** than those with the genome as DNA.
- **antibiotics are not effective** against viruses.

Influenza, SARS, rabies, Hendra and Ebola are all caused by viruses with RNA as the genetic material. It is thought that AIDS (arising from HIV infection) has been responsible for 30 million plus deaths over the last few decades. The 'Spanish' flu virus killed between 30–50 million people in a worldwide pandemic in 1918–1919.

Case Study – HIV and AIDS

The virus that causes HIV is a retrovirus, converting its RNA to DNA in host cells. Humans infected by HIV usually suffer long term damage to their immune systems with the result that they eventually succumb to one or more of the diseases associated with AIDS.

> **Note:** HIV describes the disease-causing virus and people infected are described as HIV positive (ie they produce antibodies to the antigen(s) of this virus). AIDS is the term used to describe the syndrome of diseases associated with long term infection with HIV; diseases that are a consequence of a much weakened immune system.

It is thought that the HIV virus mutated from a similar virus (SIV) that causes the same type of immunodeficiency in chimpanzees that HIV does in humans. The virus 'transferred' to human(s) in the early 1900s in central Africa, possibly through a human being bitten by a chimp or through eating or handling chimp meat.

Once HIV had evolved in humans, the disease AIDS was restricted to isolated pockets in central Africa for decades and only came to widespread public attention in western countries in the 1980s. Major reasons for AIDS 'exploding' in western populations at that time included the advent of globalisation, the development of a more casual approach to sex in many societies and the increased use of air travel. Each of these factors contributed to more opportunity for infection by HIV carriers in previously HIV-free societies.

Note 1: (Until recently) HIV meets many of the criteria associated with disease-causing microbes that can potentially cause epidemics or pandemics. It is an unstable retrovirus that has high rates of mutation, it is not controlled by antibiotics, it cannot be vaccinated against and (until recently) there are very few drugs that are effective in its control.

Note 2: New antiretroviral drug treatments have significantly reduced death rates from HIV, greatly extending the life expectancy of patients with the condition.

Animals as reservoirs of disease-causing viruses

In the case study on HIV and AIDS it was noted that HIV originated from a similar virus (SIV) in chimpanzees. Before crossing over into humans, SIV had almost certainly co-existed with its primate hosts for a very long time.

Animal species that harbour viruses that subsequently cause disease in humans are described as **reservoirs** for that virus. Reservoir species often suffer little harm from the viruses and they are not really vectors as such, as they are not adapted to transfer the pathogen to another species; if a transfer occurs, it is usually a chance event. Terms such as 'bird flu' and 'swine flu' give a clue to the reservoir origins of the viruses responsible for causing these conditions.

There are many examples of viruses transferring from other animal species to humans and then causing epidemics and pandemics. Historically, a range of bat species have had a very significant role in this inter-species spread.

Bats have been (or are) reservoirs for the viruses that cause Marburg, SARS and Nipah, and are an initial reservoir for rabies before its transfer into dogs (and then into humans).

There are several reasons why bats make suitable reservoirs for disease-causing pathogens that subsequently infect humans. These include:

- They are mammals and have a very **similar physiology** to humans.
- They are **social animals** and are in very close contact with large numbers of other bats, thereby ensuring that a high proportion of the bat population are carriers, thus increasing the possibility of cross-infection.
- They **fly large ranges** and therefore are potentially in contact with other organisms (humans) considerable distances away from their base.

A significant factor leading to the inter-species transfer of some viruses from bats to humans in recent decades has been the continual encroachment of man into habitats frequented by bats as a consequence of urbanisation and the clearing of woodland for housing and agriculture. (The bats referred to in the above paragraphs are the 'flying foxes' or 'fruit' bats found in tropical and sub-tropical areas; **not** the bats found in the British Isles.)

Note: The previous section on viruses underlines that it is not just important to find new antibiotics. It is also essential that a new generation of antimicrobials are developed. **Antimicrobial drugs** are drugs that are effective against a broader range of microbes than antibiotics, or are effective against those pathogens that antibiotics cannot combat, for example, viruses.

Diagnosing infection – an update

In recent years there has been significant progress in the **earlier**, and **more accurate**, **diagnosis** of infection. Earlier and more accurate diagnosis can lead to more effective treatment at an earlier stage of disease progression.

These advances include the use of ELISA techniques and the detection of cytokines as biomarkers. **Cytokines** are molecules involved in signalling between different types of immune cells and increase in cytokine concentration can represent an increased immune response. They are used as biomarkers to identify a number of conditions including TB and rheumatoid arthritis.

ELISA (Enzyme-linked immunosorbent assay) – This is a laboratory technique that uses antibodies, enzymes and other molecules as biomarkers to detect the presence of particular molecules in the body. ELISA assays can test for a small, or a large number, of potential antigens or biomarkers at the same time, thus screening for a large number of possible conditions.

Typically, body fluids from a patient are added to a number of wells on a plate (a sophisticated spotting tray) and a range of antibodies are added to these wells. Reaction between antibody and antigen triggers an enzyme linked to the antibody into causing a colour change thus identifying the antigens or other molecules present.

ELISA diagnostic kits can be used to detect:

- pathogens in the body
- cancer cell markers
- cardiac disease markers
- pregnancy (in home pregnancy kits)

They have the advantage of enabling **early**, **rapid screening** and can provide a wide range of diagnostic feedback from the one test. Examples include:

An ELISA test plate

© TEK Image /
Science Photo
Library /
M530/0475

Pregnancy testing – Following the implantation of an egg in the uterine wall, increased levels of the hormone chorionic gonadotropin (hCG) can be detected in the blood or urine. In a pregnancy test, hCG antigens are detected by complementary hCG (monoclonal) antibodies immobilised on the ELISA plate. The formation of this antigen-antibody complex results in a linked enzyme reacting to produce the characteristic colour change associated with pregnancy kits.

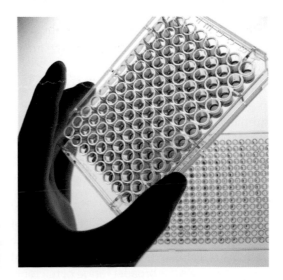

Testing for viral pathogens – An ELISA plate impregnated with the viral antigens is coated with blood serum from the patient. If the patient's blood contains complementary antibodies (evidence of infection), then the antigen-antibody complex triggers an enzyme reaction that leads to a colour change.

> **Note:** The antibody-antigen complex normally stimulates the enzyme reaction, it is not the substrate as such. The substrate for the enzyme is normally added as part of the process.

Practical work

Investigating microorganisms using aseptic techniques

Aseptic technique is used to prevent contamination when working with microorganisms. This includes preventing contamination of both the microbe culture and contamination of the individuals working with the microbes.

Solid agar or liquid broth can be used to culture microorganisms and care is needed when transferring microorganisms to Petri dishes or other containers for investigation.

Procedure for transferring microorganisms:

Metal inoculating or disposable plastic loops can be used.

- If using a metal inoculating loop it is necessary to 'flame' the loop in the hottest part of a Bunsen flame until it becomes red-hot. After sterilising the metal loop it is necessary to air-cool the loop as when red-hot it would kill any microorganisms it comes into contact with. After transfer of microorganisms, it is necessary to re-sterilise the loop. However, for safety reasons it is important not to create a microorganism-rich aerosol when doing this. Once used, disposable plastic loops should be discarded into a solution of disinfectant.

- When transferring microorganisms from a culture bottle to a Petri dish (or a fresh culture bottle), the lid of the bottle should be held in the same hand that holds the culture bottle and not allowed to touch the bench, with the other hand holding the inoculating loop. Immediately after opening the culture bottle, its neck should be quickly passed through the Bunsen flame to sterilise the lid region; this should be repeated immediately before replacing the lid on the culture bottle.

- When transferring the microorganisms to a Petri dish, the lid of the dish should be only raised enough to allow the microorganisms to be added to the agar.

Alternatively, a **spread plate** method can be used, when cells in suspension are used in inoculation. In this case an L-shaped spreader is used to spread the inoculating bacteria over the surface of the agar. Plastic sterile disposable spreaders are a suitable alternative to the glass spreaders that require sterilisation before and after use.

Petri dishes should be labelled on the outside of the base (and not the lid). They should be incubated upside down in an incubator at an appropriate temperature for the microorganism concerned.

Investigating the effect of different antibiotics on bacteria

At the very basic level, discs of antibiotics can be placed on agar in a Petri dish. The agar is inoculated with a particular type of bacterium and the effect of the antibiotic (or antibiotics) on that strain of bacteria can be investigated as shown in the diagram on the right.

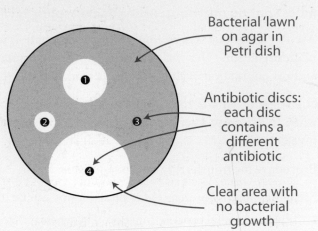

Investigating the effect of different antibiotics on a type of bacterium

Alternatively, **E-strips** are a more sophisticated way of measuring the effect of different concentrations of antibiotic on bacteria. E-strips are prepared strips that contain a concentration gradient of antibiotic (or antimicrobial compound) running the length of the strip. The process involves placing the E-strip on the agar of a Petri dish that has been inoculated with a bacterium. Following incubation (normally between 18–72 hours needed), and depending on the E-strip and microorganism used, a result similar to that in the diagram below can be observed.

As the E-strips contain markings that show antibiotic concentrations at particular points on the strip, it is possible to work out the minimum antibiotic concentration that is necessary to inhibit bacterial growth.

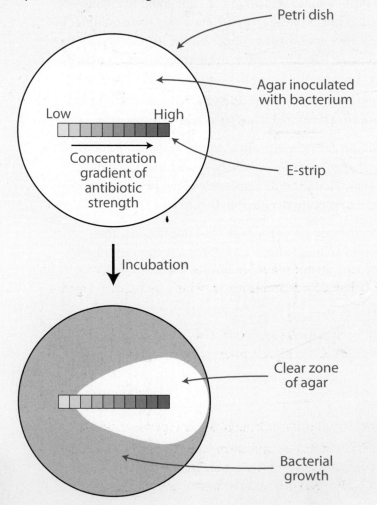

E-strips and bacterial growth

Preparation of a streak plate to isolate single colonies

This technique is commonly used to isolate single colonies of microbial cells, ie a pure culture of cells, all of which share the same parental cell.

Procedure:

1. Using an inoculating loop, spread the microorganisms over a small section of the agar in the Petri dish (the initial inoculation, stage 1 below).

2. Then, with a new/sterilised inoculating loop, 'streak' several lines of microorganism across the agar at an angle, taking care not to allow the separate 'lines' to overlap (stage 2).

3. Repeat stage 2 once or twice, making sure that a sterile loop is used on each occasion (stages 3 & 4).

4. Make a final single streak as shown (stage 5).

5. Incubate the Petri dish at a suitable temperature. After 24 hours or so it should be possible to identify isolated pure colonies (stage 6).

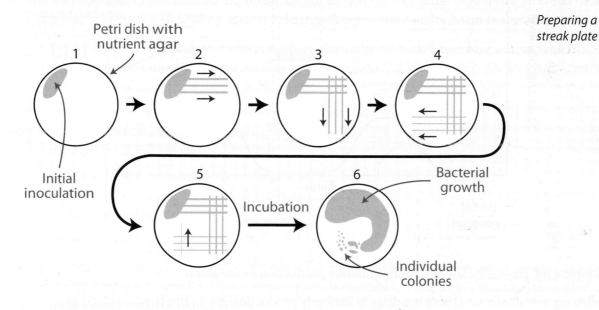

Preparing a streak plate

Investigating the antimicrobial properties of plants

Many plants have a range of defences against microorganisms. These help prevent decay and further loss in parts of plants, for example leaves, which become damaged in their natural environment.

Many common woodland plants, such as wood anemone, bluebell, lesser celandine, wild garlic and mint, produce compounds that prevent or reduce fungal and/or bacterial growth.

Procedure:

1. Grind up the leaves of each woodland plant in ethanol using separate mortars.

2. Prepare some sterile agar plates (Petri dishes) and spread a fungus or bacterium culture on the plate using appropriate aseptic techniques. The fungus *Pythium debaryanum* or *Bacillus* bacteria are suitable for this purpose. Soak a

6. *Quality of written communication is awarded a maximum of 2 marks in this section.*

Activation of the human immune system can have both positive and negative consequences. Vaccination was first carried out by Edward Jenner in 1796. Many countries now have vaccination programmes.

Meningitis is a disease which can be caused by a bacterium referred to as Meningococcal B. Each year 1 in 10 of the 1200 people in the UK who get meningitis caused by this bacterium will die. In 2015 the vaccination programme for children in the UK was widened to include Meningococcal B vaccine. The vaccine contains an inactive form of the bacterium.

(a) With reference to the human immune system, explain how Meningococcal B vaccination will result in fewer children suffering the effects of meningitis. [9]

A potentially negative consequence of the action of the immune system can arise in pregnancy, for women who are rhesus negative. To avoid complications, these women may be injected with anti-D during the later stages of pregnancy.

(b) Explain fully why rhesus negative women may need anti-D. [7]

Quality of written communication. [2]

Question taken from CCEA's Biology Assessment Unit A2 1, Physiology and Ecosystems, May 2016, © CCEA 2017

Chapter 3 – Coordination and Control in Plants

Students should be able to:

4.3.1   Demonstrate knowledge and understanding of the role of phytochromes in the control of flowering in long-day and short-day plants.

4.3.2   Demonstrate knowledge and understanding of the role of plant growth substances (hormones) in stem elongation.

As complex living organisms, plants are able to respond to many stimuli in the environment including gravity, water, chemicals and light. The effect of light on plant growth and development is easily demonstrated, and historically, much studied. One example of the effect of light on plant growth and development involves the phytochrome system.

Phytochrome and flowering in plants

Phytochrome is a pigment system found in the **leaves** of flowering plants. It is primarily involved in the timing of flowering in many species. While in some species, the flowering process is initiated when average temperatures reach a certain level, for example, tomatoes, for most British species the trigger is the **duration of light** or day length (**the photoperiod**).

For species sensitive to day length there are two categories of plants:

- **Long-day plants** (LDPs), for example, cabbage and petunia. These species flower only if the day length **exceeds** a certain minimum length.

- **Short-day plants** (SDPs), for example, chrysanthemum and strawberry. These species only flower if the days are **shorter** than a critical value (or the nights exceed a minimum length).

Phytochrome as the photoreceptor

Phytochrome pigments act as the **photoreceptor**. Phytochrome is sensitive to light and its suitability for this role is linked to its ability to exist in two inter-convertible forms:

- **P_{660}** (P_R) absorbs **red light** (light from the red part of the spectrum) with an absorption peak of 660 nm.

- **P_{730}** (P_{FR}) absorbs **far red light** with an absorption peak of 730 nm.

Due to the differences in absorption peaks, the two forms of phytochrome are known as P_{660} and P_{730} respectively. If subjected to red light the P_{660} is rapidly converted to the P_{730} form and if P_{730} is subjected to far red light it is rapidly converted to P_{660}.

Additionally, in darkness (as P_{730} is much less stable than P_{660}), P_{730} will slowly convert to the P_{660} form.

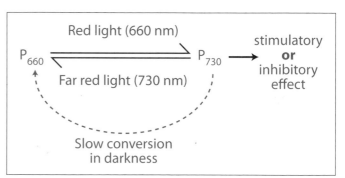

The inter-convertible forms of phytochrome

Two key points:

- As **daylight contains more red than far red light**, P_{660} is converted to P_{730} during the day. Consequently, as day length gets longer in spring/early summer the proportion of phytochrome that exists in the P_{730} form increases. In LDPs, as day length increases, the amount of P_{730} eventually reaches a critical level that initiates flowering. The *intensity* of light is also important, as the conversion is quicker in high light intensities.

- Furthermore, it is the **P_{730}** form that is the **physiologically active** form, whether it is that sufficient P_{730} has accumulated to promote flowering in LDPs or that there is too much P_{730} to allow flowering to occur in SDPs. In SDPs the inhibitory effect of high levels of P_{730} must be removed before flowering can take place.

The following table summarises the effect of different photoperiods on LDPs and SDPs.

Photoperiod 0 ---------- 24 hours	Type of plant	Phytochrome response	Effect
short day – long night	LDP	P_{660} converted to P_{730} during the day but the night (dark period) is long enough for sufficient P_{730} to be slowly converted back to P_{660} to prevent the P_{730} reaching the critical level needed for flowering.	No flowering
long day – short night		Long day length allows P_{660} to be converted to P_{730} in high concentrations. The night (darkness) is too short for enough P_{730} to be converted back to P_{660}. P_{730} builds up to critical level.	Flowering
short day – long night	SDP	P_{660} is converted to P_{730} during the day. The dark period is long enough for a sufficient level of P_{730} to be converted to P_{660} to remove the inhibitory effect of P_{730}.	Flowering
long day – short night		P_{660} is converted to P_{730} during the day but the dark period is not long enough for a sufficient level of P_{730} to be converted to P_{660} to remove the inhibitory effect of P_{730}.	No flowering

Note: It is the length of the dark period that is critical in determining whether flowering occurs in both LDPs and SDPs, as it determines how much P_{730} can be converted back to P_{660}.

Manipulating the photoperiod

Commercial plant growers need to have flowering plants available at the times of the year when sales are likely to be highest, for example, roses for St Valentine's Day and a wide range of flowers for Christmas. Most species will not naturally flower at these times of the year but manipulation of the photoperiod (the light regime) can ensure that supply and demand are matched.

Manipulating flowering in long-day plants

The onset of flowering in LDPs is stimulated by increasing day length (and reducing the period of darkness). However, there can be a time interval between the *stimulation* of the flowering process and the actual *appearance* of flowers, ie in some British LDPs the flowers may not appear until July/August, by which time the days are getting shorter!

In **LDPs** the flowering period can be brought forward or delayed by manipulating the photoperiod, for example, by using artificial lighting in glasshouses or by using screens to reduce the light period.

Interpretation of diagram – In light regimes **1** and **2** the length of day is not long enough to build up P_{730} to sufficiently high levels to initiate flowering. In **3** flowering is initiated as the period of light is sufficient to build up P_{730} to the critical level (and the period of darkness is not long enough to break down the P_{730} and keep it below the critical level). In light regime **4** the period of darkness that interrupts the light period does not reduce the P_{730} level enough to inhibit flowering (there is still enough light to allow the P_{730} to reach the critical level).

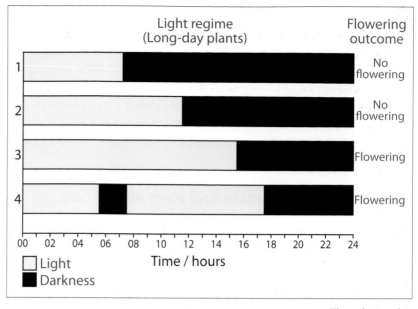

The relationship between light regime and flowering in long-day plants

Note: In the LDP exemplified by the diagram above, flowering is initiated by a light period of a critical length somewhere between about 11.5–15.5 hours. Based on the evidence in the diagram it is impossible to be any more specific.

Manipulating flowering in short-day plants

In **SDPs** flowering times can also be adjusted by manipulating the photoperiod.

Interpretation of diagram – In light regime **1** the period of darkness is not long enough to remove the inhibitory effects of high levels of P_{730}. In light regime **2** the period of darkness is long enough to allow enough P_{730} to be converted back to P_{660} (thus removing the inhibitory effect of high levels of P_{730}). In light regime **3** the short flash of light during the dark period is enough to inhibit flowering, as during the short flash of light, P_{660} will be rapidly converted to P_{730} therefore not allowing a sufficiently long continuous period of darkness for enough P_{730} to be converted to P_{660}.

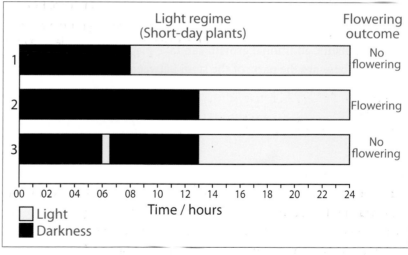

The relationship between light regime and flowering in short-day plants

Note 1: In SDPs the critical period of darkness must be **continuous** (uninterrupted) – this is because a short flash of light will rapidly convert P_{660} to P_{730} whereas the conversion of P_{730} to P_{660} in darkness is slow.

Note 2: In the SDP exemplified by the diagram above, flowering is initiated by a continuous dark period of critical length somewhere between 8–13 hours.

While light duration is perceived by phytochrome, it has been widely assumed that the photoperiod response is brought about by the action of a **hormone**. There are many reasons why this has been suggested, including the fact that there must be some form of communication between where the light stimulates the phytochrome (the leaves) and where flowering actually takes place – a considerable distance apart in some plants. However, as yet no 'flowering' hormone has been identified but a number of **plant growth substances** (hormones) and their functions in plants have been identified. Some of these plant growth substances and their functions will be reviewed in the next section.

Plant growth substances and stem elongation

Plant growth substances control many aspects of plant growth with their influence on the growth of the stem being particularly widely studied. Growth in stem or shoot tips is very similar to the growth in root tips (as discussed when covering mitosis at AS). In plants, unlike most animals, growth is localised in specific zones at the tips of roots and shoots called **apical meristems**. In these meristems, **cell division** (mitosis) takes place to produce **more cells**. This is not the whole story as much of the actual growth that takes place is due to the extra cells produced by mitosis **elongating**. Stem and root tips have clearly identified **zones of division** and **zones of elongation**. In most plants the majority of their growth is due to this division and elongation of cells at their tips.

The photograph (right) shows a cactus with a clearly defined (lighter) region of growth at the shoot tip. This region represents the growth during the year in which the photograph was taken.

In many plants, additional growth can take place in the **internodal** regions. These are the parts of the stem between the nodes (points at which leaves develop).

The clear differentiation between new and old growth in a cactus

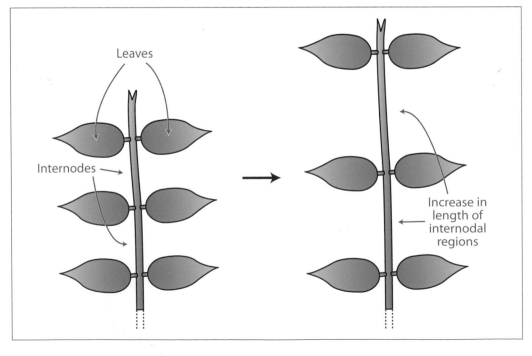

Growth of shoot internodes

The three main groups of plant growth regulators that affect growth in stems are **auxins**, **cytokinins** and **gibberellins**. Each stimulates growth in different ways, as summarised in the following table.

Plant growth substance	Site of production	Main functions
Auxins	Produced in the tip and move down the stem – the concentration of auxin decreases as it moves down the stem	Promote growth by increased **cell elongation** (in the zone of elongation)
Cytokinins	Produced in meristematic (actively dividing) tissues in zone of division	Promote growth by increased **cell division** in the apical meristems (zone of division)
Gibberellins	Produced in leaves (and in other parts of the plant)	Promote growth by **cell elongation** (in the internodes)

Note: These plant growth substances interact and seldom act in isolation, for example, cytokinins promote cell division only in the presence of auxins.

Exam questions

1. Read the following passage about the control of flowering in plants and write the most appropriate word(s) in the blank spaces to complete the account. [3]

   The pigment _____ is found in the leaves of flowering plants and occurs in two interchangeable forms. In daylight, the _____ form is rapidly changed to the _____ form. Short-day plants will flower when the period of _____ reaches or exceeds a minimum length.

   Question taken from CCEA's Biology Assessment Unit A2 1, Physiology and Ecosystems, January 2013, © CCEA 2017

2. (a) In an investigation into flowering in plants, the concentration of phytochrome P_{730} in the leaves of one species of flowering plant was measured between March and May. The results are shown in the graph below.

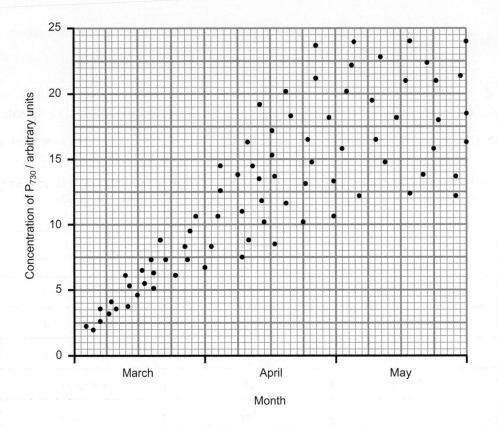

   (i) Describe and explain fully the results shown. [3]

   (ii) In May, the concentration of P_{730} ranges from 12–24 arbitrary units. Suggest one reason for this high degree of variability. [1]

   (b) In a different investigation into plant growth, a particular plant growth substance was applied to the tip of a stem and left for a period of time. The following diagram shows the results of this investigation.

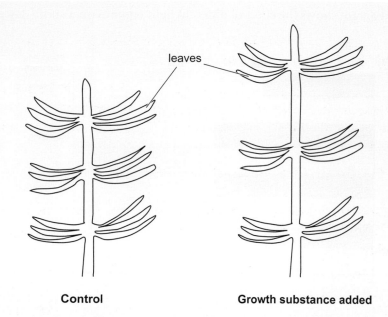

Control   **Growth substance added**

(i) Name the plant growth substance involved. [1]

(ii) The plant growth substance causes its effect mainly through the increased elongation of cells. Suggest why it produces the greatest growth when cytokinin levels are not limiting. [2]

Question taken from CCEA's Biology Assessment Unit A2 1, Physiology and Ecosystems, May 2014, © CCEA 2017

3. (a) An investigation was carried out in a laboratory to determine the photoperiod necessary to promote flowering in a species of plant. The results are shown in the table below.

Length of continuous dark period / hours	Length of continuous light period / hours	Flowering outcome
16	8	no flowering
14	10	no flowering
12	12	no flowering
10	14	flowering
8	16	flowering

(i) What is the evidence that this species is a long-day plant? [1]

(ii) Suggest why the investigation was carried out in a laboratory rather than field (outdoor) conditions. [1]

(iii) Describe how this investigation could be extended to give a more precise value for the photoperiod required to promote flowering. [1]

(b) The following diagram shows the effect of different light regimes on a short-day plant.

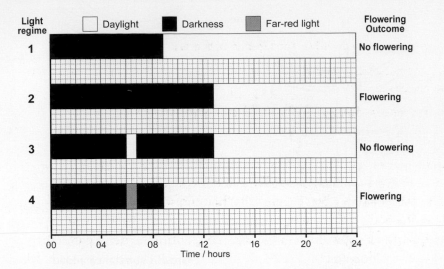

(i) In terms of phytochrome conversions, explain why the plant does not flower in light regime 3. [2]

(ii) Explain why flowering does occur in light regime 4, yet not in light regime 1. [3]

Question taken from CCEA's Biology Assessment Unit A2 1, Physiology and Ecosystems, May 2015, © CCEA 2017

Chapter 4 – Neurones and Synapses

Students should be able to:

4.3.3 Demonstrate knowledge and understanding of the structure of a neurone.

4.3.4 Demonstrate knowledge and understanding of the generation and transmission of nerve impulses.

4.3.5 Demonstrate knowledge and understanding of synaptic transmission.

Coordination in animals, as in plants, involves hormones (called plant growth substances in plants). However, animals also have a **nervous system**. The nervous system is based on a system of **neurones** (nerve cells) that transmit electrical **nerve impulses** throughout the body. Fine control and integration is provided through a system of **synapses** (junctions) between neurones that can control the nerve pathways involved.

> **Note:** Do not confuse neurones with nerves. Nerves are bundles of neurones (nerve cells) grouped together (analogous to how individual electrical wires are grouped in electrical cabling).

In general, nervous control is **faster** and more **precise** than hormone action.

Nervous control usually involves **receptors** and **effectors** with an interlinking **coordinator**. Receptors are found in, for example, the eye, ear and nose, and each type of receptor is sensitive to a particular type of **stimulus**. Using the examples in the previous sentence, a stimulus is something we see, hear or smell. **Effectors** are parts of the body that produce the **response**; in mammals effectors are often muscles. Coordination invariably involves the **central nervous system (CNS)** comprising the brain and the spinal cord. Consequently, many of the neurones in the body travel **to** the CNS from receptors and **from** the CNS to effectors.

Neurones

There are three main types of neurone:

- **Motor neurones** – carry impulses from the CNS (brain or spinal cord) to effectors (muscles and glands).
- **Sensory neurones** – carry impulses from receptors to the CNS.
- **Connector** (relay, association or intermediate) neurones – connect neurones within the CNS.

Each type of neurone has the same function – to conduct **nerve impulses**. However, the three types differ in location as outlined above. Furthermore, they have different shapes and sizes as seen in the following diagram.

> **Note:** Neurones are much longer than they appear in the diagram. Some neurones can have a thousand or more Schwann cells along the length of the axon.

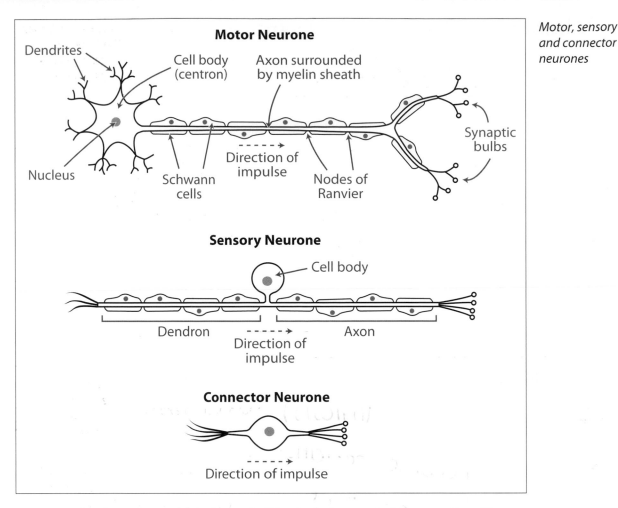

Motor, sensory and connector neurones

As seen in the diagram, neurones have a cell body and an extended nerve fibre. The **cell body** (**centron**) contains a nucleus, mitochondria and other organelles as well as Nissl's granules (large groups of ribosomes).

Terminology surrounding the **nerve fibre** depends on whether the part involved carries impulses to the cell body or away from it. If it transmits impulses away from the cell body, it is referred to as an **axon** – in motor neurones the entire fibre is an axon. However, if a part of the fibre is carrying impulses to the cell body (as in sensory neurones) it is called a **dendron** – **dendrites** are very small (and numerous) extensions that can conduct impulses into a dendron (for example, a sensory neurone) or into the cell body directly (for example, a motor neurone). Axons terminate in **synaptic bulbs** (knobs). Nerve fibres can range in length from less than a millimetre (some connector neurones) to over a metre.

In mammals, many nerve fibres (but not all) are **myelinated**. This means that their dendrons and axons are covered with an insulating **myelin sheath**. The myelin sheath, rich in the lipid myelin, is formed from the greatly extended cell surface membrane of **Schwann cells** repeatedly being wrapped round the axon (or dendron). The Schwann cells (each about 1 mm in length) are arranged at intervals along the nerve fibre with small gaps between each cell called **nodes of Ranvier**. At these nodes the dendron or axon is exposed. The myelin sheath is both protective in function and also serves to speed up nervous conduction.

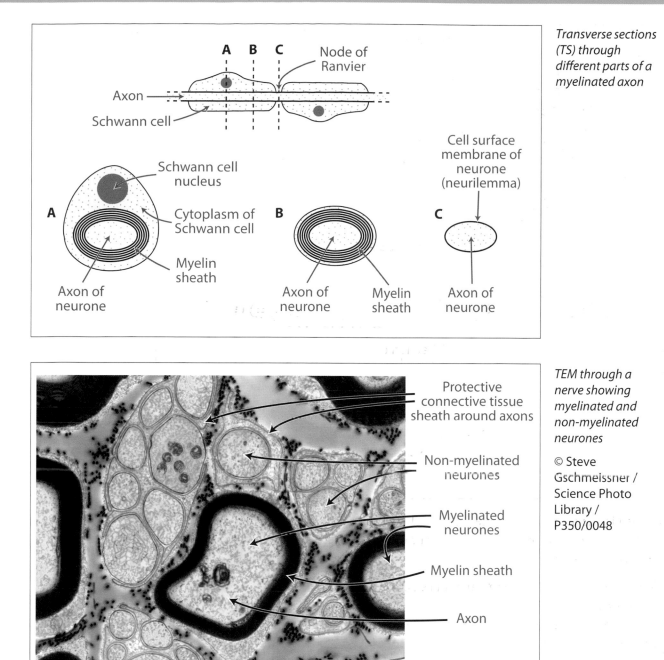

Transverse sections (TS) through different parts of a myelinated axon

TEM through a nerve showing myelinated and non-myelinated neurones

© Steve Gschmeissner / Science Photo Library / P350/0048

Note: Nerves are bundles of neurones protected within an outer protective layer. Nerves can contain sensory neurones only, motor neurones only, or can be mixed and contain both types.

The nerve impulse

The resting potential

Being able to conduct electrical impulses, neurones are highly specialised cells. They have a potential difference across their cell surface membranes called a **resting potential**, ie the neurones are **polarised** as there is an electrochemical gradient across the membrane. This potential difference is caused by there being an excess of positively charged ions (Na^+) outside the membrane compared with inside. At rest, the outside of the neurone is positive relative to the inside (or the inside is negative relative to the outside) with a potential difference of around **70 mV** (millivolts). This differential can be maintained as the cell surface membrane is **largely impermeable to the flow of sodium ions** when not conducting an impulse (an important feature as if it was permeable, the Na^+ positive ions would diffuse into the neurone down the concentration gradient).

The action potential

When a neurone is stimulated the cell surface membrane becomes **permeable** to ions. With an excess of positive ions outside the neurone relative to inside, they diffuse into the neurone down the concentration gradient. As the potential difference across the cell surface membrane decreases, a point is reached (the outside +55 mV relative to the inside) where a number of gated ion channels open, rapidly increasing the rate of diffusion of ions leading to **depolarisation** of the neurone.

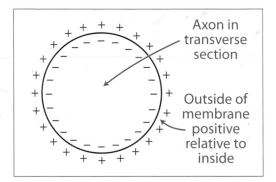

Axon in transverse section

Outside of membrane positive relative to inside

The resting potential

As positive ions flood in, the inside becomes positive relative to the outside, reaching a potential difference of around 40 mV. This depolarisation and reversal of potential difference in neurones is called an **action potential**, a sequence of events that takes about 1 millisecond.

At the peak of the action potential (inside of neurone +40 mV relative to outside) the recovery phase starts and the positive ions both **diffuse** and are **pumped out** of the neurone. This rapidly restores the resting potential and the cell surface membrane becomes largely impermeable again to Na^+. During this recovery phase (**refractory period**) a further impulse cannot occur as the gated ion channels are closed and the resting potential has not been fully restored. The entire electrochemical sequence of events associated with an action potential takes about 4 milliseconds.

Changes in the potential difference across the axon membrane as an action potential occurs

Explanation of diagram:

1. Resting potential with inside of axon –70 mV relative to outside (another way of saying outside of membrane is +70 mV relative to inside).

2. Membrane becomes permeable and positive ions diffuse into the axon – membrane is starting to become depolarised.

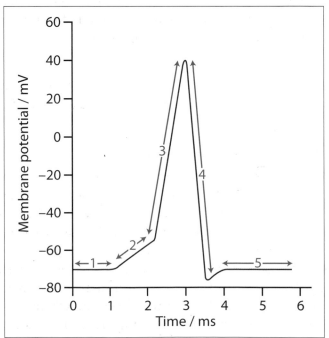

3. At –55 mV (inside relative to the outside) gated channels open and positive ions flood in at an even more rapid rate. Rapid depolarisation of the membrane takes place and the inside becomes +40 mV relative to the outside – the action potential.

4. Positive ions diffuse out and are also pumped out of the axon. This stage is called the refractory period as the membrane cannot be depolarised again until the resting potential is restored. At the end of this stage there is a slight 'overshoot' as the inside of the axon membrane becomes slightly more negative **(hyperpolarisation)** than in the normal resting potential.

5. The resting potential is restored and the axon can conduct another nerve impulse if stimulated.

Note: The sequence of events in the diagram representing the action potential describes the sequence as it occurs at one point on the axon over a very short period of time (a few milliseconds).

The **refractory period** has a number of functions:

• It ensures that the action potentials are propagated in one direction only. This is important as axons are physiologically capable of transmitting an impulse in either direction.

• It also limits the number of action potentials that can be fired and ensures that each action potential is a discrete entity.

Two more important features about nerve impulses:

• The **threshold stimulus** refers to the level of stimulus a neurone requires before an action potential is produced, for example, a small degree of depolarisation in the cell surface membrane of the neurone can occur without resulting in an action potential but at a critical point (the threshold potential) an action potential will result.

• The **all-or-nothing-law** refers to the principle that once the threshold stimulus is reached, the action potential results, ie an action potential either occurs or it does not; different intensities of action potential do not occur – they are all the same.

Once an action potential occurs it sweeps along the neurone as a **nerve impulse**. The propagation of the nerve impulse is discussed in the next section.

The threshold stimulus and the all-or-nothing-law

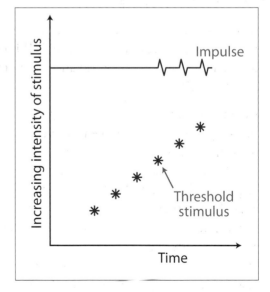

Propagation of the nerve impulse

Action potentials 'move' very rapidly along neurones. In reality a wave of depolarisation moves rapidly along the neurone. Just as quickly the region immediately behind the depolarised zone becomes repolarised. As one part of the membrane becomes depolarised, it sets up **local (electrical) circuits** with the areas immediately adjacent on either side. Positive ions from the depolarised zone pass along the inside of the membrane towards the polarised zone immediately in front. A similar effect occurs on the outside of the membrane, where positive

Local circuits and nerve impulse propagation

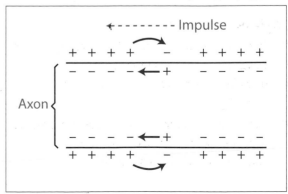

ions move back from the (as yet) still polarised zone into the depolarised zone. It is these processes occurring continuously that creates a wave of depolarisation that moves rapidly along the neurone. Similar circuits enable the resting potential to be restored directly behind the action potential.

Factors affecting the speed of the nerve impulse

The speed of the nerve impulse is affected by a number of factors including the presence or absence of a myelin sheath and the thickness of the axon.

The **myelin sheath** acts as an electrical insulator in myelinated neurones. As an insulator it prevents depolarisation in that part of the neurone. However, every 1–2 mm along the neurone the sheath is disrupted – these breaks are the junctions between adjacent Schwann cells. At these points, called **nodes of Ranvier**, depolarisation can take place. The local circuits form between the nodes only, allowing sections of the neurone to be bypassed. The action potentials 'jump' from one node to the next in a process called **saltatory conduction**.

The **diameter of the axon** also affects the speed of impulse. In general, the thicker the axon, the faster the impulse. This is because there is proportionally less 'leakage' of ions in a neurone with a larger diameter. If there is too much leakage, as can happen in axons with very small diameters, it makes it very difficult to maintain the potential gradients required to form resting and action potentials.

In myelinated neurones, there are relatively few ion channels under the fatty myelin sheath (they are concentrated at the nodes of Ranvier). Consequently myelination tends to overcome the problems presented by neurones of small diameter, in addition to producing the faster speeds associated with saltatory conduction, for example, up to 100 m s^{-1}.

As with many metabolic processes, the speed of a nerve impulse is affected by **temperature**. As temperature affects the rate of diffusion of ions involved in neurone action, it affects the speed that neurones can conduct impulses.

> **Note 1:** The zone of depolarisation is the part of the neurone where polarity is reversed, ie the inside is positive relative to the outside.
>
> **Note 2:** Some textbooks refer to the propagation of the nerve impulse as being analogous to a 'Mexican wave' moving around a sports arena.

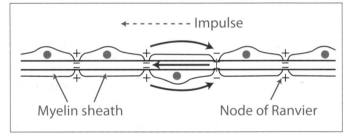

Saltatory conduction in myelinated neurones

Synapses

Synapses are junctions between the axon of one neurone and the dendrite (or dendron/centron) of an adjacent neurone.

Structure of synapses

Impulses are transmitted from one neurone to another by chemicals called **neurotransmitters** that diffuse across a very small gap, **the synaptic cleft**, which is 20–30 nm wide. Both the **pre-synaptic neurone**, the neurone that releases the transmitter, and the **post-synaptic neurone**, the adjacent neurone that receives the diffusing neurotransmitter, are specialised for their roles in synaptic transmission.

The end of the pre-synaptic neurone is thickened into a **synaptic bulb (knob)**. Synaptic bulbs contain large numbers of mitochondria (important in manufacturing the neurotransmitter) and **synaptic vesicles** in which the neurotransmitter is stored.

The membrane of the post-synaptic neurone contains **receptors** complementary to the type of neurotransmitter involved in that particular synapse. In general, the principle is that the neurotransmitters that pass across the synaptic cleft will cause depolarisation in the post-synaptic neurone allowing the nerve impulse to continue from one neurone to the next.

Note: A synapse includes the synaptic bulb, the synaptic cleft and the post-synaptic neurone membrane. If you get a question about synaptic transmission you will probably be expected to account for what takes place in each of these areas.

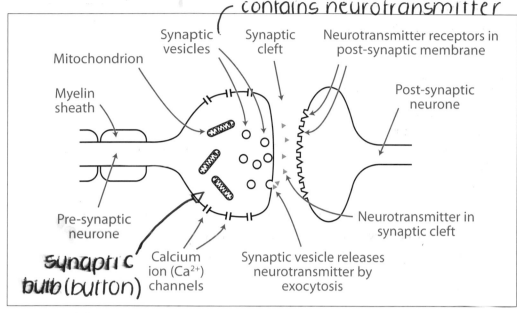

A typical synapse

Transmission at synapses

1. When an impulse arrives at the end of a neurone (synaptic bulb), calcium ion (Ca^{2+}) channels open allowing **calcium ions** to diffuse into the synaptic bulb.

2. The calcium ions cause the **synaptic vesicles** to move towards the pre-synaptic membrane.

3. The vesicles fuse with the pre-synaptic membrane, releasing the neurotransmitter (typically **acetylcholine**) by **exocytosis** into the synaptic cleft.

4. The acetylcholine diffuses across the synaptic cleft and binds to acetylcholine **receptors** in the post-synaptic membrane.

5. This causes the opening of ion (Na^+) channels in the membrane of the post-synaptic neurone. As positive ions diffuse in, the membrane becomes **rapidly depolarised** and an **excitatory post-synaptic potential (EPSP)** is generated.

6. If sufficient depolarisation takes place (dependent on the number of neurotransmitter molecules filling receptor sites), the EPSP will reach the **threshold** intensity required to produce an **action potential** in the post-synaptic neurone.

7. The enzyme **acetylcholinesterase** (attached to the post-synaptic membrane) breaks down the acetylcholine. The breakdown products, **choline** and **ethanoic acid** (acetyl), are released into the cleft. It is very important that the acetylcholine is broken down and does not continually remain in a receptor – this prevents it continuously generating a new action potential in the post-synaptic neurone.

8. The breakdown products diffuse across the cleft and are reabsorbed into the synaptic bulb. They are subsequently **re-synthesised** into **acetylcholine** which is stored in the synaptic vesicles to be used again. The ATP required is produced by the **mitochondria**.

acetylcholinesterase
↓
acetylcholine ⟶ choline + ethanoic acid

Function of synapses

The diffusion of chemicals across a short gap is necessarily slower than the conduction of an impulse along myelinated neurones. However, due to the very short distances involved it is still very fast! Nonetheless, the presence of synapses gives the nervous system many advantages.

- Synapses enable nerve impulses to pass from neurone to neurone – Synapses allow **nervous communication to continue** throughout the body, even though the nerve 'hardware' (neurones) is not continuous.

- They ensure **unidirectionality** – Nerve impulses can only pass from the pre-synaptic neurone to the post-synaptic neurone, as the neurotransmitter is only made in the pre-synaptic neurone and neurotransmitter receptors are only in the membrane of the post-synaptic neurone.

- They **prevent** the **overstimulation** of effectors (for example, muscles) – Too many impulses passing along the same neurone in a short period of time will exhaust the supply of the neurotransmitter more quickly than it can be built up – the synapses **fatigue**.

- They provide **integration** – This may involve a number of pre-synaptic neurones forming junctions with one post-synaptic neurone. In effect, synapses provide **flexibility** – if there were no synapses, nervous activity would be little more than a series of reflexes with a particular stimulus producing an automatic and never-changing response. Integration is aided through the process of summation, which is discussed in the next section.

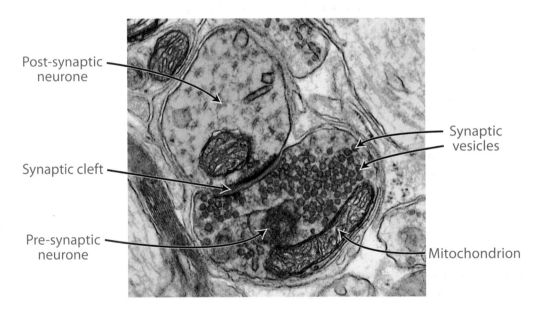

TEM of a synapse in the brain

© Thomas Deerinck, NCMIR / Science Photo Library / P360/0487

Note 1: In the TEM (transmission electron micrograph) above, the axons of the two neurones extending beyond the synapse are not evident. This is because they were in different planes to the very thin section chosen for this photograph.

Note 2: A2 examinations will test synoptic knowledge, ie AS knowledge important in understanding A2 content. For example, you could be asked for the evidence that shows that the image is a transmission electron micrograph rather than a SEM (scanning electron micrograph).

Summation is important in providing the complexity and flexibility that synapses demonstrate. For example, an infrequent action potential reaching a synapse may not be sufficient to cause an action potential in the adjacent post-synaptic neurone. However, a series of impulses travelling along the same neurone or a number of pre-synaptic neurones operating in unison, each releasing neurotransmitter chemicals, may be enough to cause a sufficient EPSP to trigger an impulse in the post-synaptic neurone.

The synapses discussed so far refer to **excitatory synapses** – neurotransmitter chemicals are released with the function of causing an EPSP and a subsequent action potential. **Inhibitory synapses** have the function of making it more difficult for synaptic transmission to take place. The neurotransmitter they release makes it more difficult for an EPSP to form in the post-synaptic membrane. The inhibitory neurotransmitters lead to an influx of negative ions in the post-synaptic membrane, making the inside of the membrane even more negative, thus creating an **inhibitory post-synaptic potential (IPSP)** in the post-synaptic neurone which is even more negative than the normal resting potential. Consequently, this **hyperpolarisation** makes it even more difficult than normal for excitatory synapses to produce an EPSP that reaches threshold level.

Whether an impulse will actually take place in the post-synaptic neurone depends on the relative contribution excitatory and inhibitory synapses make in promoting or inhibiting depolarisation.

Why have inhibitory synapses? They can help by reducing the input of background stimuli that would clutter up the nervous activity in the brain or may prevent some reflex actions.

The effects of summation and the action of inhibitory synapses provide integration and fine control through the synapse **integrating** all the different inputs (there may be hundreds) at synaptic junctions. Synapses also have an important role in filtering out low-level background stimuli thus preventing overload and overstimulation.

Neurotransmitter substances

Acetylcholine is the primary transmitter substance in the central nervous system (CNS) of vertebrates, although **noradrenaline** (typically used in involuntary nervous control, for example, the regulation of gut movements) is one of several other types. However, each synaptic bulb produces only one type of neurotransmitter.

GABA (aminobutyric acid) is an example of a neurotransmitter that is released at inhibitory synapses. It is the chief inhibitory neurotransmitter in mammals. GABA causes negative ions to flow into post-synaptic neurones, thereby causing hyperpolarisation as described above. GABA has many roles including helping reduce anxiety and 'panic attacks' through a 'damping down' of the nerve pathways in the brain.

Substance	Effect
Nicotine	Stimulates the release of acetylcholine and other neurotransmitters making action potentials more likely.
Curare	Blocks receptors (at neuromuscular junctions) preventing synaptic transmission – loss of muscle function.
Opioids	Block the calcium channels in the pre-synaptic neurone. Less transmitter substance is released and action potentials less likely. Opioids and related compounds can provide pain relief by reducing impulses coming from the pain receptors.

Note: Many examination questions involve drugs that either stimulate, or are antagonistic to, neurotransmitters. The questions often provide information concerning the function of the drug involved (as in the table above) and you would be expected to deduce the effect it would have on synaptic transmission.

Practical work

You should be familiar with photomicrographs and electron micrographs of neurones and synapses – see images earlier in this chapter as examples.

Exam questions

1. (a) Diagram X below represents a myelinated neurone in transverse section (TS).

    Two important features of the neurone are labelled A and B.

Diagram X

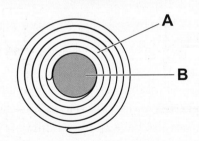

    (i) Identify the features labelled A and B. [2]

Diagram Y below represents part of the myelinated neurone in longitudinal section (LS).

Diagram Y

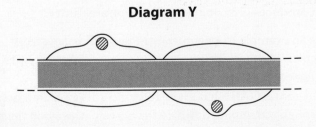

    (ii) Make a copy of Diagram Y and draw a line to show where the section represented in Diagram X could have been taken. [1]

(b) Describe how an action potential is propagated along a myelinated neurone. [2]

Neurones in an earthworm are non-myelinated and most are very thin in transverse section. However, earthworms have a small number of axons (giant axons) that are much thicker than the others. When an earthworm has pressure applied suddenly to its body surface, or the surface is damaged, the giant axons are involved in a withdrawal response.

(c) Using the information provided, explain the advantage to the earthworm of possessing giant axons. [2]

Question taken from CCEA's Biology Assessment Unit A2 1, Physiology and Ecosystems, January 2014, © CCEA 2017

2. (a) An investigation was carried out to investigate the effect of electrical stimulation on isolated neurones. This type of investigation uses neurones obtained from freshly killed animals. The experimental set-up is shown in the diagram below.

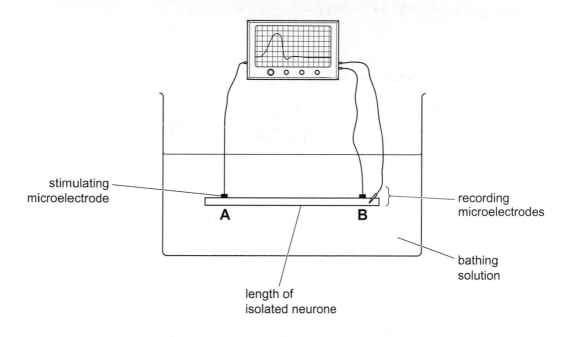

In the investigation the neurone was stimulated via a microelectrode at A, where depolarisation of the neurone was initiated. At B, a pair of microelectrodes, one external and one internal, record the potential difference as an impulse passes.

An excitatory neurone and an inhibitory neurone synapsing with a post-synaptic neurone are shown in the diagram below.

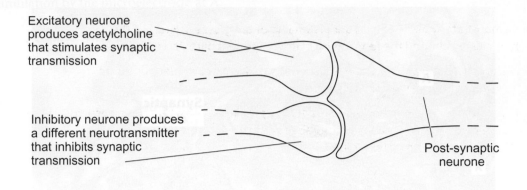

Excitatory neurone produces acetylcholine that stimulates synaptic transmission

Inhibitory neurone produces a different neurotransmitter that inhibits synaptic transmission

Post-synaptic neurone

(i) Suggest how an inhibitory synapse can prevent an excitatory synapse producing an action potential in a post-synaptic neurone. [2]

A deficit of the neurotransmitter serotonin, found in some inhibitory synapses, can create states of anxiety and panic in individuals.

(ii) The drug Prozac can be used to alleviate the symptoms caused by a shortage of serotonin. Using the information provided, suggest how Prozac affects synaptic transmission. [2]

Question taken from CCEA's Biology Assessment Unit A2 1, Physiology and Ecosystems, May 2013, © CCEA 2017

4. *Quality of written communication is awarded a maximum of 2 marks in this section.*

Neurones are specialised cells, highly adapted for rapid nervous communication throughout the body. The diagram below represents a motor neurone.

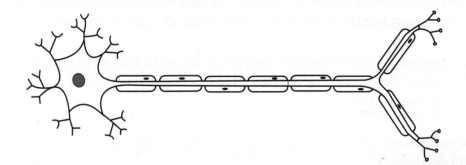

(a) Using the diagram and your knowledge, describe and explain how neurones are adapted for their function. Your answer should refer to how nerve impulses are initiated, propagated and passed on. [12]

(b) Nervous communication involves synaptic transmission. While they may limit the speed of nervous transmission, synapses have a necessary role in coordination and control. Outline why synapses are important. [4]

Quality of written communication. [2]

Question taken from CCEA's Biology Assessment Unit A2 1, Physiology and Ecosystems, May 2015, © CCEA 2017

Chapter 5 – The Eye and Muscle

Students should be able to:

4.3.6   Demonstrate knowledge and understanding of the gross structure of the mammalian eye and the functioning of its component parts in normal vision.

4.3.8   Demonstrate knowledge and understanding of the structure and function of voluntary (skeletal) muscle as an effector.

4.3.7/9 Carry out practical work including examining prepared slides, photomicrographs and/or electron micrographs, as appropriate, of the mammalian eye and skeletal, cardiac and smooth muscle.

The mammalian eye

The mammalian eye is a complex sense organ. Only a very small section of the eye contains the photoreceptors that are sensitive to light. The rest of the eye contains structures that ensure that the receptors in the retina at the back of the eye receive focused light rays at the correct intensity to form an image.

Structure of the eye

The diagram below represents a cross-section of the mammalian eye.

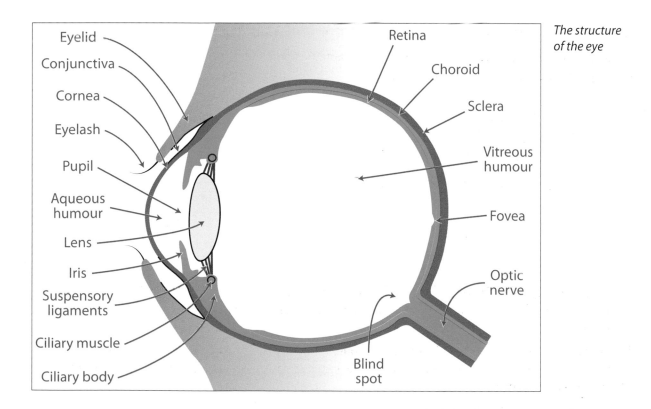

The structure of the eye

The following table summarises the functions of the main parts of the eye.

Part of eye	Description	Role
conjunctiva	thin epithelial layer covering the front edge of the sclera and the inner surface of the eyelids	moistens and lubricates the front of the eye
sclera	tough opaque connective tissue covering the eye – replaced by transparent cornea at front	protects against damage; site of attachment of eye muscles
cornea	front transparent part of sclera	transparent and most refraction (bending) of light occurs here
aqueous humour	transparent watery fluid between cornea and lens	maintains the shape of the front part of the eye
iris	muscular layer with both circular and radial muscle; contains pigment that absorbs light	adjusts the size of the pupil to control the amount of light entering the eye
pupil	gap within the iris	the area through which light reaches the lens and enters the centre of the eye
ciliary body	contains a muscular ring of (ciliary) muscle around the eye; suspensory ligaments extend from the ciliary body and hold the lens in place	adjusts the shape of the lens to focus light rays
suspensory ligaments	ligaments that connect the ciliary body to the lens	transfers tension in the wall of the eyeball to make the lens thinner; important when focusing on distant objects
lens	transparent biconvex structure with refractive properties	refracts light and focuses light rays on the retina
vitreous humour	transparent, jelly-like material between the lens and the back of the eye	maintains the shape of the rear part of the eye and supports the lens
retina	inner layer of the eyeball containing the light sensitive receptor cells (rods and cones)	when stimulated the rods and cones initiate impulses in associated neurones
fovea	region in the centre of the retina that is particularly rich in cones and does not contain rods	part of eye that gives the clearest daylight colour vision
choroid	a layer of pigmented cells between the retina and the sclera	contains blood vessels that supply the retina; prevents reflection of light back through the eye
optic nerve	bundle of sensory nerve fibres that leave the retina	transmits impulses from the retina to the brain
blind spot	part of the retina where the sensory neurones that unite to form the optic nerve leave the eye	contains no light sensitive cells so is not sensitive to light

Function of the eye

Obtaining a focused image – As light rays enter and pass through the cornea, some bending (refraction) of light automatically takes place. In reality, most of the refraction takes place in the cornea. Further bending takes place as the light passes through the lens. By adjusting the thickness of the lens, light rays can be focused on the retina, irrespective of their angle as they enter the eye. The diagram below shows how the lens focuses light from distant and close-up objects.

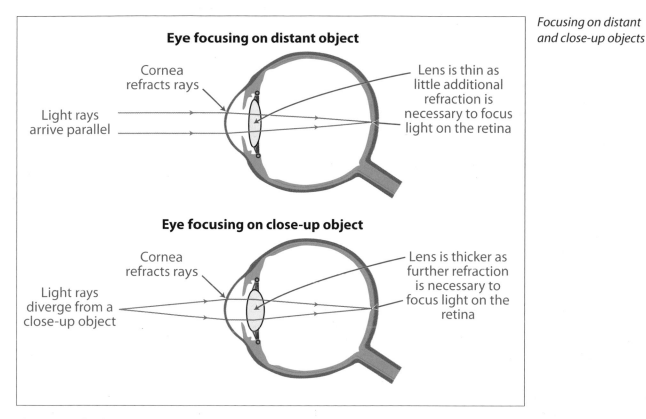

Focusing on distant and close-up objects

The **ciliary body** contains a ring of muscle (**ciliary muscle**) running around the inside of the eyeball and surrounding the lens. The lens is attached to the ciliary body by **suspensory ligaments** that resemble small pieces of nylon thread. If the ciliary body relaxes, the tension in the wall of the eyeball is transferred through the suspensory ligaments to the lens (in effect, the ciliary body springs out to form a bigger diameter pulling the suspensory ligaments taut). When this happens, the suspensory ligaments pull the lens into a thinner shape that has less refractive power.

The opposite happens to make the lens fatter when a greater degree of refraction is required. The ciliary muscle contracts to form a tighter circle with a smaller diameter. The suspensory ligaments are not pulled taut so relax and with less pressure on the lens it is able to spring back to its 'normal' thicker shape.

The adjustment of lens thickness to ensure that the light rays are focused on the retina, irrespective of the angle of light rays reaching the eye, is called **accommodation**.

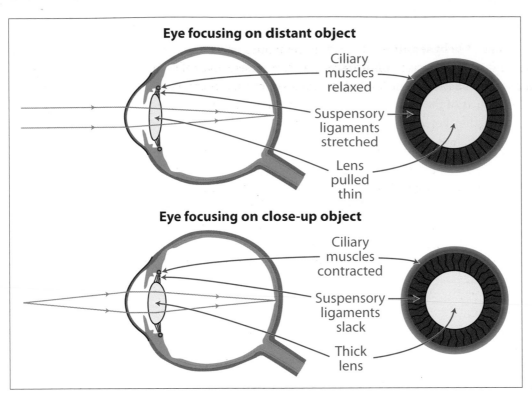

Eye focusing on distant object

Ciliary muscles relaxed

Suspensory ligaments stretched

Lens pulled thin

Eye focusing on close-up object

Ciliary muscles contracted

Suspensory ligaments slack

Thick lens

The role of the ciliary muscles and suspensory ligaments in accommodation

Note: Ligaments are tough and flexible but they do not stretch. Not being stretchable is important as this ensures that the suspensory ligaments pull the lens thin when the ciliary muscle relaxes.

Controlling the amount of light that enters the eye – It is important that the correct **intensity of light** enters the eye and reaches the retina. Too little or too much light will prevent an image being formed. In addition, too much light can damage the sensitive light receptor cells in the retina. In low light intensities a large **pupil** diameter allows as much light as possible to enter the eye to ensure that there is sufficient light to stimulate the photoreceptors in the retina. In bright light the pupil is reduced to a small size to restrict the amount of light entering. The size of the pupil is a direct consequence of the size of the iris.

The muscles of the **iris** can contract or relax to change the size of the pupil. The iris consists of two types of muscle – **radial** and **circular**. Radial muscles are like the spokes of a wheel moving out from the edge of the pupil through the iris, and circular muscles form rings within the iris around the pupil.

Note: Accommodation and the control of the amount of light entering the eye are both examples of reflex action. They are automatic responses, not under voluntary control.

- In **low light** intensities the **radial muscles contract** (and the circular muscles relax) – this makes the pupil larger.

- In **bright light** the **circular muscles contract** (and the radial muscles relax) – this makes the pupil smaller.

Adjusting the size of the pupil

Pupil dilated

Pupil constricted

Iris

Pupil

Circular muscles relaxed

Radial muscles contracted

Circular muscles contracted

Radial muscles relaxed

The retina in detail

The retina contains millions of light sensitive cells and the neurones with which they synapse. **Rod** and **cone** cells are specialised **photoreceptors** (photosensitive cells) in that light energy brings about change in the level of polarisation of their membranes – they act as transducers converting a light stimulus to a nerve impulse in their associated neurones.

Rod cells – In rods the light sensitive pigment **rhodopsin** is packed into an array of membranes in the outer part of the rod cell. Rhodopsin is formed from a protein **opsin**, combined with a light absorbing compound called **retinal** which is derived from vitamin A. When stimulated by light, the rhodopsin breaks down into its retinal and opsin components. This changes the membrane potential of the rod cell and creates a **generator potential**. If a **threshold level** is achieved, this can cause the adjacent linking neurone (bipolar neurone) to become depolarised to the extent that it will conduct an action potential.

> **Note:** A generator potential is the degree of depolarision a stimulated receptor can produce. Only if the generator potential reaches a threshold level will it produce an action potential in the neurone.

The inner segment of the rod contains the cell's nucleus and mitochondria, the latter important in producing the ATP needed for the re-synthesis of rhodopsin from retinal and opsin following light stimulation.

Rods are adapted for vision in **low light intensities**. They have **high sensitivity** as the rhodopsin will break down readily in low light levels requiring only a small amount of light energy. However, this can lead to the phenomenon of **dark adaptation**. In bright light virtually all the rhodopsin is broken down (bleached) and it takes time for it to be re-synthesised. This explains why if we move from a well lit area into a dark room, our vision in the low light environment is very poor initially but gradually improves. In effect, our eyes have changed from being light-adapted (when in bright light) to being dark-adapted, ie adapted for functioning in low light intensities.

Cone cells – The same general principles apply to the functioning of **cone** cells. However, in cones a different pigment, **iodopsin**, is situated in the membranes of the outer segment. The iodopsin is less readily broken down and will only produce a generator potential in bright light.

While rods are not sensitive to colour and provide monochromatic vision, **cones** provide **colour vision**.

Iodopsin exists in three different forms with each form being sensitive to different wavelengths of light. The absorption peaks of the three types of cone (each with a different type of iodopsin) correspond to the colours **blue**, **green** and **red** (the **trichromatic theory of**

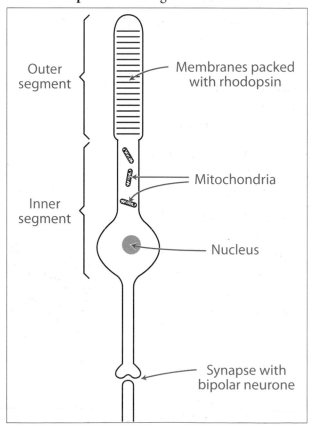

A rod cell

Outer segment

Membranes packed with rhodopsin

Inner segment

Mitochondria

Nucleus

Synapse with bipolar neurone

colour vision). Pure blue light will only break down the 'blue' iodopsin but of course most light is not pure blue, green or red. In effect, it is the degree of stimulation of each type of cone that determines colour vision.

The arrangement of rods and cones in the retina – It is not only the differences in the structure and sensitivities of rod and cone cells that are important in their functioning. Their distribution across the retina and the different ways in which they are arranged with linking neurone cells are also crucial.

As the diagram below shows, the rods and cones form a layer immediately inside the choroid. A layer of **bipolar neurones** lies immediately inside the photosensitive cells and beyond the bipolar neurones there is another layer of sensory cells (**ganglion cells**). It is the axons of the ganglion cells that group together to make up the optic nerve that carries the impulses from the retina to the brain.

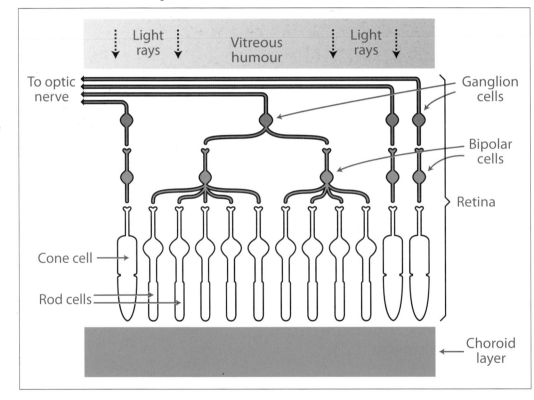

Section through the retina showing photoreceptor cells and their associated neurones

The diagram also shows that each cone cell can synapse individually with its own bipolar neurone, ie each provides its own discrete image in vision. This is the basis of **high visual acuity** – the ability of cones to provide highly precise (colour) vision of high resolution – enabling the brain to distinguish between two points that are very close together. However, the rods show **retinal convergence**. This involves a number of rods having a common bipolar neurone (and a number of bipolar cells having a common ganglion cell). Retinal convergence allows the generator potentials from individual rods to combine together (**summation**) and reach the threshold required for producing an action potential in a bipolar neurone.

Allied to the ability of rhodopsin (in rods) to break down more easily than iodopsin (in cones), retinal convergence is the basis of the **sensitivity** that rods show. The light energy reaching any one rod is not enough to stimulate the bipolar cell sufficiently but stimulation of a group of rods provides enough generator potential to produce an impulse in the bipolar neurone. This of course also explains another feature of rods –

Note 1: The different properties of rods and cones, and their retinal arrangement, explains why we can see detailed colour vision during the daytime (the light intensity is sufficient to break down iodopsin) but can only see less detailed black and white image during the night (light intensity sufficient to break down rhodopsin but not iodopsin).

their **lack of visual acuity** or high resolution as the individual rods in each 'convergence unit' only provide as much detail as one cone cell.

Note 2: Do not confuse sensitivity with visual acuity. Sensitivity is the ability to operate in very low light intensities – not the ability to provide precision vision.

Note 3: If you look again at the arrangement of photosensitive cells and neurones in the retina, you will note that the light rays have to pass through layers of neurones before reaching the light sensitive cells. This 'inverted' arrangement appears to be less efficient than if it was the opposite way round with the photosensitive cells being on the inside and the neurone 'cabling' behind. Perhaps, but the arrangement in mammals is a consequence of the evolutionary development of the eye.

The graph below shows how the cones and rods are distributed across the retina. The distribution explains phenomena such as the blind spot and why we can distinguish shapes but not colour at the periphery of our vision, ie when the light rays are focused on the edge of the retina.

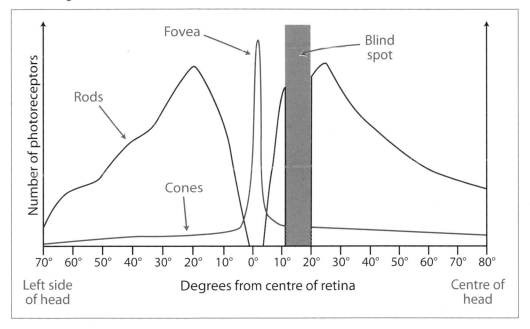

The distribution of rods and cones across the retina of the human left eye

Note: The graph above, illustrating the distribution of cones and rods across the left eye, shows that there are more rods at the right side of the retina (closer to centre of head) compared to the left. This facilitates peripheral vision on the left side of the head – the converse arrangement exists in the right eye.

Binocular vision

The presence of two eyes in mammals provides **binocular** or stereoscopic vision. If the two eyes create a single image it allows accurate **judgement of distance**. **Stereoscopic vision**, the ability to form **three-dimensional images**, is also possible.

In humans and other primates, and also in most predatory species, the eyes are positioned on the front of the head. This facilitates excellent judgement of distance and 3-D vision as discussed above. Many prey species, such as rabbits, have their eyes positioned on the side of their heads rather than at the front. This provides a wider field of view, a greater priority for prey aiding the detection of potential predators than 3-D vision.

Muscles

Muscles are specialised effectors that bring about movement through contraction. The main type of muscle in the body is skeletal muscle, muscle that is attached (via tendons) to the skeleton. Skeletal muscle is **voluntary** muscle in that it is under conscious control.

Structure of skeletal muscle

Skeletal (voluntary) muscle can vary considerably in size, for example, compare the triceps and biceps muscles with the muscles controlling the eyeball. However, the basic structure of all skeletal muscle is the same.

Skeletal muscle consists of many **muscle fibres** bunched together. Each fibre is surrounded by a cell surface membrane (**sarcolemma**). Each fibre is **multinucleate** with the nuclei typically arranged just inside the sarcolemma. The fibre, which is effectively a very specialised 'cell', contains the cell organelles typically found in any cell, but is particularly rich in **mitochondria**. At intervals, the sarcolemma folds deeply inwards to form **transverse tubules** or **T-tubules**.

The bulk of the muscle fibre is filled with highly specialised contractile units called **myofibrils**. Muscle fibres are very large structures and can be up to many centimetres long.

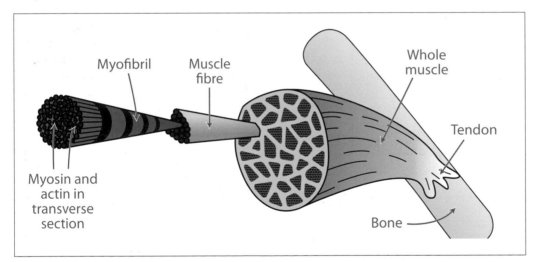

Muscle, muscle fibres and myofibrils

The ultrastructure of myofibrils – The myofibril consists largely of two types of protein, myosin and actin. **Myosin** forms **thick** filaments around 15 nm in diameter and **actin** forms **thin** filaments about 7 nm in diameter.

Myosin filaments lie in the central region of each contractile unit and are linked together by a thin disc (the **M-line**) that runs perpendicular to the orientation of the myosin filaments. The actin filaments slot between the outer edges of the myosin filaments and they are also held together by a thin disc called the **Z-line**. A section of myofibril between two Z-lines (ie the basic contractile unit) is called a **sarcomere**.

Note: Be clear that you can distinguish between the terms muscle, muscle fibre, myofibril and sarcomere.

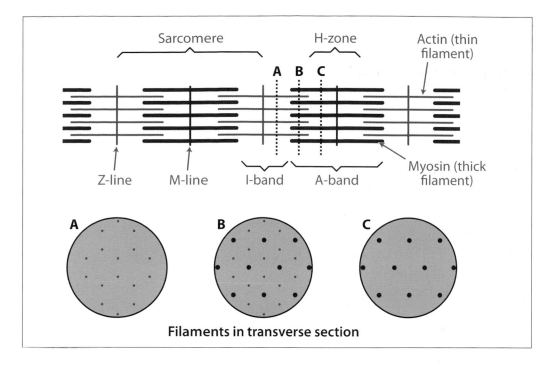

The arrangement of myosin and actin in a myofibril

The thicker myosin filaments form denser or darker striations or bands and the thinner actin filaments form less dense or lighter regions between them as seen in the diagram above. It is this alternating pattern of myosin and actin that forms the **striated (banded)** pattern of voluntary (striated) muscle as seen in electron micrographs.

The part of the myofibril containing myosin is referred to as the **A-band** (or **anisotropic band**). The A-band includes those areas where the thinner actin penetrates between the myosin filaments. The **I-band (or isotropic band)** is the part of the myofibril that contains actin only. The **H-zone** is the zone in the centre of the A-band where there is myosin only (the area beyond the ends of the actin filaments).

Furthermore, the relationship between the overlapping actin and myosin is very regular with each myosin filament being surrounded by six actin filaments in a regular hexagonal pattern, as highlighted in the enlarged image on the right.

TS of A-band (through region where myosin and actin filaments overlap)

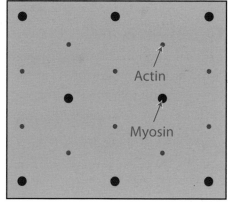

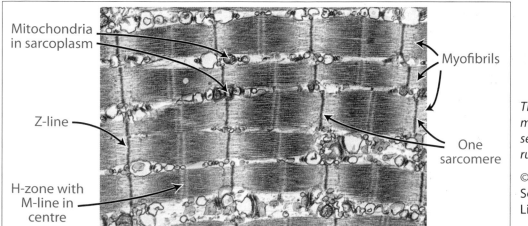

TEM of striated muscle showing series of myofibrils running left to right

Muscle contraction

The basic principle of muscle contraction is that the myosin and actin filaments slide past each other so reducing the overall length of the sarcomere (and muscle). The process is called the **sliding filament mechanism**.

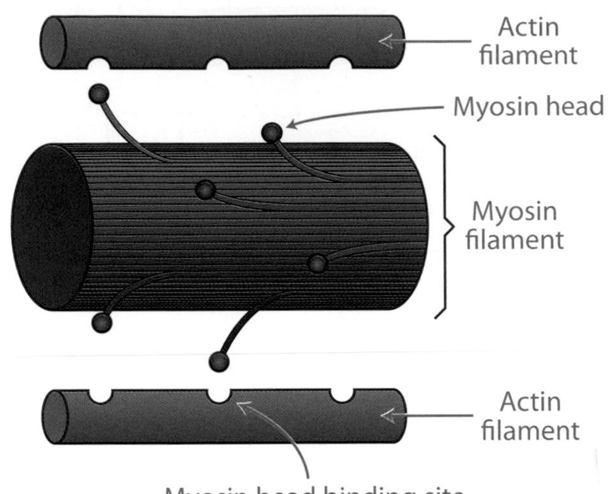

Before considering the mechanics of the sliding filament process, it is important to revisit the structure of the myosin and actin protein molecules. Although mainly a long fibrous molecule, the myosin also has small bulbous heads that protrude at intervals as shown in the diagram on the right. The thinner actin filaments have small binding sites into which the bulbous heads of the myosin fit.

When not contracting, the actin binding sites are blocked by another ancillary protein (tropomyosin) to prevent binding.

The process of muscle contraction can be summarised in the following steps:

Actin and myosin

Actin filament

Myosin head

Myosin filament

Actin filament

Myosin head binding site

- An action potential stimulates the muscle fibre as it travels through its extensive system of **T-tubules**.

- The action potential causes the calcium ion channels in the **sarcoplasmic reticulum** (the name given to the specialised endoplasmic reticulum of muscle cells) to open.

- This causes the **calcium ions** (Ca^{2+}) that have been stored in the sarcoplasmic reticulum to diffuse into the **sarcoplasm** (the cytoplasm of muscle cells) down a concentration gradient.

- The calcium ions cause **ancillary protein** (tropomyosin) that normally covers the binding sites on the actin filaments to be moved, so enabling the myosin bulbous heads to link with the actin binding sites (forming **actomyosin** bridges).

- Once attached, the myosin heads change their angle (rotate or 'rock' back to an angle about 45°) and pull the actin filaments over the adjacent myosin filaments (by about 10 nm).

- An **ATP** molecule attaches to each myosin head and the energy released from its hydrolysis enables the myosin head to detach from the stationary actin binding site and return to its original position.

- The detached myosin heads repeat the process so that the **cycle of attachment, rotation and release** is repeated in a type of ratchet mechanism, with each cycle occurring about five times each second.

- The cycle continues as long as the muscle fibre receives nervous stimulation (and has calcium ions present).

Note: You do **not** need to know about ancillary protein (tropomyosin) – see the fourth bullet point above and the following diagram. It is included here only for illustration purposes to show how calcium ions make the actin binding sites available. You **do** need to know that the presence of calcium ions enables the myosin heads to bind to (previously unavailable) binding sites on the actin.

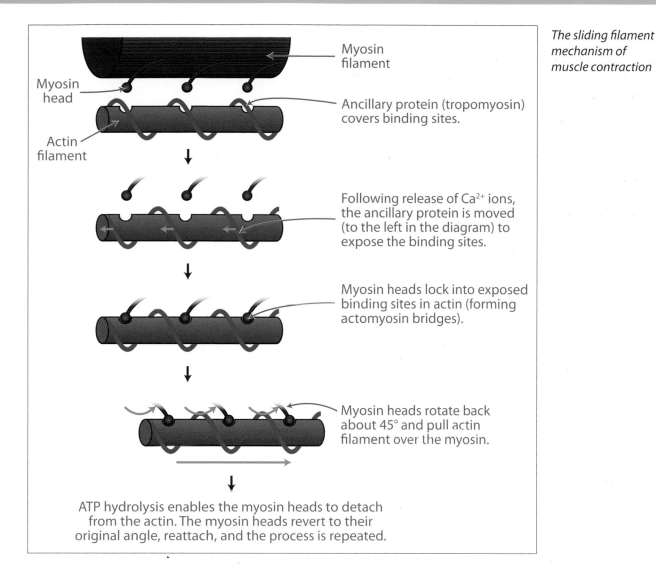

Myosin filament

Myosin head

Actin filament

Ancillary protein (tropomyosin) covers binding sites.

Following release of Ca^{2+} ions, the ancillary protein is moved (to the left in the diagram) to expose the binding sites.

Myosin heads lock into exposed binding sites in actin (forming actomyosin bridges).

Myosin heads rotate back about 45° and pull actin filament over the myosin.

ATP hydrolysis enables the myosin heads to detach from the actin. The myosin heads revert to their original angle, reattach, and the process is repeated.

The sliding filament mechanism of muscle contraction

The diagram on the right shows that as **contraction takes place** the arrangement of the myosin and actin filaments in each sarcomere changes as summarised below:

- The sarcomere shortens (distance between the Z-lines decreases).
- The H-zone becomes shorter.
- The I-band becomes shorter.

The diagram also shows that as contraction takes place, the **A-band** remains the **same length**.

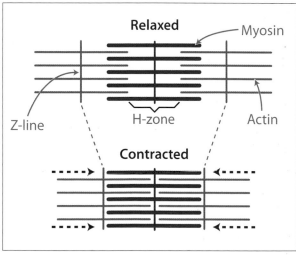

Relaxed

Myosin

Z-line

H-zone

Actin

Contracted

A sarcomere in a relaxed and contracted state

Note: myosin filaments in adjacent sarcomeres are not shown for clarity.

Note 1: With each sarcomere being microscopic in size (approx 2.5 μm) it is obvious that the contraction caused by each sarcomere shortening is almost negligible. However, with many sarcomeres lined end to end in a muscle fibre, and all contracting at the same time, the overall muscle contraction can be considerable.

Note 2: The power of muscle contraction is due to the many parallel myofibrils lined side by side in a muscle fibre (and many fibres in a single muscle) all contracting at the same time.

Note 3: The strength of muscle contraction depends on a number of factors including for how long the muscle is stimulated but also how many muscle fibres are actually stimulated and contracting. Although one motor neurone may control contraction in an entire muscle, not all the fibres may be contracted at the one time.

Skeletal muscle, although the most obvious in terms of size and extent, is not the only type of muscle in the body. Smooth and cardiac muscles also contract and bring about movement but are different in appearance and have different functions to skeletal muscle.

The three main types of muscle are summarised in the following table:

	Skeletal	**Smooth**	**Cardiac**
Appearance	Striated (banded) Multinucleate fibres	Discrete uninucleate cells are spindle-shaped Non-striated	Striated but branched with intercalated discs (seen as discrete lines) between cells
Distribution	Attached to bone throughout the body (most of the muscle in the body)	Lining gut and blood vessels Iris and ciliary body in eye	Wall of heart
Nervous control	Voluntary (conscious) control	Involuntary or automatic (for example, reflex action)	Myogenic and involuntary control

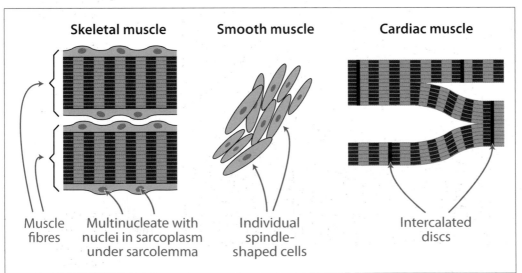

Skeletal muscle   Smooth muscle   Cardiac muscle

Muscle fibres   Multinucleate with nuclei in sarcoplasm under sarcolemma   Individual spindle-shaped cells   Intercalated discs

The three types of muscle

Practical work

You need to be familiar with prepared slides, photomicrographs and electron micrographs of muscle and muscle components in addition to the different types of muscle outlined in the table on the left.

Cardiac muscle

The electron micrograph on the right shows **cardiac muscle**.

Cardiac muscle can be difficult to distinguish from skeletal muscle – it is clear in this electron micrograph that the characteristic striated appearance of skeletal muscle is also present in cardiac muscle.

However, there are crucial differences. In cardiac muscle:

- cells branch.
- intercalated discs run across the myofibrils – these are important in synchronising electrical conduction and contraction in heart muscle.
- the cells are uninucleate.

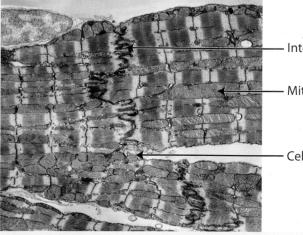

Intercalated disc

Mitochondrion

Cells branch

EM of cardiac muscle

© Thomas Deerinck / Science Photo Library / P154/0279

Smooth muscle

Smooth muscle contains elongated **spindle-shaped cells** that taper towards their ends and they do not have the striated appearance of the myofibrils of striated and cardiac muscle. There is a single **central nucleus** in each cell.

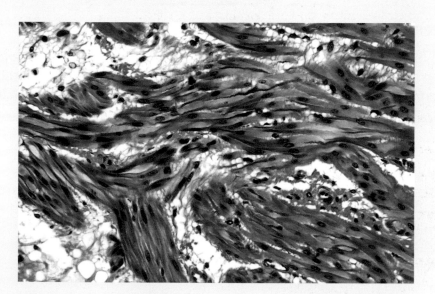

Photomicrograph of smooth muscle

© Microscape / Science Photo Library / C029/6643

Note 1: A photograph of skeletal muscle to help your understanding is present on page 77.

Note 2: You should also be familiar with preparations of the eye as prepared slides and EM photographs.

Although smooth muscle consists of discrete cells, each with a central nucleus, this is not always very obvious in photographs as many smooth muscle cells are bunched together and intertwined to form smooth muscle tissue as shown in the diagram above.

Exam questions

1. The following statements relate to the structure or function of the eye. Identify the term described by each statement.

- The structures that link the ciliary body and the lens
- The layer that prevents internal reflection of light in the eye
- The neurone arrangement that provides high sensitivity in low light intensities
- The type of vision that makes three dimensional images possible [4]

Question taken from CCEA's Biology Assessment Unit A2 1, Physiology and Ecosystems, January 2014, © CCEA 2017

2. (a) Photograph I shows a section through part of the wall of a mammalian eye.

Photograph I

© Ralph Eagle / Science Photo Library / P424/0213

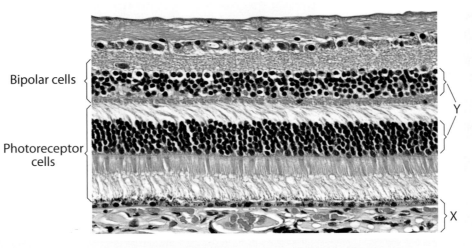

Bipolar cells

Photoreceptor cells

Y

X

(i) Identify layer X that lies immediately below the photoreceptor cells. [1]

(ii) Identify the dark circular structures in the layers labelled Y. [1]

(iii) The mammalian retina is described as being 'inverted'. Using Photograph I, suggest why the mammalian retina is described as being inverted and suggest a possible disadvantage of this. [2]

(b) Mammalian photoreceptor cells (rods and cones) and their associated neurones are represented in the diagram below.

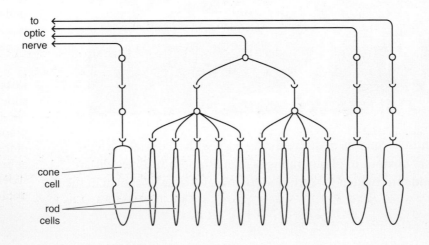

to optic nerve

cone cell

rod cells

The diagram shows that the rods and cones differ in the structural arrangement with their associated neurones. Describe and explain the significance of this to human vision. [4]

Question taken from CCEA's Biology Assessment Unit A2 1, Physiology and Ecosystems, January 2013, © CCEA 2017

3. (a) The diagram below represents a rod cell. Make a copy of the diagram.

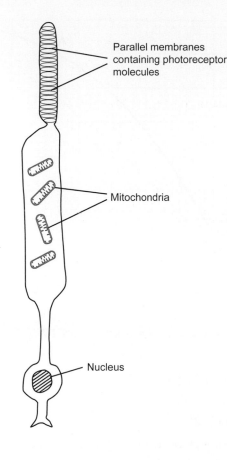

- (i) Add an arrow beside your copy of the diagram to show the direction of light entering the retina. [1]
- (ii) State the precise function of the mitochondria found in rod cells. [1]

(b) Transduction is the process of changing energy from one form to another. Phototransduction is a term that describes the general function of rod cells.

Suggest a definition for phototransduction in the context of rod cells. [1]

(c) In the retina, rod cells synapse with an adjacent bipolar cell. When a rod is not stimulated, the transmitter substance, glutamate, diffuses across to the bipolar neurone reducing the possibility of it becoming depolarised.

When the rod cell is stimulated, it stops releasing glutamate. The reduction in glutamate crossing the synaptic gap promotes depolarisation in the bipolar cell.

- (i) Using the information provided, give one similarity and one difference between the synaptic transmission described above and that in typical neurone to neurone synapses. [2]
- (ii) Give one advantage of the presence of synapses in nervous communication. [1]

(d) In an investigation concerning dark adaptation in rods, two individuals (A and B) were subjected to a period of time in very bright light. This was immediately followed by a period of time in darkness. Rod sensitivity was measured throughout the time in darkness. The results are shown in the graph below.

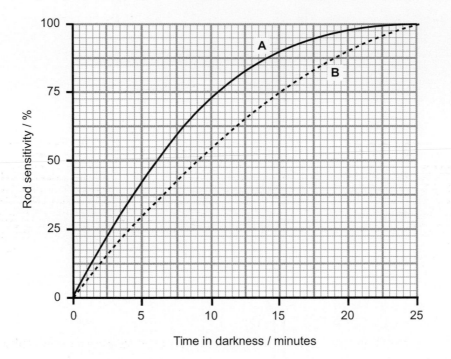

(i) Calculate the percentage change in rod sensitivity for individual A between 5 minutes and 15 minutes after entering dark conditions.

(Show your working.) [2]

(ii) Explain the results shown in the graph for individual A. [2]

(iii) Suggest one reason for the difference in response between individuals A and B. [1]

(e) When viewing objects in the night sky, people tend to view them with their eyes at a slight angle rather than focusing directly on the object of interest. Suggest a reason for this. [2]

Question taken from CCEA's Biology Assessment Unit A2 1, Physiology and Ecosystems, May 2014, © CCEA 2017

4. *Quality of written communication is awarded a maximum of 2 marks in this section.*

The mammalian eye is highly adaptable: capable of accommodating images of objects which are close-up or far-away; providing detailed colour images during daytime when the light intensity is high; and yet able to perceive images when the light intensity is low. Some species of nocturnal mammals have eyes that are highly specialised to function only in the very low light intensities during the night.

(a) Describe and explain how the typical mammalian eye provides a detailed colour image of close-up objects in high light intensities. [10]

(b) Explain how the eye is adapted to provide vision in low light intensities, and suggest how the eyes of nocturnal mammals are specialised. [6]

Quality of written communication. [2]

Question taken from CCEA's Biology Assessment Unit A2 1, Physiology and Ecosystems, May 2013, © CCEA 2017

5. The diagram below represents a section through a myofibril in a skeletal muscle.

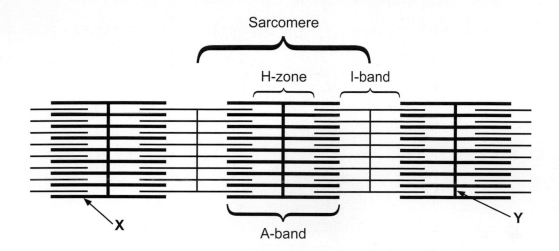

(a) Identify the structures labelled X and Y. [2]

(b) The diagram above shows the myofibril in its relaxed state. Make a copy of the table below and complete it by adding a tick (✓) in the appropriate box to describe what happens to each feature when the muscle contracts.

Feature	Increases in length	Decreases in length	No change in length
A-band			
I-band			
H-zone (H-band)			
Sarcomere			

Question taken from CCEA's Biology Assessment Unit A2 1, Physiology and Ecosystems, May 2014, © CCEA 2017

6. State the most appropriate word or phrase that matches each of the following descriptions:

   - the protein which forms thick filaments in a myofibril
   - the theory which describes the contraction of skeletal muscle
   - the ions stored in the sarcoplasmic reticulum of muscle cells, which are released to initiate muscle contraction
   - the region of a sarcomere which remains the same length in both contracted and relaxed muscle
   - muscle which consists of spindle-shaped cells [5]

   Question taken from CCEA's Biology Assessment Unit A2 1, Physiology and Ecosystems, May 2016, © CCEA 2017

7. (a) The main proteins involved in skeletal muscle contraction are represented in Diagram A.

   Diagram A

   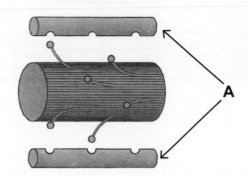

   (i) Identify protein A. [1]

   (ii) Explain the process of muscle contraction in a myofibril following nervous stimulation. [4]

   (b) An experiment was carried out to investigate muscle contraction in skeletal muscle. This type of investigation uses muscles obtained from freshly killed animals. The experimental set-up is shown in Diagram B.

   Diagram B

   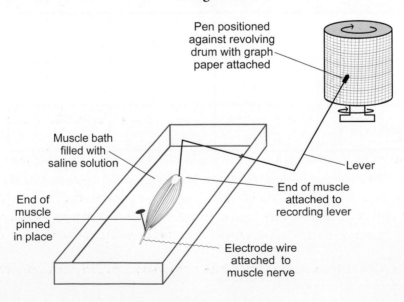

If a single electrical stimulus is applied to the muscle (by the electrode wire), the following trace (graph line) is produced on the graph paper on the revolving drum.

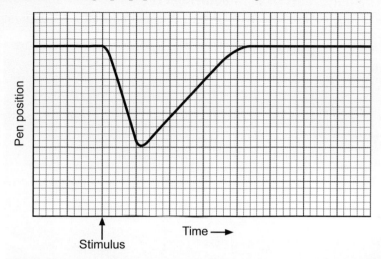

(i) Make a copy of the graph above and mark with an X a part of the trace that represents muscle contraction. [1]

The graph below represents the trace from a muscle that was stimulated repeatedly over a period of time, with very short intervals between successive stimuli.

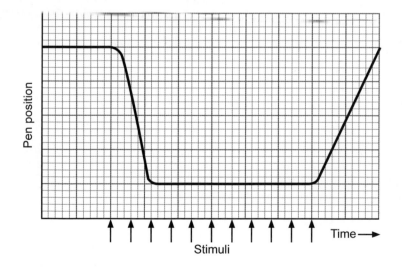

(ii) Identify two differences between the muscle response to repeated stimuli and a single stimulus. [2]

(iii) Suggest one example of human activity that would involve this type of contraction. [1]

(c) When using the experimental set-up shown in Diagram B to compare different types of contraction in muscle, it is important to ensure that variables are controlled as far as possible. Describe two variables that need to be controlled in this investigation to ensure valid results. [2]

Question adapted from CCEA's Biology Assessment Unit A2 1, Physiology and Ecosystems, May 2015, © CCEA 2017

8. (a) Photograph II is a photomicrograph of muscle tissue.

Photograph II

© Dr Gladden Willis / Visuals Unlimited / Science Photo Library / C005/5281

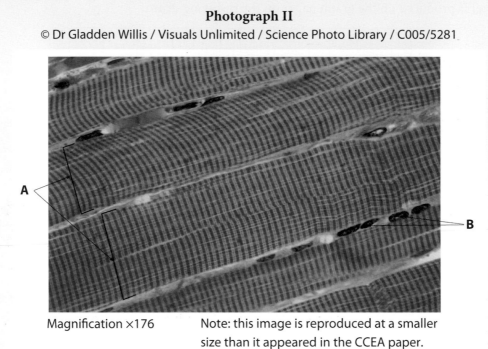

Magnification ×176   Note: this image is reproduced at a smaller size than it appeared in the CCEA paper.

(i) Identify the features labelled A and B. [2]

(ii) Identify the evidence from the photomicrograph which indicates that this section is:

- skeletal muscle and not cardiac muscle
- skeletal muscle and not smooth muscle [2]

(b) The graph below shows the length of a sarcomere during muscle contraction.

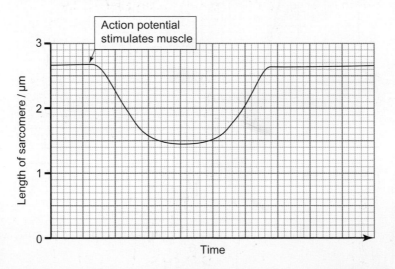

(i) Explain the role of calcium ions, myosin and actin in bringing about the changes in the length of the sarcomere, as shown in the graph. [3]

(ii) The graph shows that a sarcomere will only shorten by a very small amount (approximately 1.2 µm) when it contracts. Explain how muscle tissue is able to contract many centimetres when stimulated. [2]

Question adapted from CCEA's Biology Assessment Unit A2 1, Physiology and Ecosystems, January 2014, © CCEA 2017

Chapter 6 – Populations and Communities

Populations

A **population** is a group of organisms of the **same species** living in a particular area. Population numbers can remain relatively stable or can grow or decline over time. Factors influencing population growth include birth and death rates, immigration and emigration. Some of the main types of population growth are discussed in the following sections.

Population growth

One of the most studied examples of population growth is the growth of bacteria (or yeast) in nutrient medium in closed conditions, for example, in a beaker or conical flask. The graph below shows the characteristic pattern of population growth typically seen in these circumstances. Population growth (or decline) is measured as the change in number of organisms in bacteria increase occurs when a bacterium divides (splits) to produce two new daughter cells.

The growth of bacteria in closed conditions

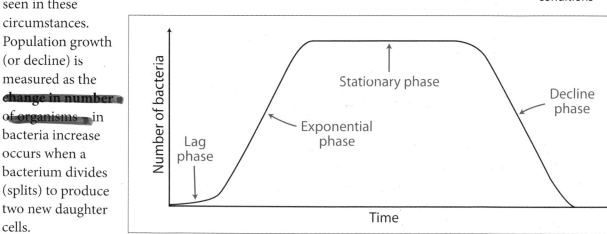

The pattern of growth evident in the diagram can be divided into four distinct phases, the lag phase, the exponential (or log growth) phase, the stationary (or stable) phase and the decline phase.

1. **Lag phase** – In this phase there will be a very slow increase in number (numbers may even decrease for a time). This is a stage when **nutrient assimilation** takes place – this may involve the bacteria activating genes and producing the appropriate enzymes to metabolise a particular food substrate.

2. **Exponential (log) phase** – The bacteria divide **exponentially**. There is no **restriction to growth** (for example, abundant resources present and insignificant waste accumulation) and the bacteria can divide to produce new bacteria at the maximum rate. A bacterium can divide to produce two new bacteria as often as once every 20 minutes and consequently the increase in numbers can be exponential.

3. **Stationary (stable) phase** – In this stage food supplies may begin to become limiting so the number of new individuals produced falls. Waste products and toxins may have also accumulated to a level that restricts growth. During the stationary phase the 'birth' and death rates approach equilibrium.

4. **Decline phase** – The death rate exceeds the birth rate and the population declines, sometimes very rapidly in a population 'crash'. In the bacterial population in the diagram, this can be due to the accumulation of toxic waste and/or the nutrient supply running out.

Note 1: The **sigmoidal** (S-shape) growth curve comprising the lag, exponential and stationary growth phases in the graph on page 89 applies to the populations of many species in particular circumstances, such as when colonising a new area. The same principles apply but other factors can contribute to particular parts of the growth curve, for example, the lag phase can be due to the time taken for egg or larval production or the gestation period or even the time to grow and reach sexual maturity. However, most natural populations are most likely to remain in the stable phase rather than progress into the decline phase – a phase typically associated with 'closed' conditions.

Note 2: A logarithmic scale can be used when representing the change in numbers of microbes over time as the increase can be over several orders of magnitude. Typically the time (on the x-axis) is scaled as normal but number (on the y-axis) has a log scale as shown below. Special 'semi-log' graph paper can be used for this purpose.

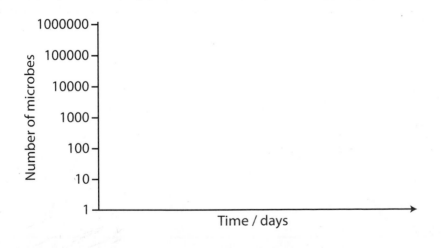

Outline of a semi-log graph

The diagram of bacterial growth on page 89 really represents a log scale on the y-axis, as exponential growth is seen as a straight line only when using a log scale.

Some key terms describing population growth are discussed below:

- **Biotic potential** – The maximum rate of growth of the population as seen in the exponential phase reflects the population's **biotic potential** – the reproductive potential (rate) of a population under optimum environmental conditions with unlimited resources.

- **Environmental resistance** – The environmental restrictions on population growth, for example, as evident in the stationary phase, create what is described as an environmental resistance. **Environmental resistance** is the restriction by the environment on the population reaching its maximum growth rate and its biotic potential. Environmental resistance can be due to many factors including nutrient shortage or accumulation of waste (as discussed on page 90) but also climate, competition from other organisms, predation and disease. The factors that influence populations can be grouped into two main categories. **Abiotic factors** are factors in the chemical or physical environment and are loosely referred to as non-living; examples include water, nutrient, light and oxygen availability. **Biotic factors** are the effects of other organisms whether the same or other species, for example, food supply or predation.

- **Carrying capacity** – The **carrying capacity** is the maximum number of a population that the ecosystem can support. The carrying capacity is very much determined by the amount of **resources available**. In our example of bacterial growth, if extra resources were provided – for example, a larger volume of medium which would have additional nutrients (and which also would dilute the waste/toxins produced) – there would be a higher carrying capacity.

Renewable and non-renewable resources – The characteristic flattening out in the stationary phase and rapid fall of the decline phase in our bacterial example are due to the resources being **non-renewable**. The nutrients that were there at the start of the investigation were not replaced (as well as the waste not being removed).

If resources are **renewable**, as in a broadleaved, deciduous woodland where trees shed their leaves each year and provide food for earthworms, the earthworm population tends to remain in a stationary or stable phase.

A J-shaped growth curve

Some other growth curve examples

The diagram on the right shows the growth of an algal (planktonic protoctistan) population over the course of a year; a **J-shaped** growth curve that is characteristic of many protoctistan species.

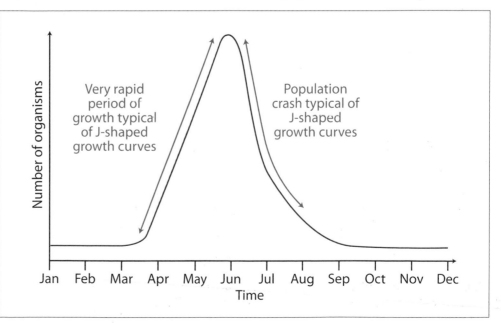

The graph shows that there is a very rapid period of growth in spring as there is abundant nutrient availability in the water, both temperature and light levels are increasing and there are relatively few herbivores in the water at this time of the year. However, in mid-summer the population often 'crashes' (with no stationary phase) and rapidly falls largely because the nutrient supply becomes exhausted but also because herbivores (zooplankton) increase in number and because wastes accumulate. In this example, resource availability is again a key determinant of the growth pattern.

Note: The human population growth curve is a J-shaped curve with very rapid and increasing growth over the last 200 years. The big difference with the algal populations is that, as yet, there has been no crash!

Competition between organisms – is when different organisms are competing for the same resource. **Competition** is also an important factor in providing environmental resistance and influencing the carrying capacity. Competition can be either intraspecific, among members of the same species as in our example of bacterial growth, or interspecific, among members of different species. The graphs below summarise a very famous investigation involving interspecific competition carried out by the Russian zoologist G.F. Gause over 80 years ago.

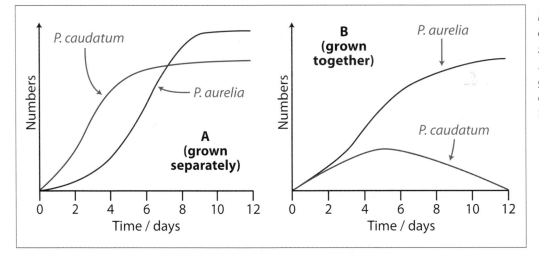

Population growth curves for two species of Paramecium when grown separately (A) and when grown together (B)

Gause investigated competition between populations of two species of *Paramecium* – *P. aurelia* and *P. caudatum*. When cultured separately in the laboratory and fed on bacteria the *P. aurelia* reached a higher final density compared to *P. caudatum*, as shown above in **A**. However, when cultured together in the same conditions (**B**), the *P. aurelia* population increased at only a slightly reduced rate compared to when grown separately. However, the *P. caudatum* was eliminated as a consequence of being losers in the competition for the food resource. Clearly, the smaller *P. aurelia* was better adapted for utilising the food resources available.

This example highlights a point made during the AS course, in that no two species occupy the identical ecological niche. When this happens one species loses out as a consequence of the competitive exclusion principle.

Predator-prey interaction – The oscillating growth curves produced as a consequence of predator-prey interactions with alternating peaks and troughs are shown in the following graph (opposite, top).

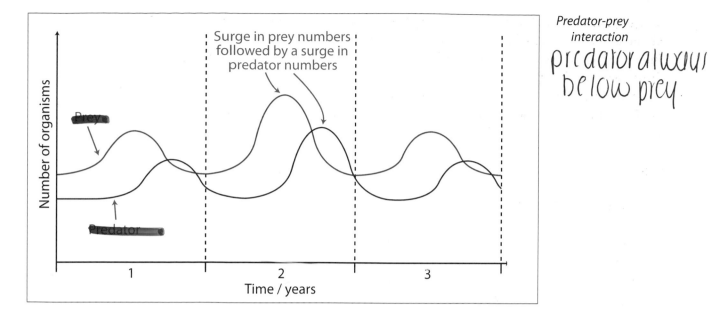

Predator-prey interaction

predator always below prey

If there are large numbers of prey there will be more food available for predators so their numbers will increase. In due course the increased numbers of predators will cause the numbers of prey to decrease, which in turn will cause the number of predators to decrease and so on. The type of growth curve shown above, demonstrating the classical predator-prey interaction, generally has a number of common features:

- The predator peaks and troughs lag behind the prey peaks and troughs – the time lag depends on a number of features including the rate and time involved in which the predators can produce offspring.

- Although lagging behind, the length of the predator cycle is usually similar to the length of the prey cycle.

- The number of predators is normally significantly lower than the number of prey individuals at equivalent points on the cycle.

Note: Predator-prey relationships such as the one in the diagram above are only as obvious as this when the predator relies on one particular prey. In reality, most predators have more than one prey species, so the growth curves often have a smoother pattern and there is less of a correlation between any one prey and any one predator.

Population dynamics

As the growth curves show, the number of individuals making up populations fluctuates over time. However, the change in size of any population is determined by the birth and death rate, and any migration that takes place.

Population growth = (births – deaths) + (immigration – emigration)

This equation holds true whether the population is increasing or decreasing and can be applied to any example we review. In the lag-exponential-stationary-decline growth pattern of bacteria cultured in a laboratory, migration is not a factor so the different stages are dependent on the balance between 'births' and deaths. The rapid increase in the populations of migratory bird species throughout spring and summer is a combination of both immigration and a high birth rate.

The example of migratory birds highlights another feature of populations in general. In many species there is a very obvious seasonal effect on population size. Thousands of migrant birds may be all too obvious during spring and summer but in contrast there may be no local population during the winter. For most species the seasonal effect on population size is not a migration effect but is determined by the balance between births and deaths. Many species of animals give birth in spring or early summer, so there are large populations at this stage, when temperatures are high and food resources are plentiful. Seasonal effects can often be represented by survivorship curves which show the percentage of individuals surviving over a year as the seasons progress. Survivorship curves can also be used to show the number of individuals of a particular species surviving over a period of years. The graph below shows a typical survivorship curve for tawny owls over their first five years of life – the percentage survival values represent the number of chicks from one particular year that survive over successive years as they age.

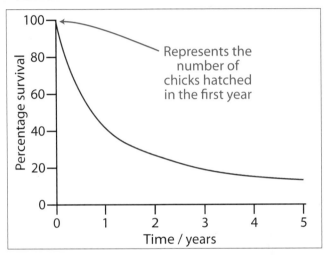

Survivorship curve for tawny owls over their first five years

Population sizes can also change from year to year. This can be for many reasons including being part of a normal predator-prey cycle, changes in food supply or abiotic factors such as a colder winter.

r- and K-selected species (r- and K-strategists)

The characteristics of the species itself influences the population dynamic. Most species can be broadly grouped into either r- or K-selected species.

r-selected species tend to be 'opportunistic' and grow both very quickly as individuals and increase the population number very rapidly when conditions are ideal. Their numbers also decline very rapidly when conditions are less favourable. They tend to exhibit 'boom and bust' patterns of growth as the emphasis is on reproduction and the colonisation of new areas rather than survival. Examples of r-selected species typically include bacteria, protoctistans and annual plants (many species of weeds).

K-selected species have more stable populations and the population size usually remains at or close to the carrying capacity for the species. In K-selected species, the emphasis is more on survival and dominance rather than expanding the population or colonising new areas. K-selected species include many large mammals such as humans and many species of trees. The table opposite (top right) shows features of typical r-selected and K-selected species.

rcsad nul   opponic

r-selected (r-strategists)	K-selected (K-strategists)
Small body size	Large body size
Short lived	Long life cycle – usually a number of years before mature and able to produce offspring
Reproduce rapidly with usually many offspring	Few offspring
Very little parental care	Large amount of parental care – high investment in young – few young produced so important that they have high chance of survival
Able to disperse rapidly and colonise new habitats	Low dispersal ability – colonisation of new habitats less frequent
Population size (density) very variable	Population size (density) more constant
Low competitive ability – unlikely to become dominant	High competitive ability – may be a dominant species in the ecosystem
Not specialised so adaptable to change in environment – can evolve rapidly, for example, antibiotic resistance in bacteria	Tend to be highly specialised so less resistant to environment change – prone to becoming endangered or extinct in changing environment, for example, polar bears and global warming
Often inhabit unstable or short lived habitats, for example, weeds colonising a ploughed field	Typically occur in stable habitats that remain relatively undisturbed for many years, for example, oak trees in a forest

Note 1: r is the designation for the **intrinsic rate of natural increase** (the biotic potential). r-strategists, as indicated in the table, have short life cycles and reproduce very rapidly and therefore have a high value for r – they approach the biotic potential.

Note 2: In population growth curves **K** represents the **carrying capacity**. Consequently K-strategists have population sizes that remain close to the carrying capacity (K).

Population interactions – winners and losers

We have already seen how predator and prey populations can interact. This is only one example of how the populations of two **different species** can interact and influence each other.

Predator-prey interactions are an example of a + / – interaction, where one species gains and the other loses. Herbivores grazing on plants is a similar type of + / – interaction, where one species (eg the cow) gains and another (eg the grass) loses.

Parasitism is a third type of + / – interaction. The parasite gains at the expense of the host.

A parasite can be defined as an organism that lives in or on another organism (the host) benefiting from it and causing it harm over an extended period of time.

Cows grazing in a field, a + / – interaction

The differences between a predator-prey relationship and a parasite-host relationship can often be very subtle and difficult to distinguish with no clear demarcation. However, as a general rule, parasites differ from predators in four ways:

- The parasite lives in or on the host.
- The parasite causes harm to the host over an extended period of time.
- The parasite is usually smaller than the host.
- The parasite seldom kills the host (or if it does, it is a very slow process).

Examples of parasites include the flea, the human tapeworm and the malarial parasite *Plasmodium* that is transferred between humans by female mosquitoes. Parasites are not restricted to the animal kingdom; the common tar spot fungus is an example of a fungal parasite that infects sycamore leaves and mistletoe is an example of a plant parasite that infects trees across much of north-west Europe. The amount of harm that parasites cause varies considerably – normally a flea is little more than an irritant but malaria is often fatal.

Tar spot fungus in sycamore

Mistletoe

Mistletoe has evergreen leaves and forms dense spheres that hang from the host tree – the photograph on the right was taken in March before the tree leaves opened, making the mistletoe even more obvious. The mistletoe can photosynthesise to produce its own carbohydrate but produces special structures to penetrate the tree and absorb water and minerals for its needs – it has no roots as such that reach the ground.

There are also – / – interactions, where both species suffer. This is often the case with **competition.** If you revisit the growth curves of *Paramecium aurelia* and *P. caudatum* on page 92 you will observe that when the two species are grown together, neither species grows as well as it does when growing on its own. The graphs also show another common feature of competition, the loser is often eliminated by competitive exclusion.

Although this example of competition shows that the species with better competitive ability can lead to the elimination of another **species,** in nature there is as much competition among members of the same species (intraspecific competition) as there is among different species (interspecific competition). For example, the oak seedlings growing around an oak tree are competing with each other (and with the parent tree). Over time, fewer and fewer **individuals** survive due to competition for resources such as space, light, water and minerals.

Mutualism is the interaction where **both partners benefit** (a + / + interaction). Mutualistic relationships can be complex and often have evolved to the extent where at least one of the species cannot survive on its own.

Lichens are an example of an obligate mutualistic relationship between fungi and green algae. The fungi provide the supporting framework and absorb water and minerals (as well as sheltering the algae and protecting them from desiccation), and the algae photosynthesise thus providing carbohydrates and other organic compounds, some of which are available to the fungi.

Mutualistic **nitrogen-fixing bacteria** live in the nodules of the roots of legumes such as peas and beans. The nitrogen-fixing bacteria benefit through gaining carbohydrate from the plants and the plants benefit through gaining amino acids (or other nitrogen-containing compounds) from the bacteria.

Cellulose digestion in many herbivores is a consequence of mutualism between the herbivores and bacteria and/or protoctistans in the gut of the herbivore. In cows and other ruminants the bacteria possess the cellulases required to hydrolyse cellulose. The cows benefit as they can utilise a very abundant source of food not accessible to so many other animal species, and their mutualistic partners gain a ready supply of food and are maintained at a relatively high and constant temperature, ensuring rapid metabolic activity.

Lichen growing on a tree trunk

The biological control of pest species

Man often deliberately manipulates the relationship between other species for his own ends. This can be seen in the control of pests. Due to the harm caused by the use of chemical pesticides, the biological control of pest species is seen as an attractive alternative. What exactly is a pest and what is biological control?

- **A pest species** can be defined as a species that damages a **valuable/commercial crop** species, causing **economic damage**.
- **Biological control** involves deliberately introducing an organism that will target and cause harm to the pest. This can be a **predator**, a **competitor**, a **parasitic** or a **pathogenic** organism.

Biological control will benefit the environment by reducing the need for chemical pesticides and the harm that they cause but are also used because 'broad-spectrum' pesticides (such as insecticides and herbicides) may not work particularly well. Broad-spectrum pesticides may kill many beneficial organisms, including many natural enemies of the pest. The graph below shows an example of what can happen if a broad-spectrum insecticide is used to target a population of pest insects.

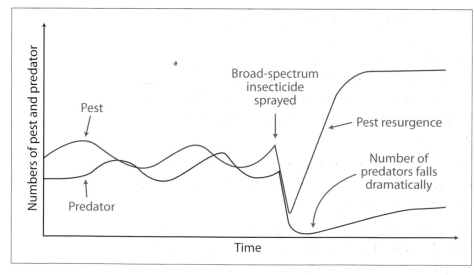

Pest resurgence following application of a broad-spectrum insecticide

The graph shows that the pest can experience **pest resurgence** in that its numbers increase rapidly due to the elimination of a natural predator.

In pest resurgence after the use of insecticide, the number of pests can rise to well above what it was before the insecticide was applied.

The graph below shows how **effective biological control** can reduce pest numbers below the threshold of economic damage.

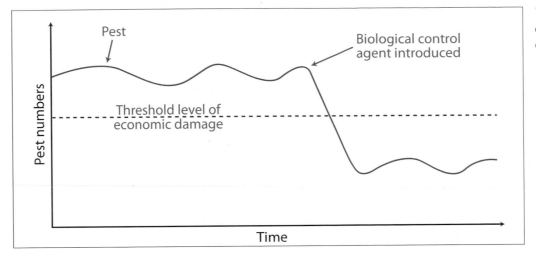

The potential of effective biological control

With effective biological control the introduced predator integrates naturally into the ecosystem, building a sustainable population and therefore does not need to be continually re-introduced. Effective biological control possesses the following **advantages**:

- There is **no chemical damage** to the environment with the risk of significant ecological harm and **bioaccumulation** in food chains.

- Biological control **targets only the pest species** – there is reduced collateral damage affecting other organisms.

- The development of **resistance** by the pests is unlikely (see note below).

- Pest resurgence is unlikely.

- Biological control, if successful, needs **little additional action** and **saves money** on the continued use of pesticides.

Note: Insect **populations** treated with insecticides frequently develop resistance to the pesticide and it ceases to become effective. Before the pesticide is applied, a small number of **individuals** in a population will have resistance due to mutation. However, when the pesticide is used, the non-resistant individuals are killed leaving only the resistant individuals (that survive and reproduce) resulting in the **population** becoming resistant.

Biological control has its **limitations** though and it is not always successful. These limitations (potential disadvantages) include:

- The **pest is unlikely to be totally eliminated**. However, with effective biological control, its density will be reduced to below the threshold for economic damage.

- Biological control will only work well if the biological control species can adapt well and **thrive in the ecosystem** into which it is introduced. Often an 'unnatural' crop ecosystem not found in the wild can be hostile to the introduced biological control species.

- It is important that the introduced control species **does not outcompete native species** (cause harm to non-target species).

This section on populations has focused on how populations of individual species grow over time and how these populations interact with another (or small number of) species. The next section on communities addresses the relationships between many species as communities and ecosystems develop.

Communities

A **community** is the sum total of **all the populations** (species) in a particular area (habitat or ecosystem). A more complete definition is that it is the **biotic** component of an ecosystem involving interaction between the autotrophic and heterotrophic populations present.

An **ecosystem** is the community plus its physical environment – it consists of **both biotic** and **abiotic** components. In an ecosystem many of the species are interdependent on each other. However, it is the abiotic environment, such as rock type and climate, that determines the type of community that can develop and the different species present will interact in areas such as energy flow, nutrient and gas exchange.

Succession (community development)

Ecosystems are constantly changing and **succession** is the term used to describe the changes over time in ecosystems. It is important to note that succession involves changes to both the community (the species present) and the abiotic environment due to the ongoing interaction between these two components.

Primary succession

Primary succession occurs on newly formed, barren substrates that have not been previously colonised. This could be the lava fields produced after a volcanic eruption, the sudden appearance of a volcanic island or the exposed rock at the base of a disused quarry. A key point is that the exposed land (rock) provides a very harsh and hostile environment for life. There will be no soil present to support plants.

The first stage in the succession is usually the appearance of colonising **pioneer species**. Pioneer species such as **lichens** are able to survive the hostile conditions. The lichens can grow on the bare rock, tolerating desiccation. Over time the lichens begin to degrade the rock and help promote the weathering (aided by the climate, for example, frost action) that forms the embryonic **soil**. Initially the soil will accumulate in cracks in the rock. As the lichens die and decompose, the 'soil' will develop to a stage where it can support **mosses**.

Lichens and mosses on a rock

Lichen

Lichens (and mosses) grow in shelter of rock crevices. 'Debris' containing moisture and minerals from decomposed lichens and mosses accumulates in these crevices.

Note 1: The communities present at each particular stage of the succession help to modify the abiotic environment thus creating the abiotic conditions necessary for the next stage, for example, the decomposing lichens and mosses form the embryonic 'soil', increasing mineral availability.

Note 2: The colonising plant species that succeed lichens and mosses in the early stages of succession are usually short lived r-strategists that have excellent dispersal mechanisms allowing them to rapidly colonise new areas.

Lichens colonise bare rock.

Mosses and plant species grow in rock crevices.

Soil accumulates and builds up in hollows between exposed rocks enabling a wider variety of grasses and other plants to grow.

Further successional stages

Typically with time, as the succession develops, **soil depth** and **fertility** increase, so does the number of different plant species (although plant biodiversity often decreases again as the succession approaches maturity). The plant **biomass** also tends to increase as succession progresses, as seen in the graphs opposite.

Each stage in the succession is called a **sere** – the two photographs (above and on page 99) could be regarded as representing successive seres in a succession. Eventually after a number of seres, the climax community develops. The **climax community** is the stable end stage of a succession which is in equilibrium with the environment. In most of lowland Britain the climax community is mixed broadleaf deciduous forest dominated by oak and other common species. In harsher upland environments, moorland is often the climax community.

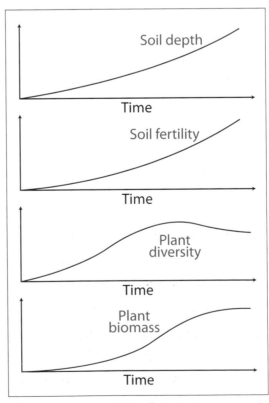

Features typical of primary succession

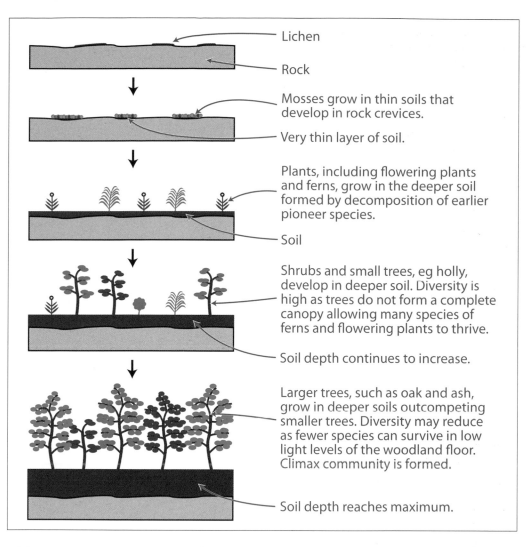

Lichen

Rock

Mosses grow in thin soils that develop in rock crevices.

Very thin layer of soil.

Plants, including flowering plants and ferns, grow in the deeper soil formed by decomposition of earlier pioneer species.

Soil

Shrubs and small trees, eg holly, develop in deeper soil. Diversity is high as trees do not form a complete canopy allowing many species of ferns and flowering plants to thrive.

Soil depth continues to increase.

Larger trees, such as oak and ash, grow in deeper soils outcompeting smaller trees. Diversity may reduce as fewer species can survive in low light levels of the woodland floor. Climax community is formed.

Soil depth reaches maximum.

The typical sequence of succession in lowland Britain

If the composition of the climax community is determined by the climate (as in the examples described opposite) it is called a **climatic climax**. If it is determined by biotic factors, such as grazing, it is called a **biotic climax**.

Although the actual succession that will take place depends on a number of factors, including climate, all primary successions tend to have a number of features in common:

- They are **predictable** in pattern – pioneer species will always be the initial colonisers and a similar climax community will develop in the same conditions.

- The **abiotic environment becomes less hostile** as soil forms and the growth of plants provides shelter for the organisms in the later stages.

- The **height** and **biomass** of vegetation increases.

- Communities become **increasingly complex**, with more complex food webs, as a greater number of niches are provided for animals.

- There is **increased biodiversity** (at least until mid-succession).

- Communities in later stages of the succession are usually more **stable** than in earlier seres.

Case study – a sand dune succession

At any one time most successions will be at a particular stage or sere. If you visit a mature mixed deciduous woodland you will be in a climax community – a community that used to dominate most of Britain and Ireland but is much rarer now. You have to imagine what the pioneer stage was like many years ago as this type of succession will take several hundred years to develop.

Young dune at edge of shore

Sand dunes are a particularly interesting type of succession in that they can demonstrate all the different seres at the same time. A sand dune ecosystem is continually developing as sand blown by the wind or carried by the force of the sea is forming new dunes close to the high tide mark. As dune renewal takes place at the hostile interface with the sea, there is a progression of increasingly older dunes further inland as conditions become more benign and the dune system becomes more stable and mature.

Roots of marram grass bind the sand particles together

In the **young dunes** at the shore edge, **marram grass** is the principal **pioneer species** and coloniser. The marram grass is highly specialised in a number of ways – it is a xerophyte and able to survive in the sand which is unable to effectively retain the (usually abundant) rain that falls in these ecosystems. The roots of the marram grass can rapidly penetrate through the sand and have a very important role in binding the sand together and stabilising the dunes.

Dune slack immediately behind the young dunes

Just behind these young developing dunes, small areas of 'grassland' called **dune slacks** have a degree of protection and are rich in mosses and many other ground-hugging plant species such as birdsfoot trefoil and thyme. Animal species such as snails are also becoming more common as the food webs are becoming increasingly complex. Typically, these areas have the greatest biodiversity in the sand dune system. The continuing cycle of the growth and decomposition of the plants allows a thin soil to develop.

Further inland, as the dunes are more **mature**, the ground is stable enough and the soil developed enough to allow shrubs such as **heather** to dominate. The increasing height of the plant community shades out many of the plants that dominated the ground cover in the previous sere. Not surprisingly, the biodiversity begins to fall although there is a significant increase in biomass at this stage.

Marram

Heather

Mature dune with heather and marram

This trend continues as we move inland and reach the **old dunes** – dunes that have been formed for hundreds of years. The old dunes are even more stable and are colonised by **bracken** and **gorse**. These species allow very little light to penetrate to ground level. Few species other than mosses are common under the bracken and gorse.

Gorse

Bracken

Old dunes with bracken and gorse

Further inland again, the heather and gorse community is often replaced by **woodland**.

Dune system merging into woodland

Reading through this case study of sand dune succession you will note that it has all the typical characteristics of primary succession, as listed earlier in this chapter (page 101).

In reality, most successions that take place do not show the relatively slow sequence from bare land – usually rock but sand in the case of a sand dune succession – to climax community. Instead, they are successions that take place when the normal primary succession is interrupted or the climax community damaged or destroyed due to, for example, **fire**, **flooding**, **wind damage** or through **human interference** (for example, woodland clearance or ploughing land). This type of succession is called secondary succession.

Secondary succession

Secondary succession does not usually begin with the typical pioneer species, such as lichen, as the **soil** is already formed and will contain the **seeds** of many species as well as other plant parts that can rapidly regenerate, for example, roots. Many other **soil organisms**, such as nitrifying bacteria and detritivores, are also usually present in the soil. As a consequence of all these factors, secondary succession is invariably much **quicker** than primary succession, with the climax community being reached in a much shorter time.

Foxglove – a common species early in a woodland secondary succession following clearance

A common secondary succession in Britain is the succession that takes place after woodland is cleared. Although some of the cleared land is often used for urban development, or for farming activity, some frequently remains untouched and has the opportunity to revert to climax community through secondary succession. The sequence of seres generally represents the sequence at the latter end of a primary succession but there are often some differences compared to the typical primary succession.

For example, some species are particularly adapted to the ecological niches associated with cleared woodland. They can either regenerate very rapidly from seed banks in the soil or colonise from surrounding areas.

For this reason, foxgloves are common plants in the years immediately following woodland clearing, as shown in the photograph (top right).

The photograph opposite (bottom right) shows secondary succession taking place in an area of land that was formerly woodland. Many of the trees in the original woodland were destroyed by a very severe storm and the land is now largely covered by bracken. This photograph was taken about 15 years after the storm that destroyed the woodland.

Part of original woodland remaining after storm

Occasional tree left undamaged

Bracken growing as early sere in secondary succession

Secondary succession following woodland destruction

Practical work

The haemocytometer

The haemocytometer is an instrument for counting cell numbers (density). As its name suggests it was originally designed for counting blood cells, but can also be used to count yeast or any type of cells that are large enough to be seen under the microscope.

If carrying out an investigation on yeast populations in the laboratory, the yeast can be cultured in a conical flask containing glucose solution.

The haemocytometer resembles a modified microscope slide with a grid (or grids) containing squares of known size. The design enables the central area (counting platform) containing the grid to be slightly lower by a fixed distance (0.1 mm) than the coverslip. This ensures that the squares in the grid represent not only a known area, but the liquid above them has a known volume.

The diagram below represents a haemocytometer.

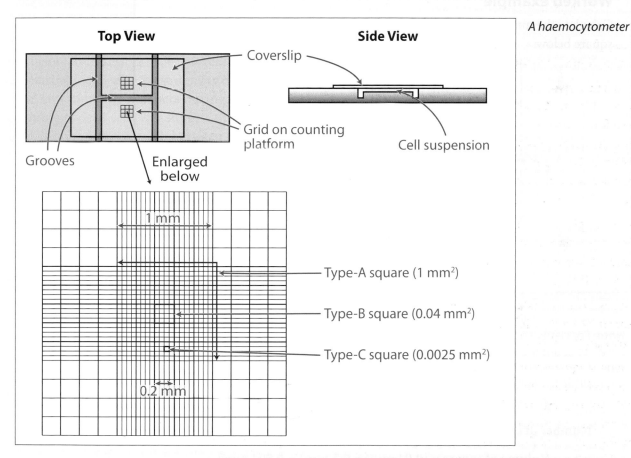

A haemocytometer

The volume enclosed (volume = area × depth [0.1 mm depth for all squares]) for the different size of squares is:

$$\text{type-A} = 1 \text{ mm}^2 \times 0.1 \text{ mm} = 0.1 \text{ mm}^3$$

$$\text{type-B} = 0.04 \text{ mm}^2 \times 0.1 \text{ mm} = 0.004 \text{ mm}^3$$

$$\text{type-C} = 0.0025 \text{ mm}^2 \times 0.1 \text{ mm} = 0.00025 \text{ mm}^3$$

Detailed procedure for the capture-recapture technique

1. A **large sample** of the species is caught or trapped using an appropriate technique (for example, pitfall trap for beetles, sweep net for grasshoppers).

2. The caught animals are marked in a way that will last over the sampling period (the marking is **permanent** or **semi-permanent** using, for example, waterproof ink, correction fluid or bird ringing).

3. The marking should be done in a way that does not harm the animal or make it any more likely to be **predated** than other non-marked animals. This can be done by marking the animals on their underside, which is out of sight to most predators.

4. The marked animals are released. There must be sufficient time to allow the animals caught in the first sample to **mix** throughout the overall population.

5. The population is then **re-sampled** using the same trapping process as before and the population size estimated using the Lincoln index formula.

Assumptions – Estimating population size by this method makes a number of assumptions. These include:

- There are no significant gains or losses through immigration or emigration. This can be avoided through carrying out the sampling in a discrete area where mixing with other populations is less likely (for example, sampling the beetles in one wood rather than just part of the wood).

- There are no significant gains or losses through births and deaths respectively.

- The trapping process (or subsequent marking) does not affect the animal in any way (for example, making it more wary of the trapping mechanism and reducing its possibility of being trapped in the re-sample or being more likely to be predated).

- The marked animals have mixed throughout the population by the time of the re-sampling period.

The mark-recapture technique works particularly well for small, mobile animals that are easily trapped such as beetles and grasshoppers.

Exam questions

1. (a) In relation to the study of population growth, explain what is meant by the term 'biotic potential'. [1]

   (b) *Paramecium* are mobile protoctistans. The graphs below show the population growth curves of two species (A and B) of *Paramecium* when cultured in separate beakers (Graphs 1 and 2) and when cultured together in the same beaker (Graph 3). Each beaker contained a rich supply of bacteria, the preferred food source of both species.

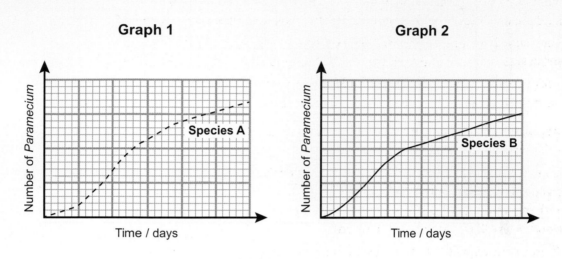

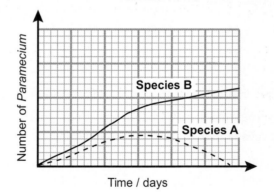

   (i) Describe and give a possible explanation for the population growth curves of the two species when cultured together (Graph 3). [3]

   (ii) Protoctistan numbers can be estimated using a haemocytometer. Suggest one reason why it might be difficult to estimate *Paramecium* numbers accurately using this technique. [1]

   (c) Other species of protoctistans can photosynthesise. They live in the surface layers of seas and lakes. Numbers of individuals of these species often increase rapidly in spring and fall very sharply in mid to late summer, producing J-shaped growth curves.

   Suggest reasons for the J-shaped growth curves of these species. [3]

Question taken from CCEA's Biology Assessment Unit A2 1, Physiology and Ecosystems, May 2014, © CCEA 2017

2. Yeast, cultured in a conical flask containing glucose solution, will produce the population growth pattern shown in the graph below. Increase in population size is due to the yeast cells growing and producing daughter cells as outgrowths (buds) that break off as they reach an appropriate size.

The graph shows how the number of living yeast cells changes over time.

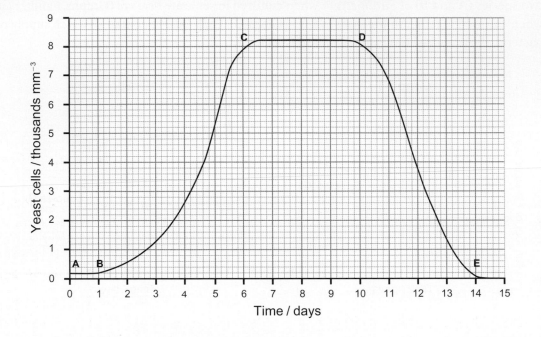

(a) Explain the population growth pattern between positions:

A–B

D–E [4]

(b) (i) Determine the carrying capacity for this particular culture. [1]

(ii) Suggest how a higher carrying capacity could have been achieved in this investigation. [1]

In a class experiment investigating the population growth of yeast, the culture was sampled at intervals and the number of yeast cells estimated using a haemocytometer.

(c) The diagram below represents the results obtained by a student from one type-B square. The distance between the surface of these type-B squares and the overlying coverslip is 0.1 mm.

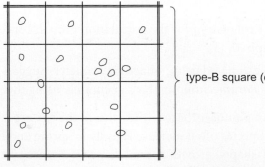

type-B square (of area 0.04 mm²)

(i) Using the information in the type-B square above, calculate the number of yeast cells per mm³. (Show your working.) [2]

Other students also took samples from the conical flask at the same time. The table below shows the values calculated by three students.

Student	Number of yeast cells / mm^{-3}
A	4900
B	2800
C	3300

(ii) Apart from inaccurate counting of yeast cells, suggest **two** reasons that could account for the large variation among the results obtained. [2]

The students found that the number of yeast cells sampled did **not** fall as expected nearing the end of the investigation, but remained relatively constant (as shown in the plateau part of the graph).

(iii) Suggest an explanation for this observation. [1]

(d) In investigations of this nature, it is possible that there could be too many cells to clearly see the grid lines on the haemocytometer.

Suggest what steps can be taken to ensure that the number of cells can be accurately estimated. [2]

Question taken from CCEA's Biology Assessment Unit A2 1, Physiology and Ecosystems, January 2014, © CCEA 2017

3. A haemocytometer can be used to count small unicellular organisms such as yeast.

Students were asked to compare the densities of two yeast populations, each growing in a 2% glucose solution.

The yeast populations were incubated for 24 hours at 30°C and 60°C respectively, in separate conical flasks.

(a) (i) Describe an appropriate procedure for sampling each of the populations and filling the haemocytometer. [3]

If yeast cells in a suspension are too numerous to count, even in a haemocytometer type-C square, the suspension can be diluted.

1 cm^3 of yeast suspension incubated at 30°C was added to 9 cm^3 of buffer. The diagram below shows yeast cells in one type-C square, **after** dilution. The depth of the suspension below the coverslip is 0.1 mm.

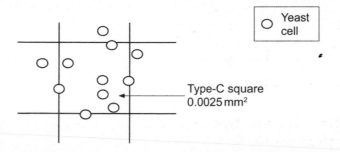

(ii) Calculate the population density of the yeast in the flask. (Show your working.) [3]

(iii) Explain how the yeast population density at 60°C would be expected to differ from that at 30°C. (Assume all other relevant variables were controlled). [2]

(iv) Apart from time, identify **two** other variables that should have been controlled in order to ensure the validity of the investigation. [2]

(b) One of the limitations of the haemocytometer is that it is hard to distinguish between dead and living yeast cells. A chemical dye, trypan blue, can be added to the yeast suspension. The dye can enter dead cells but not living cells.

Suggest an explanation for this and explain how the use of the dye would improve the investigation. [2]

Question taken from CCEA's Biology Assessment Unit A2 1, Physiology and Ecosystems, May 2016, © CCEA 2017

4. The growth of a population depends on various factors which influence birth and death rates. The population will grow until it reaches carrying capacity.

(a) Define what is meant by the term 'carrying capacity'. [1]

(b) Owls are highly-skilled, predatory hunters that feed on mice, shrews and other small mammals. The following graph represents survivorship data for the owls in a large woodland from when the eggs are laid in March until the birds are one year old.

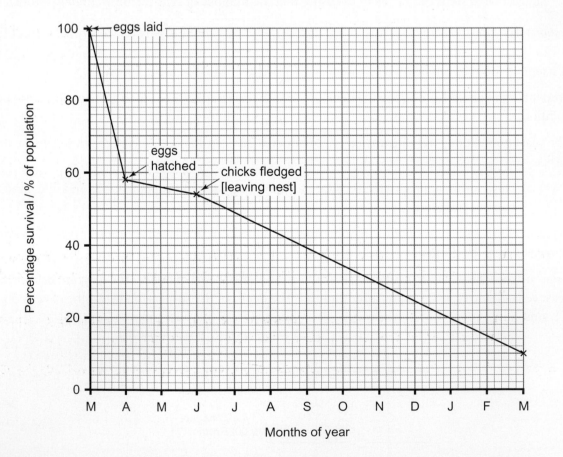

(i) At which stage is there the highest rate of mortality (death)? [1]

(ii) Suggest **one** cause of death in the months immediately after fledging. [1]

(c) Describe a suitable procedure that could be used to produce a reliable estimate of owl numbers in the woodland. (You do not need to describe techniques involved in sampling or trapping owls.) [4]

(d) In owls, as in most other species, mortality rates are very high during the first year of life. Mortality can be due to density-independent or density-dependent factors.

- **Density-independent** factors reduce the population by the same proportion regardless of the size of the population, eg in insect populations cold weather may cause up to a third of the population to die, whether the population is large or small.

- **Density-dependent** factors reduce the population to a greater extent as the population increases in size, eg competition for a resource will become greater as the population increases in size.

The graph below shows the effect of population size on each of density-independent and density-dependent mortality.

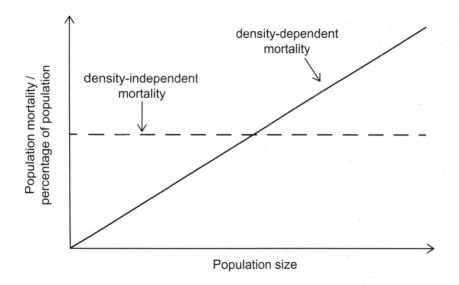

(i) Density-dependent mortality tends to result in population size becoming stable. Suggest which type of population strategy maintains stable population numbers through density-dependent factors. [1]

(ii) Using the information available, suggest how a **named** density-dependent factor is important in regulating owl numbers and keeping population numbers stable. [3]

Question taken from CCEA's Biology Assessment Unit A2 1, Physiology and Ecosystems, May 2013, © CCEA 2017

Chapter 7 – Ecological Energetics and Nutrient Cycling

4.4.10 Demonstrate knowledge and understanding of food chains and food webs.

4.4.11 Demonstrate knowledge and understanding of trophic levels.

4.4.12 Demonstrate knowledge and understanding of the quantitative relationship between trophic levels.

4.4.13 Demonstrate knowledge and understanding of the implications for agriculture.

4.4.14 Demonstrate knowledge and understanding of the cycling of carbon in the ecosystem.

4.4.15 Demonstrate knowledge and understanding of the role of decomposers, nitrifying bacteria and nitrogen-fixing bacteria to provide nitrogen in a usable form for plants.

The organisms belonging to the populations that make up the community in any ecosystem are usually interrelated at many levels. In the previous chapter we reviewed how the organisms associated with one sere modify the environment making it more suitable for the organisms in the subsequent sere. The feeding relationships that exist within an ecosystem are another very obvious, and important, example of the links between the different individuals, and species, in an ecosystem.

Energy flow

Feeding involves the **transfer of energy** between living things. Some key terms relating to the feeding relationships and transfer of energy in ecosystems are described and explained in the next section.

Food chains and food webs

Producers are organisms that manufacture **organic substances** from **inorganic substances** using energy. Almost all producers (plants) use light energy to produce organic compounds by photosynthesis.

> **Note:** A very small number of producer species, the **chemoautotrophs**, use chemical energy (rather than light) to produce organic compounds from inorganic materials. Examples include some species of prokaryotes that live in deep cave systems far from available light (and with no possibility of organic content seeping into the system from above). These prokaryotes are able to make organic substances using the minerals in the rock as a source of chemical energy. Communities in these ecosystems have only been able to develop and survive as the producers have evolved an energy source other than light. Nitrifying bacteria are chemoautotrophs – we will meet these later in the chapter.

Consumers are organisms that obtain their energy by feeding on other organisms. Animals are consumers. **Primary consumers** feed on producers (plants). **Secondary consumers** being next in the link feed on primary consumers. **Tertiary consumers** feed on secondary consumers. Primary consumers are also called **herbivores** (plant feeders) and secondary and tertiary consumers are **carnivores**, as they feed on other animals.

Decomposers and **detritivores** are groups of organisms involved in **decay** and **decomposition**. While energy flows through an ecosystem as a consequence of photosynthesis by producers and the subsequent feeding relationships involved, the flow through the **detritus pathway** is equally important. **Decomposers**, for example bacteria and fungi, and **detritivores** (small animals such as earthworms, millipedes and woodlice) are important groups of organisms involved in decay and decomposition.

Food chains and **food webs** – A **food chain** shows the link between a producer, a primary consumer, a secondary consumer and possibly a tertiary consumer, as shown

A food chain with four trophic levels

in the example on the right. Each stage is referred to as a **trophic level** with producers being at the first trophic level, primary consumers at the second trophic level and so on.

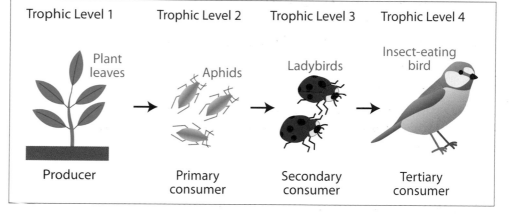

In reality, food chains are usually not a realistic representation of the feeding relationships involved, as most animals do not rely on a single food source – this would be far too risky in most ecosystems. A **food web** is the pattern of interrelated 'food chains' that operate in an ecosystem. In complex ecosystems, such as the climax community stage, food webs tend to be very complex involving many different species.

The quantitative relationships between trophic levels

Food chains and food webs are useful in that they show the path of energy flow but they do not provide any information concerning the number, or biomass, of organisms at each trophic level, ie the **quantitative relationships**. The relative number, biomass, or even energy of the organisms involved can be represented through the display of **ecological pyramids**.

Pyramids of numbers – A pyramid of numbers represents the total **number** of organisms at each trophic level in a food chain or web. The length of the bars in a pyramid of numbers is usually drawn proportional to the number at each level (the depth of bars should be the same for each level). Normally as there will be more organisms at the producer level than there are primary consumers, and so on, this gives a pyramid shape, hence the term pyramid of numbers.

A pyramid of numbers

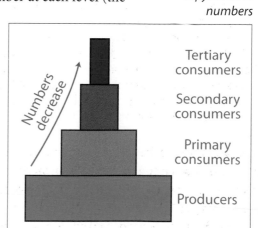

Pyramids of numbers are often a very simplified or inaccurate picture of the energy flow between trophic levels. They do not take account of the **size** of the organism. The diagram on the next page shows an example of a 'typical' pyramid of numbers representing a common food chain in grassland (**a**) and an inverted pyramid from woodland (**b**).

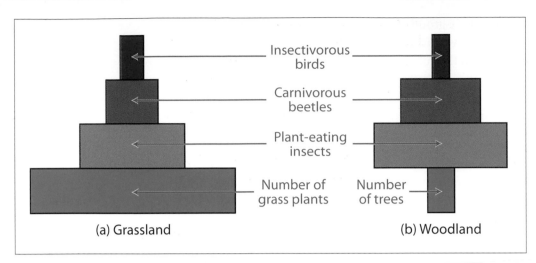

'Typical' and inverted pyramids of numbers

When **very large numbers** are involved at any trophic level it is very difficult, or impossible, to scale the bars accurately. For example one large oak tree may have several million insects operating as primary consumers.

Pyramids of biomass – Pyramids of biomass represent the **biomass** of the organisms at a particular trophic level in a food chain or food web. Biomass can be measured as fresh mass or dry mass. Fresh mass is more variable but will still normally give an accurate representation. Dry mass (drying the organism(s) until constant mass is achieved) is more accurate but time consuming and also means that the organisms are killed in the process.

With a pyramid of biomass (as with a pyramid of numbers), only the organisms present at any one time (the standing crop) are considered. Consequently, inverted pyramids of biomass can result, but often for different reasons than pyramids of numbers. Inverted pyramids of biomass for food webs are much less common than inverted pyramids of numbers.

Commonly used examples include some marine or aquatic pyramids of biomass as they do not take into account the biomass over the whole year but only represent an instantaneous value. In early spring the biomass of zooplankton (protoctistans and small animals that feed on phytoplankton) may exceed that of the phytoplankton. The food web is only sustainable because the phytoplankton reproduce at such a rapid rate that their numbers are quickly replenished.

Note: While **inverted pyramids of biomass** for **food webs** are very uncommon, inverted pyramids of biomass in a particular **food chain** are much more common. This can be explained by the consumer(s) having a number of different food sources (ie other sources outside a particular chain). Inverted **pyramids of numbers** in food chains can also arise for the same reason.

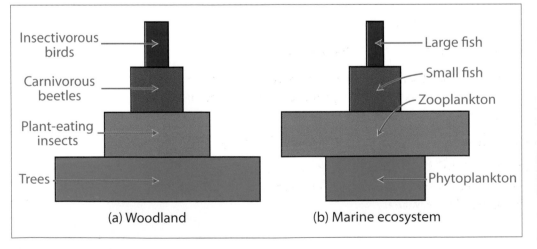

'Typical' and inverted pyramids of biomass

Pyramids of biomass are **more representative** than pyramids of number but their disadvantages include problems with obtaining the data required – we have already noted the problems associated with dry mass but how do you obtain even the fresh mass of an oak tree? Additionally, pyramids of biomass can sometimes give a false picture of the amount of energy available to be transferred. A single oak tree can provide food for millions of leaf-eating insects but should the value represented in the pyramid be the mass of the entire tree or just the edible leaves?

Pyramids of energy (productivity) – The term productivity means how much new material is produced. Pyramids of energy reflect the new material produced (productivity) over a period of time. Pyramids of energy give the **most accurate** representation of the energy at a particular level but the values are more **difficult to obtain** as values need to be obtained over a time period to compare the before and after.

The data may be presented as kJ m^{-2} yr^{-1} (kilojoules per square metre per year) and this indicates how much new material, represented as the energy it contains, is produced in a square metre of ecosystem over the period of one year. Pyramids of energy are particularly useful in comparing ecosystems (including agricultural ecosystems). Stable ecosystems will always represent energy flow as a pyramid.

The efficiency of energy flow through ecosystems

As the Sun is the ultimate energy source for all ecosystems, photosynthesis is the principal route by which the energy is made available to the communities within the ecosystem.

However, only a very small percentage of the energy reaching the Earth's atmosphere is used by producers to make organic compounds in the process of photosynthesis and even less is available to consumers. The following sections explain why energy flow can be relatively inefficient.

Energy losses between the Sun and the plants – Less that 1% of the Sun's energy reaching the atmosphere is available to plants for a number of reasons, as over 90% of the energy is **reflected** back into space by dust particles or clouds, or is **absorbed** by the water vapour or dust in the atmosphere and then re-radiated as heat energy.

Of the small percentage of the Sun's energy reaching the surface of the Earth, only a small proportion of this is used as most will fall on bare ground and will therefore **miss the leaves of a plant**. As much as 99.9% of the light energy **reaching** the Earth's surface will not be available to plants for this reason.

Of the Sun's energy that actually strikes a **leaf**, most is lost through:

- being **reflected** from the surface of leaves – this process is often exacerbated by the presence of a thick waxy cuticle (a necessary compromise between maximising light harvesting and reducing water loss).

- some energy is used in the **evaporation** of water (on the leaf surface).

- missing the **chloroplasts** within the leaf. Although the chloroplasts are arranged in the cells of the palisade layer to trap as much light as possible, the volume of the chloroplasts in a palisade cell is very small.

- over half of the light reaching the leaves is of the **wrong wavelength**. Most plants have pigments that absorb the blue and red parts of the visible spectrum with the green part of the spectrum being reflected.

- the **photosynthetic (photochemical) reactions** are **inefficient**, with much of the energy being lost as heat.

Between **0.5 and 1%** of the incident light that **reaches the leaf surface** will be converted into chemical energy (organic compounds) as a result of photosynthesis.

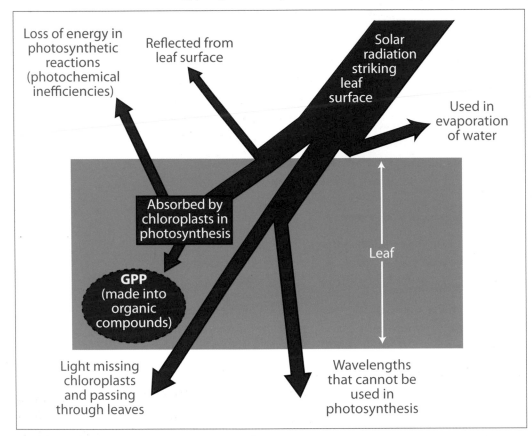

The fate of light energy reaching the leaf surface

Gross Primary Production and Net Primary Production – The energy in the organic compounds produced by plants in photosynthesis is called the **gross primary production (GPP)**. However, plants use up to 50% of the GPP in **respiration (R)**. The remainder, the **net primary production (NPP)**, is available for plant growth, or for the other trophic levels in the ecosystem should the plant die or be eaten.

Therefore NPP = GPP – R

Note 1: GPP or NPP is often represented as kilojoules per square metre per year ($kJ\ m^{-2}\ yr^{-1}$) as it is usually taken to represent the energy in the ecosystem as opposed to being a calculation based on individual plants. GPP and NPP are indicators of the **productivity** of an ecosystem.

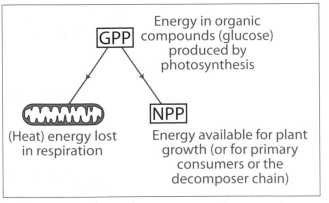

The relationship between gross primary production, net primary production and respiration

Note 2: In terrestrial (land based) ecosystems, the GPP (and NPP) is generally limited by temperature and moisture – the most productive natural ecosystems are tropical swamps and tropical forests where both temperature and moisture availability are approaching optimum levels. In aquatic and marine ecosystems, nutrient (mineral) availability is often the limiting resource.

Energy transfer between producers and consumers – The transfer of energy between producers and primary consumers and among consumers is much more efficient than the conversion of solar energy into organic compounds. Nonetheless, it is still relatively inefficient.

The least efficient stage is between **producers and primary consumers** (typically between 5–10%). Much plant material **cannot be accessed**, for example, plant roots and tree trunks are not grazed to the extent that succulent and accessible leaves are. Much plant material is **very difficult to digest** – very few species have the enzymes necessary to digest cellulose and lignin. Therefore, herbivores typically can only assimilate a small percentage of the plant material they eat with considerable quantities of indigested material being egested. **Excretory losses** also contribute to energy losses – metabolic waste, for example urea, is excreted and this represents energy that is not available to be transferred to the next trophic level.

Much of the organic content that is eaten by primary consumers is used in **respiration** to generate ATP. The energy 'lost' through respiration is lost as **'heat'** – heat is produced as a byproduct of the respiratory process.

Respiratory losses are particularly high in mammals and birds (**endotherms**). The maintenance of a high and constant body temperature requires high metabolic activity and consequently high levels of respiration and unavoidable heat loss.

Additionally, some plants (or plant parts, for example, leaves from deciduous trees in autumn) enter the **decomposer food chain** and are not available to primary consumers.

Energy transfer between consumers – Energy transfer between animals (consumers) is more efficient (typically between 10–20%) than between plants and herbivores. Generally, more of an animal can be eaten and digested. However, again only a small proportion of the energy in any animal will be built up into organic compounds in the next trophic level due to excretory losses, uneaten structures, or being used in respiration or through death and entry into the decomposer food chain.

Energy flow through the different trophic levels of a food chain

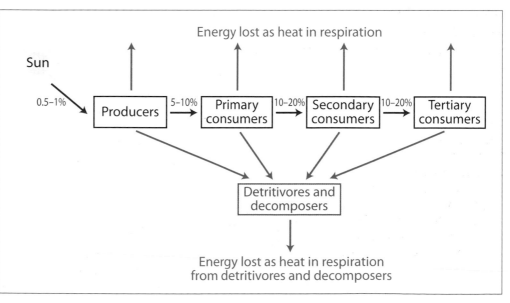

Note 1: The values used in the diagram on page 121 are very approximate. The actual amount of energy that flows (and is lost) in a particular ecosystem depends on the species involved and may vary considerably from the 'typical' values used here.

Note 2: There are typically no more than three steps in a food chain (and very seldom more than four or five) due to the inefficiency of energy transfer and the huge efficiency losses that take place at each step.

Note 3: The transfer of energy through trophic levels is **energy flow**. It is not a cycle – energy needs to continually enter the system from the Sun.

Implications for agriculture

Agricultural ecosystems are particularly important in Northern Ireland. These ecosystems can be crop or animal based. For both crop and livestock systems, key aims are the increased efficiency of energy transfer into the crops (and animals) and the reduction of losses through unwanted consumption by consumers, through respiration or losses through the decomposer pathway.

There is much investment in increasing agricultural **productivity**.

Increasing primary productivity in plants – Plant (crop) growth can be increased by removing or reducing the limiting factors affecting growth. This can be done artificially in, for example, glasshouses by providing extra light, heat and carbon dioxide. However, most crops are grown outside and the most realistic way of increasing productivity is through the use of **fertiliser** and reducing the effect of **pests**.

Even spacing of maize for maximum productivity

Productivity can also be enhanced through the **appropriate spacing of crops** in a field. Sowing seeds at the optimum density ensures that competition among adjacent crop plants is reduced yet allows the crop to maximise coverage of the land used – another delicate balancing act.

Intensive farming of domestic livestock – The general principle is that by making energy conversion more efficient and restricting energy losses, where possible, more energy (meat products) will be available to humans.

Intensive farming of domestic livestock often involves the **confinement** of the animals to very specific areas – this can be cattle in a fenced-off section of a field or pigs in an outhouse, ensuring that less energy is used in movement. Keeping cattle in a small section of a field also ensures that less land is utilised at any one time and that manure from the animals is more evenly spread over the land.

Keeping animals indoors in **warm conditions** (much of the warmth, in all but the coldest conditions, is often produced by the animals themselves) reduces the energy required to produce heat and maintain body temperature.

The use of **high energy** foods such a silage and **high protein** foods (for example, soya meal) are other measures geared to increasing productivity.

Note: Silage is cut grass or maize that is chopped into small pieces and stored in anaerobic conditions. The anaerobic conditions can be produced through covering the silage by large sheets of plastic (often held in place by old tyres) or through producing plastic covered bales. Microorganisms respire in the anaerobic conditions created and produce lactic acid. The low pH, as a consequence of lactic acid buildup, restricts other (decomposing) microbial growth thus preserving the high nutrient status of the grass throughout the winter. The grass can be cut several times during the growing period and preserved as silage at the time when it is most productive and nutritious, and therefore provides a highly nutritious winter fodder (at a time when other sources are in short supply).

Baled silage

The intensive farming of domestic livestock raises many **ethical** issues (intensively farmed animals suffer high stress levels and often bone and joint damage; the hooves of cattle did not evolve for movement on concrete, especially slats) but also **management** issues. **Disease** is much more likely to spread rapidly when animals are confined in close proximity. The overuse of antibiotics to control (and often to prevent) disease has been significant in the spread of **antibiotic resistance** in bacteria. Reduced **genetic diversity** results through the selective breeding of the most productive and profitable varieties. Increased **pollution** from the increased use of fossil fuels or general farmland waste is another consequence.

Energy efficiency and the human diet – The production of animal products is **much less efficient** than using crops. The inefficiency of energy transfer through food chains means that much more energy is available to humans through eating plant products rather than animal products. In effect, each human who eats meat as a significant part of his/her diet requires much more land to produce the food required than does a vegetarian. For this reason very highly populated countries, such as some of those found in parts of Asia, have human populations that have a staple diet of plant products (for example rice) with meat being an uncommon luxury. In much of Europe and North America, meat products are more commonly used. Due to the inefficiency of eating meat products, this is possible only through the relatively low population densities involved (for example, in France) or through importing meat from other countries (for example, as happens in Britain).

Productivity in animals (secondary productivity) – The energy used in the production of new tissue in animals is referred to as **secondary productivity**. Crop farmers are concerned with increasing primary productivity (crop growth) but farmers of livestock are concerned with both primary productivity (if producing own animal feeds) and secondary productivity in the animals themselves.

The efficiency of secondary productivity can be worked out using **energy budgets**.

In the worked example below, the net secondary productivity (**P**) is the energy consumed (**C**) minus the energy lost through respiration (**R**), faeces (**F**) and urine (**U**).

$$P = C - (R + U + F)$$

In intensive farming, maximising **P** (by using high energy foods) and reducing any of **R**, **U** and/or **F** (most easily done with **R** by, for example, confinement) can lead to increases in growth and profit.

The energy budget of a bullock

R = 25

Values in arbitrary units

C = 100
100
P = 14.5
F = 60
U = 0.5

P = C – (R + U + F)
P = 100 – (25 + 0.5 + 60)
P = 14.5

Nutrient cycling

In the previous section we reviewed **energy** flow in ecosystems, a process that requires the input of energy from the Sun. However, there is no input of **nutrients** from another source, therefore the finite supply we have on Earth is **recycled** through ecosystems. The recycling of nutrients can be considered in terms of the recycling of the elements they contain, for example, **carbon** and **nitrogen**.

There are many similarities between the flow of energy and the recycling of nutrients. The recycling of nutrients also involves transfer from producer to consumer, between consumers, and through the decomposer chain. The key difference is that the nutrient enters the producer from **within** the ecosystem (for example, plants absorbing carbon dioxide from the atmosphere for photosynthesis). In this section we will consider the carbon and nitrogen cycles.

The carbon cycle

Carbon is an essential component of all the major macromolecules found in living organisms – essentially the 'building block of life'. Carbon is recycled through the processes of photosynthesis and respiration, the two key biochemical processes in the evolution of life. In **photosynthesis**, producers (plants) are able to fix inorganic carbon dioxide and incorporate it into a range of organic products. In **respiration**, organic products such as carbohydrates, fats and occasionally proteins (all containing carbon) are broken down to produce ATP, with carbon dioxide being released as a waste product.

Consumers gain carbon through **feeding**. Both plant and animal tissue are rich in carbon and complex organic compounds are broken down and built up in the ongoing cycle of feeding, digestion and the assimilation of food products in animals.

Saprobiotic microorganisms (decomposers) break down the organic molecules 'trapped' in dead organisms during **decay** and **decomposition**, and release the carbon as carbon dioxide, again in the process of respiration.

However, at certain stages of the Earth's history some dead organisms have been preserved in environments hostile to decay (**fossilisation**). Fossil fuels such as coal and peat contain 'locked in' carbon that has not been released as the process of decay and decomposition could not take place. This carbon is released (often many millions of years later) by the process of **combustion**.

The following diagram summarises the carbon cycle.

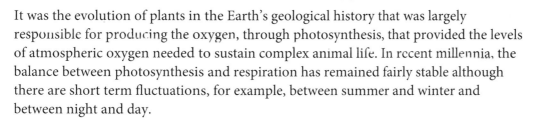

The carbon cycle

Note: The world's oceans contain a vast reserve of carbon dioxide dissolved in water as hydrogencarbonate (HCO_3^-) ions. This acts as a buffer being able to take up (or return) carbon dioxide from (or to) the atmosphere.

It was the evolution of plants in the Earth's geological history that was largely responsible for producing the oxygen, through photosynthesis, that provided the levels of atmospheric oxygen needed to sustain complex animal life. In recent millennia, the balance between photosynthesis and respiration has remained fairly stable although there are short term fluctuations, for example, between summer and winter and between night and day.

However, over the last few centuries, there has been an increase in atmospheric carbon dioxide levels. The main reasons for this are an increase in the combustion of fossil fuels and deforestation.

The nitrogen cycle

A source of nitrogen is necessary for living organisms to make the nitrogen-containing compounds essential for life. These include proteins, the nitrogenous bases in nucleic acids (DNA and RNA) and ATP.

The nitrogen normally enters the producers (plants) as **nitrate ions** (NO_3^-), absorbed from the soil by the process of active transport. Within the plants the nitrate is then used to build the nitrogen-containing organic compounds, such as amino acids and nucleotides, and subsequently into compounds, such as those listed in the previous paragraph.

The nitrogen-containing compounds in plants enter the consumer pathway when eaten by animals. Eventually the nitrogen-containing compounds are excreted (for example, as urea), egested in faeces, or end up in non-living organic matter following death.

Decay and decomposition by saprobiotic microorganisms are necessary to recycle the nitrogen contained in dead organisms, excreta and faeces to its usable inorganic form (nitrate), a process called **mineralisation**. The decay/decomposition and mineralisation of nitrogen-containing compounds involves two distinct stages, ammonification and nitrification.

Ammonification – This **decay** stage ends with the production of **ammonium ions** (NH_4^+). Decomposing microorganisms (fungi and bacteria) use the nitrogen-rich compounds (for example, protein, urea, or in faeces) as food and eventually break them down into ammonium ions.

Note: The process of decay (ammonification) is aided by the action of detritivores such as earthworms. The detritivores feed on the dead organisms, breaking them into small pieces (with larger surface area) and help distribute the dead material through the soil.

Nitrification – Nitrification is the conversion of **ammonium ions** to **nitrate**. The process is carried out in two stages by **nitrifying bacteria**:

- In the first stage nitrifying bacteria of the genus *Nitrosomonas* oxidise ammonium ions to **nitrite ions** (NO_2^-).

- In the second stage nitrifying bacteria of the genus *Nitrobacter* oxidise nitrite ions to **nitrate ions** (NO_3^-).

Note: The nitrifying bacteria are chemoautotrophs. They obtain their energy from the oxidation reactions involved rather than the Sun.

As oxidiation reactions are involved, **nitrifying bacteria need oxygen** (the process is **aerobic**) to carry out the process of nitrification. The nitrates produced by nitrification are available in the soil to be absorbed by plants and the cycle continues.

The processes already reviewed as part of the nitrogen cycle are summarised in the following diagram.

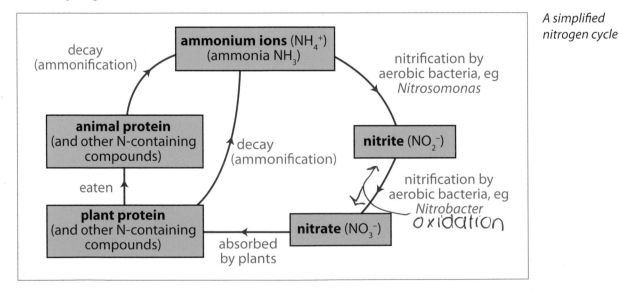

A simplified nitrogen cycle

Superimposed on the basic process involved in the cycle above, two other processes, **nitrogen fixation** and **denitrification**, are important in the recycling of nitrogen.

Nitrogen fixation – In nitrogen fixation, **nitrogen-fixing bacteria** convert nitrogen gas into nitrogen-containing compounds. The bacteria are mainly of the genus *Rhizobium* and they contain the enzyme **nitrogenase** responsible for fixing the nitrogen. Some species of nitrogen-fixing bacteria are **aerobic** and some are **anaerobic**.

The nitrogen-fixing bacteria can be **free living** in the soil or may form **mutualistic** relationships with a number of plant species. Legumes (for example, beans, peas and clover) contain nitrogen-fixing bacteria in **root nodules**. The legumes gain by obtaining nitrogen-containing compounds from the bacteria and the bacteria have a stable environment and a ready supply of carbohydrate.

Clearly nitrogen fixation is a very beneficial process as it enriches the soil. Farmers make use of this fact by growing legumes and allowing them to decay in the soil as part of a crop rotation cycle. The value of nitrogen fixation in crop systems can be very significant – white clover can provide as much as 150 kg ha^{-1} yr^{-1} of nitrogen in agricultural grasslands.

Note 1: Nitrogen fixation also takes place as a result of **lightning**. The lightning breaks the bonds holding the two atoms together in atmospheric nitrogen (N_2). These atoms combine with oxygen in the air forming nitrogen oxides. These dissolve in the rain, forming nitrates that are carried to the Earth. However the amount of nitrogen fixed by this method is insignificant compared to that fixed by microorganisms.

Note 2: As well as farmers making use of nitrogen-fixing microorganisms, nitrogen fixation is also important **ecologically**. Nitrogen fixers are important colonisers of barren land as they can survive in nitrogen deficient soils. Gorse (whin) is able to fix nitrogen, and consequently able to survive in nitrogen deficient soils. This is why it is very common in old quarries where there is virtually no soil in the early stages of succession.

Denitrification – Denitrification is the process whereby **denitrifying bacteria** convert nitrates into atmospheric nitrogen. This process can significantly reduce soil fertility. Unlike nitrifying and some nitrogen-fixing bacteria, denitrifying bacteria, for example *Pseudomonas*, are **anaerobic**. Anaerobic conditions are particularly likely to occur if the soil is compacted or waterlogged. Consequently, denitrifying bacteria are more numerous and more active in waterlogged or very compacted soils that are deficient in oxygen.

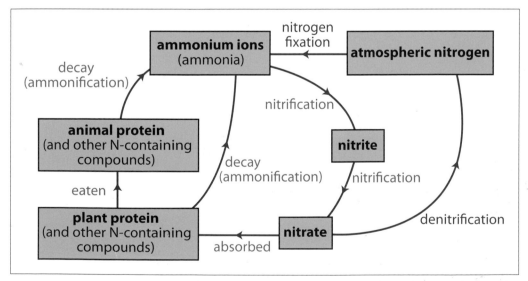

The nitrogen cycle

Note: The role of earthworms (and other detritivores) in decay was noted in an earlier section. Earthworms provide additional benefits in that their burrows aerate the soil (encouraging nitrification and nitrogen-fixing activity) and also drain the soil (reducing the activity of denitrifying bacteria).

Exam questions

1. (a) The diagram below shows the flow of energy through part of a food web in a grassland ecosystem. The figures are in kJ m^{-2} year^{-1}.

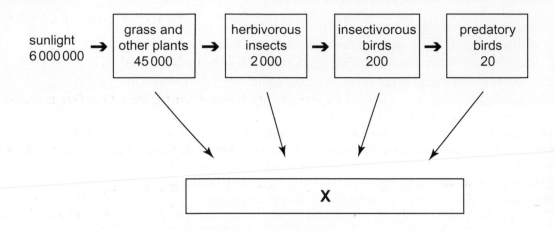

(i) Name the group of organisms represented by **X** in the box above. [1]

(ii) State **one** reason why only a very small percentage of energy reaching the leaf surface of the grass is utilised by the plants in photosynthesis. [1]

(iii) The efficiency of energy transfer between the grass and the herbivorous insects is less than that in subsequent stages of the food web. Explain the reason for this. [2]

(b) Many countries with very high populations do not use meat products as a significant human food source. For example, in much of Asia, a diet consisting largely of rice is common and seldom contains meat from birds or mammals.

In terms of energy transfer through trophic levels, explain the reason for this. [2]

Question taken from CCEA's Biology Assessment Unit A2 1, Physiology and Ecosystems, May 2013, © CCEA 2017

2. (a) The diagram below shows part of the energy budget of a cow grazing in a field. Figures are in kJ m^{-2} year^{-1}.

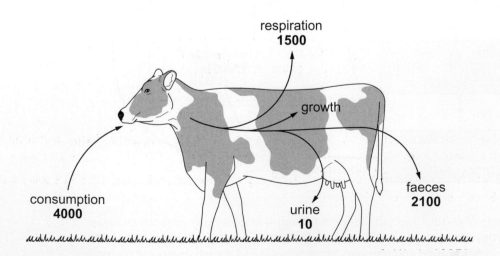

(i) Calculate the percentage of energy consumed that is available for the growth of the cow. (Show your working.) [2]

(ii) In terms of energy loss, explain the reason for the high values shown for respiration and faeces in the cow. [2]

(b) One method of increasing the efficiency of energy transfer in livestock is to confine the animals in small enclosed areas.

(i) State **two** ways that confining livestock in small enclosed areas can increase the efficiency of energy transfer. [2]

(ii) Apart from ethical considerations, give one argument against the practice of confining animals in small enclosed areas in intensive farming. [1]

Question taken from CCEA's Biology Assessment Unit A2 1, Physiology and Ecosystems, January 2014, © CCEA 2017

3. (a) When plants photosynthesise, light energy is converted into chemical energy.

The diagram below shows the fate of light energy falling on 1 m² of meadowland beside Lough Erne (units $kJ\ m^{-2}\ yr^{-1}$).

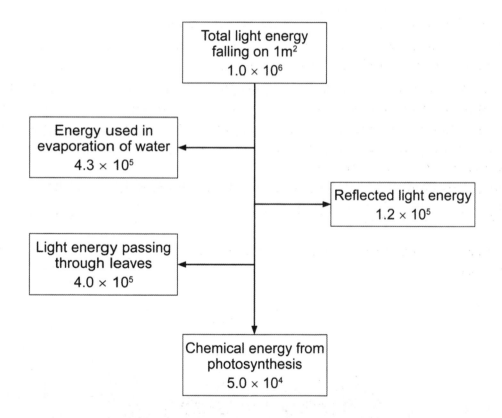

(i) Calculate the percentage of the total light energy falling on 1 m² which is converted into chemical energy by plants. (Show your working.) [2]

(ii) State **two** reasons why the chemical energy available to herbivores would be less than $5.0 \times 10^4\ kJ\ m^{-2}\ yr^{-1}$. [2]

Unit A2 2: Biochemistry, Genetics and Evolutionary Trends

Chapter 8 – Respiration

5.1.1   Demonstrate knowledge and understanding of the nature and function of ATP.

5.1.2   Demonstrate knowledge and understanding of glycolysis.

5.1.3   Demonstrate knowledge and understanding of aerobic respiration.

5.1.4   Demonstrate knowledge and understanding of anaerobic respiration.

5.1.5   Demonstrate knowledge and understanding of the Krebs cycle.

5.1.6   Demonstrate knowledge and understanding of the electron transport chain.

5.1.7   Demonstrate knowledge and understanding of the comparison between aerobic and anaerobic respiration.

5.1.8   Demonstrate knowledge and understanding of the respiratory quotient (RQ).

5.1.9   Carry out practical work to include using the respirometer to calculate oxygen uptake, carbon dioxide production and RQ values, and demonstrating the role of hydrogen acceptors using redox indicators (for example methylene blue).

ATP

Throughout the AS course and in earlier sections of the A2 course there have been many references to ATP. This has often been in the context of the mitochondrion being the organelle that makes ATP in respiration or that ATP is the molecule that allows work, for example active transport, to take place. But what exactly is ATP?

ATP is **adenosine triphosphate** and as the name suggests has **three phosphate groups** combined with the nucleotide base **adenine** and a **ribose** sugar. It is the presence of the phosphate groups that provides ATP with its energy-releasing properties.

ATP is the **immediate source of energy** in a cell, a (very) short-term store. It is the ATP that drives metabolism. Glucose can be used to make ATP but it cannot release energy directly.

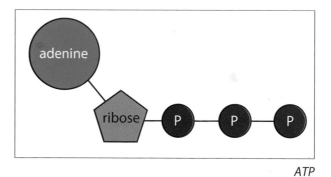

ATP

ATP is synthesised from **ADP** (**adenosine diphosphate**), a molecule with two phosphate groups and **inorganic phosphate** (P_i) as shown in the following diagram.

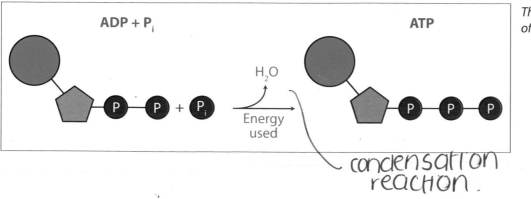

The synthesis of ATP

condensation reaction.

This process is known as **phosphorylation** (the addition of phosphate to a molecule) and the effect is to make the molecule with the extra phosphate (ATP) more energy rich. The synthesis of ATP involves condensation with the removal of a water molecule.

When the terminal (third) phosphate is subsequently removed from ATP, **energy is released** as shown in the next diagram.

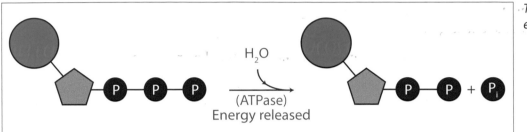

The release of energy from ATP

The breakdown of ATP (to ADP and inorganic phosphate with the release of energy) involves **hydrolysis** – the splitting of a molecule using water. The reaction is catalysed by the enzyme **ATPase**.

Note 1: ATP **releases energy** – Energy cannot be created or destroyed; it can only be changed from one form to another.

Note 2: Many students incorrectly use the terms **ATP** and **energy** synonymously. ATP is an energy-rich molecule that releases/provides energy when hydrolysed.

Note 3: Cells do not store large amounts of ATP – there may be as little as 5 g of ATP in the body at any one time. However, it can be rapidly built up from ADP and P_i. In cells there is a continuous cycle between ADP and P_i, and ATP.

What makes ATP so suitable as an immediate energy store?

- The hydrolysis of an ATP molecule releases a relatively **small amount of energy** (compared to glucose). This allows energy to be released in **small, manageable steps** during energy-requiring reactions.

- The hydrolysis of ATP is a **single reaction** (involving the breaking of one bond) releasing immediate energy, again providing the cell with fine control over its immediate energy budget. Compare this with the number of steps required to break down a molecule of glucose (see following sections).

- As a small, soluble molecule, ATP can be **transported** around the cell easily. This enables it to be transported from mitochondria (the main site of synthesis) to any part of the cell.

Using ATP in the cell

We have already reviewed in detail the role of ATP in **active transport** and **muscle contraction**. However, anywhere 'work' is required, ATP is used. It provides the energy for many **metabolic processes** including anabolic reactions involving the building up of macromolecules. The role of ATP in the **activation of molecules** (through phosphorylation) will be discussed in detail on page 137.

Note: Most ATP is made in respiration. However, ATP is also made in the light-dependent stage of photosynthesis (see Chapter 9).

The biochemistry of respiration

The conversion of glucose into ATP takes place during respiration. In mammals, and most living organisms, the principal respiratory substrate is **glucose**. Although the cellular respiration of glucose is a complex integrated process, it is convenient to divide the process into four stages:

1. **Glycolysis** – The splitting of glucose (a hexose sugar) into two 3-carbon pyruvate molecules.

2. **Link reaction** – The conversion of the pyruvate into 2-carbon acetyl coenzyme A (acetyl CoA).

3. **Krebs cycle** – The feeding of acetyl CoA into a cycle of oxidation-reduction reactions.

4. The **electron transport chain** – The use of electrons (and hydrogens) produced (mainly) in the Krebs cycle to synthesise ATP.

Glycolysis

Glycolysis, the first step in cellular respiration, is a series of reactions that take place in the **cytoplasm**. Glycolysis can be simplified into the following stages.

The initial stage is the **activation** of glucose by **phosphorylation**. This makes the glucose more reactive. The two phosphates required come from the hydrolysis of **two ATP molecules**. The phosphorylation of the glucose converts it into **fructose bisphosphate**.

Following phosphorylation, the 6C fructose bisphosphate splits into two 3-carbon molecules of **triose phosphate**. The triose phosphate is **oxidised** through the loss of hydrogen atoms to eventually form **pyruvate**. The hydrogen atoms are collected by the **hydrogen carrier** molecule **NAD** (nicotinamide adenine dinucleotide) which becomes reduced to form **reduced NAD (NADH)**. The removal of hydrogen involves dehydrogenase enzymes in a process called **dehydrogenation**.

In converting **each** molecule of triose phosphate into a pyruvate molecule **two ATP molecules** are produced.

However, as each glucose molecule **splits** to form two triose phosphate molecules (and therefore two molecules of pyruvate) this produces two ATP molecules for **each** of the triose phosphate molecules, a gain of four ATP. This gives a **net gain of two ATP** for glycolysis (as two were initially used to activate the glucose).

Glycolysis can be summarised as:

- The initial stage of the cellular respiration of glucose that **does not require oxygen** and takes place in the **cytoplasm**.

- The reduction of NAD between the triose phosphate and pyruvate stages to give **two reduced NAD (NADH)**.

- A net gain of **2 ATP**. because 2 were initially used to activate glucose.

Note 1: Glycolysis involves the oxidation of triose phosphate and the reduction of NAD. **Reduction** involves the gain of hydrogen or electrons or the loss of oxygen. Conversely, **oxidation** involves the gain of oxygen or the loss of hydrogen or electrons. Reduction involves the gain of energy and oxidation the release of energy.

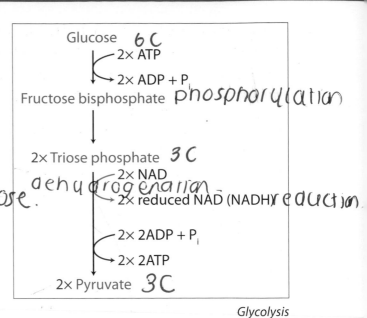

Glucose 6 C

2× ATP

2× ADP + P$_i$

Fructose bisphosphate phosphorylation

2× Triose phosphate 3 C

dehydrogenation

2× NAD

2× reduced NAD (NADH) reduction

2× 2ADP + P$_i$

2× 2ATP

2× Pyruvate 3 C

Glycolysis

Note 2: The hydrogen carrier NAD is a **coenzyme**. It is needed for the dehydrogenases to pass on the hydrogen they remove. The hydrogen cannot simply build up in the cell as a waste product! In effect, NAD carries hydrogen from one molecule to another. We will find out very soon the contribution the reduced NAD makes to the process of respiration.

The link reaction

The pyruvate produced in glycolysis is transported into the **matrix** of a **mitochondrion**. During the link reaction the pyruvate is converted to **acetyl coenzyme A (acetyl CoA)**.

The pyruvate is **decarboxylated** with the removal of one molecule of CO_2. **Dehydrogenation** also takes place with the removal of hydrogen leading to the formation of **reduced NAD (NADH)**. Following decarboxylation and dehydrogenation, the resulting 2-carbon acetate combines with coenzyme A (CoA) to form the 2-carbon acetyl CoA.

Pyruvate (3C)

NAD

CO$_2$

reduced NAD (NADH) decarboxylation,

dehydrogenation

Acetate (2C)

coenzyme A (CoA)

Acetyl CoA (2C)

The link reaction

The Krebs cycle

The Krebs cycle also takes place in the **matrix of the mitochondrion**. It involves a cyclical series of reactions.

The key stages in Krebs cycle include:

- The **2-carbon** acetyl CoA from the link reaction combines with the **4-carbon** acid (oxaloacetate) to produce a **6-carbon** acid (citrate).

- **Decarboxylation** of the 6-carbon acid (citrate) results in the formation of the 5-carbon acid (oxoglutarate) with the loss of a molecule of CO_2.

- **Decarboxylation** of the 5-carbon acid (oxoglutarate) results in the formation of the 4-carbon acid oxaloacetate with the loss of a molecule of CO_2 and the cycle continues.

- The reactions in the cycle also involve **dehydrogenation** (and dehydrogenase enzymes). At three points in the cycle, hydrogen is released that subsequently reduces NAD to form **reduced NAD (NADH)**. At one point the hydrogen is picked up not by NAD but by another hydrogen carrier FAD (flavin adenine dinucleotide) to form **reduced FAD (FADH$_2$)**.

- One molecule of **ATP** is produced by the transfer of a phosphate group from an intermediate compound to ADP. ATP produced in this way is referred to as **substrate-level phosphorylation**.

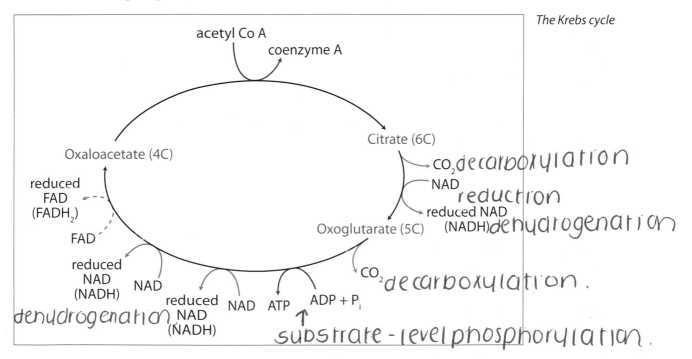

The Krebs cycle

Note: As there are two molecules of acetyl CoA formed for every molecule of glucose there will be two turns of the cycle for each glucose. Consequently, when working out the energy produced from each molecule of glucose it is important to double the values referred to above and in the diagram.

So far we have not discussed what happens to the reduced coenzymes (**reduced NAD** and **reduced FAD**) – their very important role in the respiration process will be discussed in the next section, the **electron transport chain**.

Note: The description of the Krebs cycle given here is a very simplified version. In reality, it is much more complex with many more intermediate steps.

The electron transport chain

The electron transport chain is based in and on the **inner mitochondrial membranes (cristae)**. The hydrogen atoms collected by **NAD** from the process of dehydrogenation in glycolysis, the link reaction and Krebs cycle (and by **FAD** in the Krebs cycle) are carried into the next stage of the process (as NADH and FADH$_2$ respectively). In the **electron transport chain** the energy in the hydrogen (and more particularly their electrons) is converted into **ATP**, the form of energy that cells can use.

Revisiting the mitochondrion – You will remember from AS that the inner mitochondrial membrane is highly folded. The coenzymes and many of the enzymes involved in the electron transport chain are attached to the inner mitochondrial membrane. The more deeply infolded the cristae, and the more infoldings there are, the more extensive the ultrastructure that exists for ATP production in the mitochondrion.

The NAD, FAD and other coenzymes and carriers in the electron transport chain are highly organised and arranged in a sequence of decreasing potential energy. Each carrier downstream has slightly stronger reducing power than the one immediately before it. Therefore, the hydrogens (and electrons) are able to move along the chain with carriers being successively reduced and oxidised as hydrogen/electrons pass along the chain in a series of oxidation-reduction (**redox**) reactions.

The carriers of the electron transport chain – The **NAD/FAD** operate as hydrogen carriers. Although the next diagram shows NAD at the start of the electron transport chain, it (and FAD) also functions by bringing the hydrogen to the chain.

Note: In the inner mitochondrial membrane the NAD can be arranged in such a position that it is 'physically' situated at the 'start' of the electron transport chain. This is clearly not the case for the NAD that becomes reduced in the **cytoplasm** as a consequence of the reactions that take place during glycolysis. The reduced NAD from glycolysis has to be transported into the mitochondrion from the cytoplasm to deliver these hydrogen atoms to the electron transport chain.

Initially **hydrogen** passes along the carriers **NAD**, **flavoprotein** and **coenzyme Q**, as seen in the following diagram. Following the coenzyme Q stage, the hydrogen dissociates into **electrons** (and protons) and the electron transport chain subsequently acts as an **electron carrier**. The electrons pass along the **cytochromes** in a series of redox reactions.

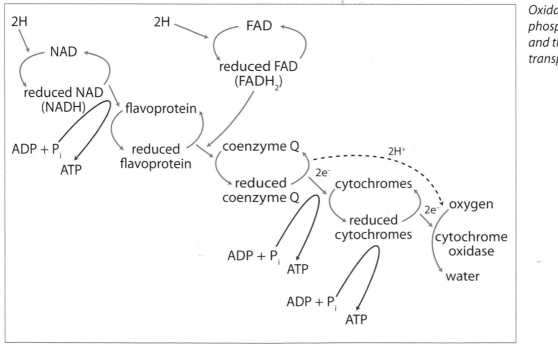

Oxidative phosphorylation and the electron transport chain

The **final hydrogen (electron) acceptor** is **oxygen**; it is at this stage that oxygen is used in respiration. The oxygen combines with hydrogen (at this stage the electrons and protons from the original dissociation of hydrogen rejoin) to form **water**, a waste product of respiration. This final stage in the electron transport chain is catalysed by the enzyme **cytochrome oxidase**.

As the carriers lie at progressively lower energy levels along the chain, energy becomes available as the redox reaction takes place. At certain points there is enough energy to produce **ATP** by **oxidative phosphorylation**.

Note: Oxidative phosphorylation is the coupling of electron transport and ATP production in the presence of oxygen.

How much ATP is produced in respiration?

It is generally assumed that for each reduced **NAD** sufficient energy is released to produce **3 ATP** molecules in the electron transport chain. Reduced **FAD** enters the chain further along than reduced NAD and there is only sufficient energy available to produce **2 ATP**.

The overall energy budget for aerobic respiration of one glucose molecule can be summarised in the following table.

Stage of respiration	Site	Reduced NAD	Reduced FAD	ATP by substrate-level phosphorylation	ATP by oxidative phosphorylation
Glycolysis	cytoplasm	2		2 (net)	
Link reaction	mitochondrial matrix	2			
Krebs cycle	mitochondrial matrix	6	2	2	
Electron transport chain	inner mitochondrial membrane				$34 (10 \times 3) + (2 \times 2)$
Totals				4	34

Theoretically each molecule produces up to **38 ATP**, as shown in the table.

Note: The 38 ATP produced from a molecule of glucose is a theoretical maximum. In reality for each molecule of glucose the value is likely to be closer to 30 as explained below. On average, reduced NAD is likely to produce closer to 2.5 ATP molecules and reduced FAD 1.5 rather than the idealistic 3 and 2 respectively. This can be for a number of reasons, for example the NAD can be used as a reducing agent for other metabolic compounds, not just those involved in respiration. Energy is also used in transporting the reduced NAD (and other molecules, for example pyruvate) from the cytoplasm into the mitochondrion, energy which should be incorporated into the respiration budget.

Summary of the biochemistry of respiration

The following diagram summarises the four stages of respiration.

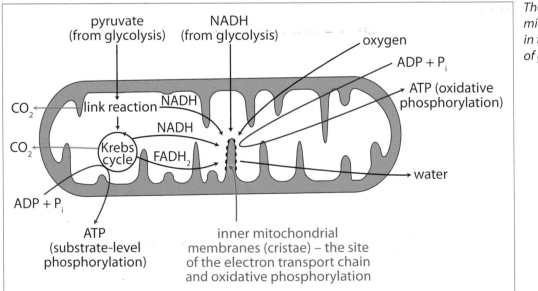

Summary of the biochemistry of respiration of glucose

As we have worked through the biochemistry of respiration we have referred to the mitochondrion on many occasions. The mitochondrion is the organelle of respiration – although you should not forget that a small amount of ATP is produced by glycolysis in the cytoplasm. The following diagram summarises the role of the mitochondrion in respiration.

The role of the mitochondrion in the respiration of glucose

The process of the respiration of glucose can be summarised by the following equation.

$$C_6H_{12}O_6 + 6O_2 \rightarrow 6CO_2 + 6H_2O + energy \textbf{ (38 ATP)}$$

On page 141 we reviewed where the (theoretical) 38 ATP are produced. The oxygen is necessary for the electron transport process to be completed and it is used as the final electron acceptor – without oxygen the carriers would remain reduced. The water is produced as a waste product at the same point where the oxygen is used. The origin of the six molecules of carbon dioxide produced for each molecule of glucose respired can be identified from pages 138–139 – the decarboxylation reaction in the link reaction and the two decarboxylations in the Krebs cycle (each × 2).

Other respiratory substrates

While glucose is the primary respiratory substrate in many living organisms, it is not the only one. If glucose supplies are low, **fat** (and eventually **protein** in near-starvation conditions) can be utilised.

When triglycerides are hydrolysed into glycerol and fatty acids, the **glycerol** enters the glycolysis pathway with the **fatty acids** entering at the acetyl CoA stage. Triglycerides are very energy rich (39 kJ g^{-1}) compared to carbohydrate (16 kJ g^{-1}). Proteins are hydrolysed to **amino acids**. Following the removal of the amino group by deamination, the residue enters the cycle as acetyl CoA (main point), pyruvate, or as one of the intermediate compounds in the Krebs cycle. Other carbohydrates can be used; fructose enters glycolysis and other more complex carbohydrates can be broken down to glucose or a similar sugar before entering glycolysis. The various pathways for the different respiratory substrates are summarised in the next diagram.

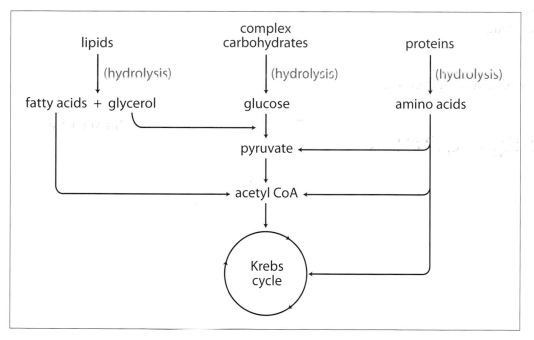

The metabolism of different respiratory substrates

The diagram highlights that other respiratory substrates originating from fat or protein are eventually channelled through the Krebs cycle with many entering at the acetyl CoA stage. For this reason **acetyl CoA** is often referred to as the 'hub' of the various respiratory pathways.

Aerobic and anaerobic respiration

The processes discussed in the earlier sections describe what happens when oxygen is available, ie **aerobic respiration**. When oxygen is not available, **anaerobic respiration** can take place.

Although oxygen is only used in the electron transport chain, without it the link reaction, Krebs cycle or the electron transport chain (the processes that take place in the mitochondrion) cannot take place.

In anaerobic respiration, glycolysis will only continue if its products are removed and not allowed to accumulate. The pyruvate is converted to lactate in animals and ethanol in plants and yeast. However, it is also necessary that the reduced NAD formed during glycolysis is oxidised again so that (oxidised) NAD will be available to take up further hydrogen atoms from glycolysis. If this did not happen all the NAD would be reduced and glycolysis would stop as there would be no hydrogen acceptors available. The 'mopping up' of these hydrogen atoms is achieved by the hydrogen being used in the reactions between the pyruvate and the lactate or ethanol.

Glycolysis is the only energy releasing (ATP production) stage of anaerobic respiration. There is a net gain of only **2 ATP**, clearly very inefficient when compared to aerobic respiration. However, it is a relatively **fast process** – it takes place throughout the **cytoplasm** and substances do not have to diffuse in and out of the mitochondrion in addition to it being only a very short part of the normal aerobic pathway.

Not surprisingly, aerobic respiration is the main respiratory pathway in active and complex living organisms. However, most living organisms can carry out anaerobic respiration in some of their tissues for a short period of time.

Anaerobic respiration in animals

Anaerobic respiration in animals is summarised by the diagram below.

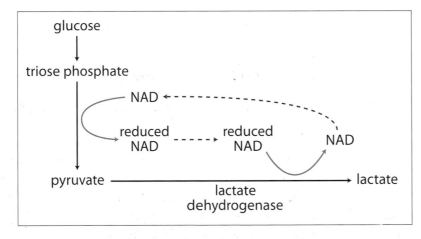

The anaerobic pathway in animals

In animals the ability to respire anaerobically can be very advantageous. In healthy mammals, including humans, anaerobic respiration is most likely to take place in the skeletal muscles as a consequence of strenuous exercise. It is important to note that during strenuous exercise, the muscles will be respiring **both** aerobically and anaerobically, but that the additional anaerobic respiration releases **extra energy** above and beyond what the aerobic respiration can provide. This extra ATP may not be much compared with that produced in aerobic respiration, but it may be enough to make the crucial difference between escaping from a predator or not, or if human, winning that race.

Note: Before the anaerobic pathway is used, the animal will physiologically maximise ATP production from aerobic respiration. This will involve increased breathing and heart rates to ensure that as much oxygen (and glucose) reaches the muscles and the operation of the Bohr shift to maximise the release of oxygen by haemoglobin. Anaerobic respiration is very much the last resort.

The lactate produced by anaerobic respiration accumulates in the muscles and can cause muscle fatigue and cramp. It is eventually removed when sufficient oxygen becomes available again and anaerobic respiration is no longer necessary. The lactate can be converted back to glucose or metabolised in other ways, processes that require oxygen. As the body is dealing with the lactate produced because of an oxygen shortage earlier on, the extra oxygen used to metabolise lactate is called the **oxygen debt**. The 'extra' oxygen is also used to resynthesise depleted ATP.

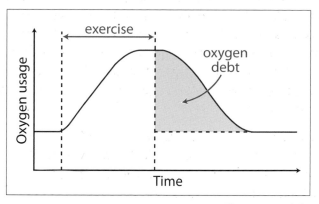

The oxygen debt

Anaerobic respiration in plants and fungi

In plants and fungi the end product of anaerobic respiration is **ethanol**, not lactate.

Additionally, anaerobic respiration in plants and fungi produces **carbon dioxide** as a waste product. Anaerobic respiration in plants and fungi is summarised by the diagram on the right.

The ethanol is **not reconverted** back to pyruvate but is eliminated as a waste product. The value of anaerobic respiration to plants and fungi is different to that in animals. A significant part of most plants

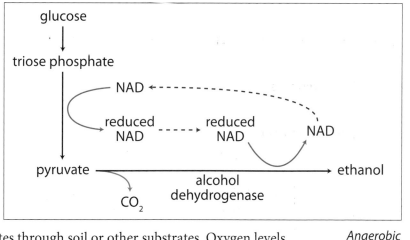

Anaerobic respiration in plants and fungi

(for example, roots) or fungi penetrates through soil or other substrates. Oxygen levels can often be low in these environments and the ability to respire anaerobically allows the production of ATP to be maintained. The much lower metabolic rate in plants/fungi, compared to the more complex animals, means that the lower ATP yield from anaerobic respiration is not as significant an issue.

Note: Anaerobic respiration can only use glucose (or other carbohydrate) as a respiratory substrate. As the breakdown products of fat and protein enter the pathway well through glycolysis, or beyond, they cannot be used for anaerobic respiration.

The respiratory quotient

Analysis of the volume of carbon dioxide released during respiration relative to the amount of oxygen consumed provides information about the type of respiratory substrate used and the type of respiration (aerobic or anaerobic) taking place.

The respiratory quotient (RQ) is the volume (or number of molecules) of carbon dioxide released divided by the volume (or number of molecules) of oxygen consumed and can be represented by the following equation:

$$RQ = \frac{\text{Volume (molecules) of } CO_2 \text{ released}}{\text{Volume (molecules) of } O_2 \text{ consumed}}$$

In the following examples the RQ can be worked out by using the number of molecules equating to carbon dioxide and oxygen in the equations.

Glucose

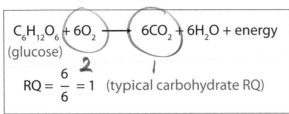

$C_6H_{12}O_6 + 6O_2 \longrightarrow 6CO_2 + 6H_2O + \text{energy}$
(glucose)

$RQ = \dfrac{6}{6} = 1$ (typical carbohydrate RQ)

Palmitic acid (a fatty acid)

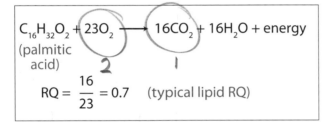

$C_{16}H_{32}O_2 + 23O_2 \longrightarrow 16CO_2 + 16H_2O + \text{energy}$
(palmitic acid)

$RQ = \dfrac{16}{23} = 0.7$ (typical lipid RQ)

The RQ values obtained for glucose (carbohydrate) and palmitic acid (a fatty acid) represent the typical overall values for carbohydrates and lipids.

The table below shows the RQ values for the main groups of substances used as respiratory substrates.

Respiratory substrate	RQ
carbohydrates	1
lipids (triglycerides)	0.7
proteins	0.9

The values in the table represent RQ values when only the substrate in question is being respired. In many organisms, a mixture of respiratory substrates is used. Therefore, the actual RQ value obtained is likely to fall somewhere between 1–0.7. In humans, a value around 0.85 is normal; this is because humans typically use a combination of carbohydrates and lipids as respiratory substrates.

What else can RQ values tell us?

A RQ value of **more than 1** suggests that **anaerobic respiration** is taking place. Remember that when anaerobic respiration is taking place, normally both aerobic and anaerobic respiration are taking place. The aerobic component will give a RQ value between 0.7–1 but anaerobic respiration will involve the production of carbon dioxide (in plants and fungi) without the input of oxygen. If enough anaerobic respiration is taking place this will push the RQ value above 1. The higher the value is above 1, the higher the proportion of anaerobic respiration.

> **Note 1:** If data shows a RQ value of more than 1, it will almost certainly be for plant or fungal tissue. Remember anaerobic respiration in animals does not produce carbon dioxide.

> **Note 2:** If the RQ value exceeds 1, **both** aerobic **and** anaerobic respiration are taking place. The RQ value for anaerobic respiration only is infinity.

Under normal conditions the RQ value can vary considerably. In humans, following a meal rich in carbohydrate the RQ can approach 1, but after a number of hours without eating it is likely to drop as lipids will be used. Variation is also very likely when measuring plant RQ values during the daytime. Photosynthesis also involves gas exchange and will almost certainly cloud the RQ values.

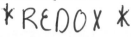

Practical work

Use of a respirometer to calculate oxygen uptake and carbon dioxide production

There are many different types of respirometer but they all operate using the same principles.

Calculating oxygen uptake – Oxygen uptake in living organisms is calculated by adding **potassium hydroxide** (KOH) to the respirometer. When the respirometer is set up, the living organisms (for example, blowfly larvae or woodlice) respire taking in oxygen from within the system. The carbon dioxide produced is absorbed by the potassium hydroxide. The consequent reduction in pressure causes the liquid/dye in the respirometer to move in the direction of the biological material. The distance (volume) moved represents the oxygen used in respiration. Normally respirometers are calibrated

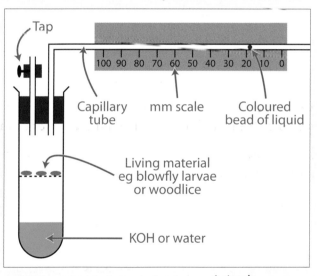

A simple respirometer

so it is possible to calculate the initial and final levels of the potassium hydroxide (as in the diagram on page 148) or dye (as in the diagram above).

Calculating carbon dioxide production – This can be calculated by repeating the process but replacing the KOH with **water**. The respirometer needs to be left for the **same length of time** and in the **same conditions** as that for measuring oxygen uptake. This time the CO_2 produced is not absorbed. If there is no change in the movement of the liquid in the manometer or calibrated scale, then the volume of carbon dioxide produced is the same as the volume of oxygen absorbed – in effect, the carbon dioxide produced **exactly** replaces the oxygen used in the tube.

For example, if the respiring tissue originally used 20 mm³ of oxygen (calculated with KOH present) in 10 minutes, then if the same tissue (organism(s)) is used for 10 minutes with water replacing the KOH, and the position of the liquid does not move, then it can be assumed that 20 mm³ of carbon dioxide is produced.

In practice, there may be more or less carbon dioxide produced than oxygen used, therefore the liquid may move a short distance in either direction from its starting position. If the liquid moves **away** from the living material, there is **more carbon dioxide produced than oxygen taken in** but if it moves **closer** to the living material there is **less carbon dioxide produced than oxygen taken in** (ie the carbon dioxide produced does not fully compensate for the pressure reduction caused by the oxygen uptake). In our example (above), if the level of liquid moved 3 mm³ on the scale further away from the living material, when the water is used, the amount of carbon dioxide produced is 20 + 3 = 23 mm³.

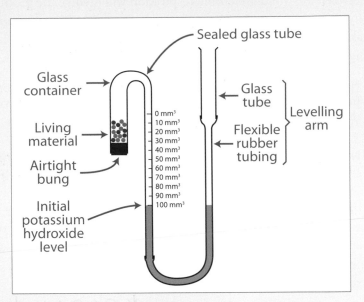

Calculating oxygen uptake and carbon dioxide production using a respirometer

Calculating the carbon dioxide produced and the oxygen taken in allows us to calculate **respiratory quotient (RQ)** values.

Using the example described above, the RQ is 23/20 = 1.15, suggesting that anaerobic respiration is taking place.

In this type of investigation it is crucial that **all possible variables are controlled**. Where possible it is best to use the same apparatus for calculating the oxygen uptake (with KOH) and for calculating carbon dioxide production (with water) with the **same living organisms** (this ensures factors such as age and the metabolic rate of the organisms are controlled as far as possible). Other variables such as **temperature** can be controlled by placing the apparatus in a **water bath** at the same temperature for both parts of the investigation. It is also important to calculate oxygen production and carbon dioxide production over the same **time period**. If using germinating peas (or other plant material), it is important to cover the living material with **foil** to prevent photosynthesis taking place.

> **Note:** Temperature needs to be controlled for two main reasons. It will affect the respiration rate (and hence oxygen intake and carbon dioxide production) and if variable can cause changes in gas volume due to expansion or contraction.

Using redox indicators

At several stages in respiration, hydrogen atoms are removed from molecules in reactions. Dehydrogenase enzymes catalyse these reactions and the process is described as dehydrogenation. The hydrogen atoms are taken up by NAD (or FAD) forming reduced NAD (or reduced FAD).

It is possible to use **redox indicators**, chemicals which are a different colour when reduced compared to their oxidised state to demonstrate dehydrogenation taking place. The indicators (as opposed to NAD/FAD) take up the hydrogen and become reduced.

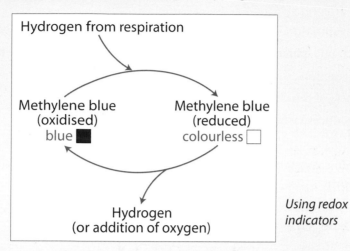

Using redox indicators

There are many different practical activities that demonstrate this principle. One example is described below:

1. Crush soaked peas/mung beans to a paste in a pestle and mortar, and place in a boiling tube.
2. Repeat with boiled peas/mung beans.
3. Make up some methylene blue of a suitable concentration.
4. Add 2 cm³ of the methylene blue to each boiling tube and place in a water bath at 35°C.
5. Observe the colour changes in the boiling tubes over time.

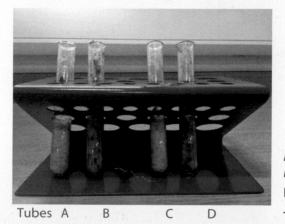

Tubes   A   B   C   D

Mung beans and redox indicators

Image courtesy of Jacqueline Gray

Results: Tubes **A** and **C** contained living tissue and tubes **B** and **D** contained the boiled tissue. The boiling denatured the dehydrogenase enzymes therefore no H atoms were produced in respiration and the methylene blue was not reduced.

Note: Investigations similar to this can be used to demonstrate respiration taking place or even to compare rates of respiration in different tissues or in different environmental conditions.

Exam questions

1. (a) Identify the word or phrase which is described by each of the following statements about respiration:

   • the initial stage of respiration, during which there is a net gain of 2 ATP molecules
   • the process in which phosphate is added to a molecule and which requires the presence of oxygen
   • the site of the link reaction
   • the two end-products of the electron transport chain
   • the process that produces lactate [5]

   (b) Tripalmitin is an organic substance which is used in the manufacture of soap. The aerobic respiration of tripalmitin is described by the equation below:

   $$2C_{51}H_{98}O_6 + 145O_2 \rightarrow 102CO_2 + 98H_2O + energy$$

   (i) Calculate the respiratory quotient (RQ) for the aerobic respiration of tripalmitin. [1]
   (ii) Give two pieces of evidence which indicate that tripalmitin is a fat (lipid). [2]

   (c) Respiration by yeast is involved in the production of alcoholic drinks such as wine. The apparatus shown below can be used to make wine from grape juice. The antimicrobial liquid and the S-shaped capillary tube help prevent contamination of the flask's contents.

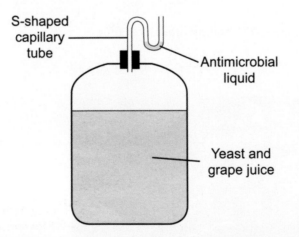

   (i) An airtight bung can also be used to prevent contamination. Suggest why this would not be appropriate in the apparatus shown. [1]

The yeast RQ values in the apparatus described on the previous page were calculated over time. These are shown in the graph below.

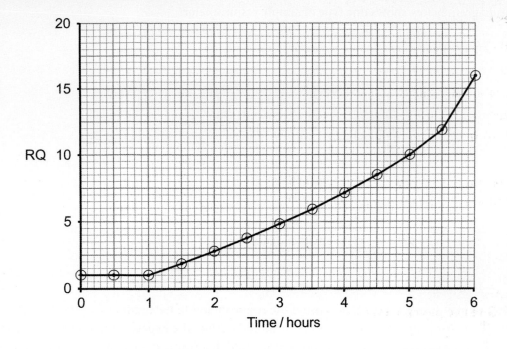

(ii) Describe and explain the results shown. [3]

Question taken from CCEA's Biology Assessment Unit A2 2, Biochemistry, Genetics and Evolutionary Trends, June 2016, © CCEA 2017

2. (a) The diagram below summarises anaerobic respiration in muscle cells.

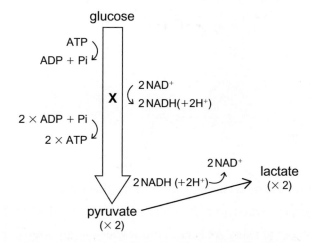

   (i) Name process X in which glucose is converted to pyruvate. [1]

   (ii) The production of lactate allows process X to continue where oxygen is limited.
        Explain how. [2]

(b) (i) Anaerobic respiration takes place where the availability of oxygen is limited. Describe one advantage of this in highly active muscle cells. [1]

   (ii) Anaerobic respiration in muscle cells leads to the build up of an oxygen debt. Describe what is meant by an 'oxygen debt'. [1]

(c) Anaerobic respiration in muscle tissue does not produce carbon dioxide as a waste product. However, anaerobic respiration in fungi and plants produces carbon dioxide.

The diagram below shows one type of simple respirometer.

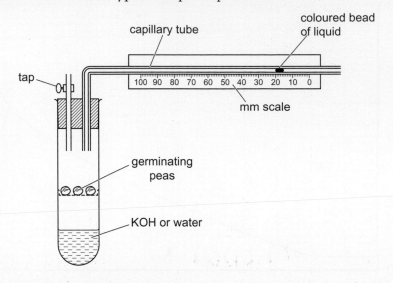

Devise a plan for an investigation using the respirometer to determine if a sample of germinating peas is respiring anaerobically. Your plan should outline the experimental set-up, the control of variables, the collection of data and how you could determine if anaerobic respiration is taking place. (You do not need to give a detailed procedure for the investigation.) [4]

Question taken from CCEA's Biology Assessment Unit A2 2, Biochemistry, Genetics and Evolutionary Trends, June 2013, © CCEA 2017

3. (a) The structure of an ATP molecule is represented in the diagram below.

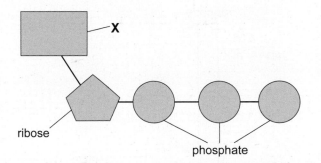

(i) Identify the part of the molecule labelled X in the diagram. [1]

(ii) Explain what happens when an ATP molecule is hydrolysed to ADP. [1]

(iii) Give two advantages of using ATP as an immediate energy source within the cell, rather than glucose. [2]

(b) It was noticed that one variety of a pea species (A) had a more rapid growth rate than another variety (B). It was suggested that this was due to variety A having a faster respiration rate.

In an investigation to compare respiration rates in the two varieties, two sets of the apparatus shown in the following diagram were used. (This apparatus is similar in principle to a standard respirometer.)

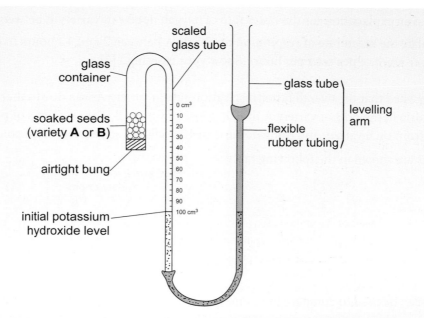

For each variety, 10 g of soaked peas were placed in the glass container with an airtight bung. The level of potassium hydroxide was adjusted to 100 cm³ on the scale by raising or lowering the levelling arm.

Both sets of apparatus were placed in a dark cupboard for 12 hours. The readings on the scales were recorded every two hours.

(i) Explain why the investigation was conducted in darkness. [2]

The results of the investigation are shown in the graph below.

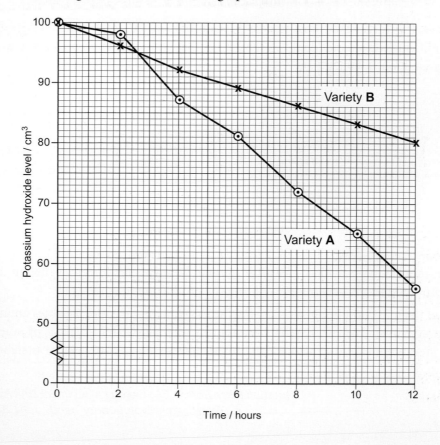

(ii) Suggest an explanation for the faster rate of oxygen uptake in variety B between 0–2 hours. [1]

(iii) Calculate the mean rate of respiration of variety A between 2 and 12 hours in cm^3 of oxygen used per gram of pea seed per hour. (Show your working.) [3]

(c) It was suggested that the overall faster respiration rate in variety A was due to there being more mitochondria in the cells of variety A than in those of variety B. Thin sections of pea tissue were prepared from each variety and mitochondria in 100 cells of each variety were counted.

The results are shown in the following table.

	Variety of pea	
	A	B
Number of cells in section (n)	100	100
Mean number of mitochondria in each cell ($\bar{x}$)	6.3	5.8
Standard deviation (error) of the mean ($\hat{\sigma}_{\bar{x}}$)	0.62	0.68

The t-test can be used to compare the number of mitochondria in the two varieties.

(i) State the null hypothesis for this test. [1]

(ii) Calculate the value of t using data from the table above. (Show your working.) [2]

(iii) State the probability value for the calculated t. [1]

(iv) State your decision regarding the null hypothesis and comment on this outcome. [2]

Question taken from CCEA's Biology Assessment Unit A2 2, Biochemistry, Genetics and Evolutionary Trends, June 2015, © CCEA 2017

4. *Quality of written communication is awarded a maximum of 2 marks in this section.*

Mitochondria are the organelles most associated with ATP production in the cell. The diagram below represents a mitochondrion and identifies substances that typically enter and leave the organelle as it carries out its function.

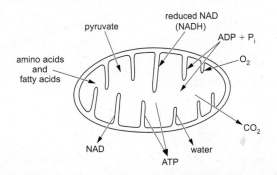

(a) Using the information provided, give an account of how the substances labelled in the diagram are used or produced in a mitochondrion during the production of ATP. [12]

(b) Analysis of the mitochondria in a cell, using the electron microscope, provides an insight into the metabolic activity of that cell. Explain how appropriate microscopic analysis of mitochondria, in terms of their number and structure, can provide information about cellular metabolic activity. [4]

Quality of written communication. [2]

Question taken from CCEA's Biology Assessment Unit A2 2, Biochemistry, Genetics and Evolutionary Trends, June 2014, © CCEA 2017

Chapter 9 – Photosynthesis

In photosynthesis energy in sunlight is used to make complex organic compounds from inorganic compounds. Chlorophyll is the major light-trapping pigment involved in harnessing the Sun's energy. Water and carbon dioxide are the raw materials used and glucose is an initial end product. The process of photosynthesis can be summarised by the equation:

$$6CO_2 + 6H_2O \rightarrow C_6H_{12}O_6 + 6O_2$$

The site of photosynthesis

In most plants the **leaf** is the organ specialised for photosynthesis. In the leaf, the cells in the layer immediately under the upper epidermis, the **palisade layer**, are highly adapted for this role. The palisade cells are therefore close to the leaf upper surface (where most light enters the leaf), are tightly packed together and have numerous chloroplasts in their cytoplasm. The spongy mesophyll layer below the palisade cells is less tightly packed and has numerous large air spaces that form a continuous pathway with the stomata in the lower epidermis. This facilitates gas exchange between the palisade cells and the outside environment.

Leaves tend to orientate themselves in such a way that they maximise incident light reaching their upper surfaces (as with these nettle plants)

The chloroplast

In green plants photosynthesis takes place in the **chloroplast**. The chloroplast is a large organelle (up to 20 μm in length and 5 μm wide) highly adapted for photosynthesis. The chlorophyll is arranged in a system of flattened membranes called **thylakoids**. The thylakoids contain the **chlorophyll** (and other plant pigments) that absorb the light energy. They also contain systems of **electron carriers** and associated enzymes involved in the photosynthesis reactions. Thylakoids are typically arranged in clumps or 'stacks' of membranes called **grana** (singular **granum**). As the grana contain concentrated areas of light-absorbing photopigments, much of the light harvesting takes place at these points in the chloroplast. The thylakoids are linked together by **intergranal lamellae**.

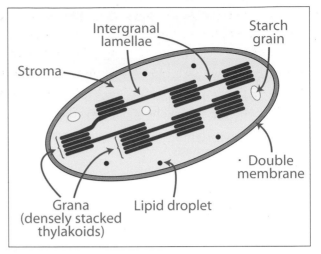

The chloroplast

Although light harvesting takes place in the thylakoids, the carbon dioxide is used ('fixed') and sugars and other compounds are made in a cyclical series of reactions that take place in the **stroma**. In effect, photosynthesis involves two distinct, but interlinked phases, which take place in the thylakoids and the stroma. The reactions that take place in the stroma are dependent on a steady supply of products from the reactions associated with the absorption of light energy.

Absorption and action spectra

Not surprisingly, there is a close association between light absorption and the rate of photosynthesis in the chloroplast.

The absorption spectrum – The absorption spectrum can be represented by a graph that shows the relative **absorption of light** at particular wavelengths. It can show the overall absorption of light by all the pigments that absorb light in photosynthesis and/ or show the light absorbed by individual pigments, for example chlorophyll *a*, chlorophyll *b* and carotene. Absorption spectra of individual pigments show that the pigments complement each other by absorbing light over a different range of wavelengths. This ensures that by absorbing light over as great a range of wavelengths

Absorption spectra of the main photosynthetic pigments

as possible, more light energy can be harvested. The relationship between the different pigments and their roles in harvesting light energy will be discussed in the following sections.

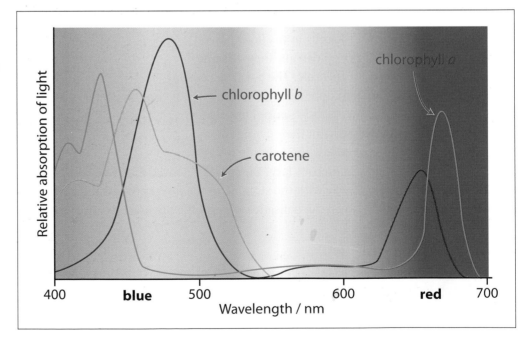

Note: Absorption spectra show the relative proportions of light that can be absorbed at different **wavelengths**. It is not necessarily linked to light **intensity**.

The action spectrum – The action spectrum is the **rate of photosynthesis** that takes place at different wavelengths. Comparison of the graphs of the absorption spectra of the main pigments (see graph on page 156) or the overall absorption spectrum (showing the light absorbed by all pigments) and the action spectrum show a very close correlation as seen in the graph below – the rate of photosynthesis is high for those wavelengths over which most light is absorbed (and converse).

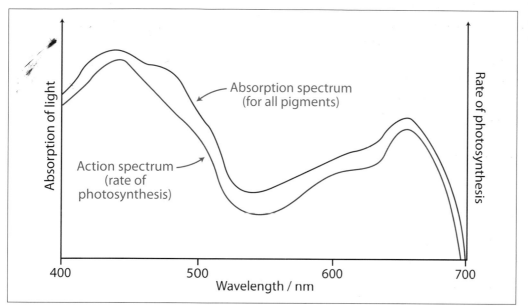

Absorption and action spectra

The biochemistry of photosynthesis

The process of photosynthesis can be conveniently separated into three main stages:

- **light harvesting** – the absorption of light in the thylakoid, a consequence of which is to raise the energy level of the electrons in chlorophyll.

- the **light-dependent stage** – energised electrons are used to make the energy-rich compounds ATP and reduced NADP. These reactions take place in or on the thylakoid membranes of the grana.

- The **light-independent stage** – the products of the light reaction are used to make simple carbohydrate. Carbon dioxide is fixed as part of the cyclical series of reactions that take place in the stroma.

Light harvesting

The chlorophyll and other pigments (**accessory pigments**) are located in the **thylakoid membranes**. They are arranged in clusters, with each cluster containing several hundred molecules. Each cluster is called an **antenna complex**. A molecule of **chlorophyll *a***, called the **primary pigment**, is situated at the base of the antenna complex in a region called the **reaction centre**.

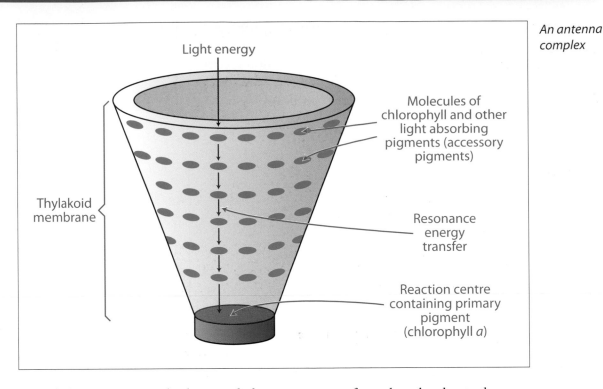

An antenna complex

The whole antenna complex harvests light over a range of wavelengths, due to the presence of different pigments with different absorption maxima. As light energy is absorbed throughout the complex, special proteins help pass the absorbed energy from one molecule to its adjacent molecule by the process of **resonance transfer**. The energy is funnelled in the direction of the reaction centre. The nature of resonance transfer requires the molecules in the antenna complex to be part of a regularly arranged structure.

Note: A key feature of resonance transfer is that it is energy that is transferred, not electrons – compare this with the reactions of the light-dependent stage in the next section.

Each antenna complex forms a **photosystem**. In the light-dependent stage of photosynthesis, there are two different types of photosystem as we shall see in the next section.

The light-dependent stage

The reactions of the light-dependent stage also take place in the **thylakoid membranes** and are very tightly linked to the process of light harvesting.

The arrangement of many accessory pigments in an antenna complex ensures that if sufficient light is available, enough energy can pass to the reaction centre allowing electrons in **chlorophyll a** (the **primary pigment**) to move to higher energy levels – they become **excited** in the process of **photoactivation**. If enough energy is available the electrons are **emitted** and taken up by an **electron acceptor** – in effect, the chlorophyll becomes an **electron donor**. The electron acceptor that accepts the emitted electrons is arranged at the start of an **electron carrier chain**, with **cytochromes** forming the carriers in the chain itself.

Note 1: Carriers are progressively reduced and oxidised in a series of redox reactions as they take up and pass on electrons.

Note 2: Each new carrier is at a slightly lower energy level than the previous one, so the electrons lose energy as they pass along the chain.

Note 3: At certain stages in the electron transport chain there is sufficient energy available to make ATP from ADP and P_i.

Note 4: Note the similarities in the previous three points to the process of electron (hydrogen) transfer in respiration.

In photosynthesis (as with the electron transport chain in respiration), the formation of ATP is tightly coupled with electron transport. However, in photosynthesis the energy comes from light so it is called **photophosphorylation**.

Of course, it is necessary that the electrons that are excited and subsequently emitted from the antenna complex are replaced in the reaction centre. These come from the **splitting of water** (**photolysis**). When the water is split the hydrogen dissociates into hydrogen ions (protons) and electrons. The electrons are used to replace the electrons lost during photoactivation and the hydrogen ions are used later in the light-dependent reaction (see next diagram) with **oxygen** being given off as a waste product.

The photosystem that emits the electrons that leads to the electron transfer, as described above, is **photosystem II** (**PS II**). Photosystem II is also referred to as P680, as the absorption peak of the chlorophyll *a* molecule is **680 nm**.

As the diagram on page 160 shows, the electron carrier chain is linked to another photosystem – **photosystem I** (**PS I**) or P700, as it has a chlorophyll *a* primary pigment molecule with an absorption peak of **700 nm**.

The chlorophyll *a* molecule in photosystem I emits electrons, as happens in photosystem II described earlier, if enough light energy reaches the antenna complex. These electrons are trapped by another electron acceptor and subsequently passed on to **NADP** to form **reduced NADP** or **NADPH**. To provide the hydrogen necessary to reduce NADP the electrons combine with the hydrogen ions (protons) provided by the splitting of water in photolysis.

Note: NADP is nicotinamide adenine dinucleotide phosphate – a very similar but subtly different coenzyme to the NAD hydrogen acceptor involved in respiration.

In photosystem I electrons lost from the chlorophyll *a* are replaced by electrons passing down the electron carrier chain, electrons that originated in photosystem II.

The electron pathway and reactions of the light-dependent stage, as summarised in the diagram on the right, is described as the **Z-scheme**.

Note 1: NADP is the **final electron acceptor** in photosynthesis (it is oxygen in respiration).

Note 2: The production of ATP as described in this chapter (also applies to oxidative phosphorylation in respiration) is non-cyclic with the electrons passing through the electron transport chain needing to be continually supplied from earlier reactions. Consequently the production of ATP in photosynthesis is referred to as **non-cyclic photophosphorylation**.

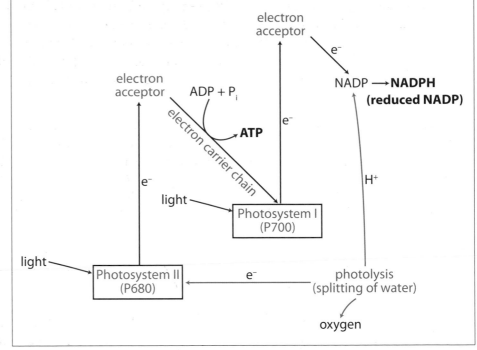

The light-dependent stage of photosynthesis

The end products of the light-dependent reaction are **ATP** and **NADPH (reduced NADP)**, both of which are used in the light-independent reaction.

The light-independent stage

The light-independent stage takes place in the **stroma** of the chloroplast and it is dependent on products (ATP and NADPH) of the light-dependent stage. It is during this light-independent stage that the inorganic carbon dioxide is 'fixed' (incorporated) into organic compounds.

Carbon dioxide that has diffused into the chloroplast combines with the **5-carbon** compound **ribulose bisphosphate (RuBP)**, a reaction catalysed by the enzyme ribulose bisphosphate carboxylase (**rubisco**). This forms two molecules of the **3-carbon glycerate phosphate (GP)**. The **NADPH (reduced NADP)** is used to provide the reducing power to reduce the glycerate phosphate to **triose phosphate (TP)** and energy released from ATP drives the process.

Five out of every six molecules of triose phosphate produced are used in the recycling of ribulose bisphosphate. ATP (also from the

The light-independent stage of photosynthesis

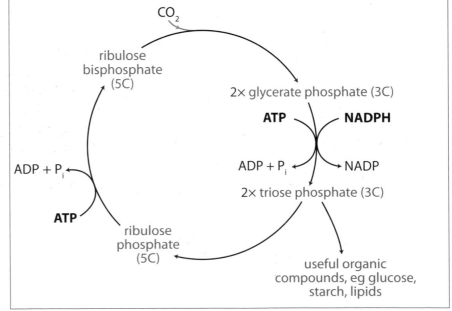

light-dependent reaction) is used to provide energy and also to provide the phosphate to make the RuBP. The regeneration of the RuBP is a cyclical process, as seen in the diagram at the bottom of page 160. One sixth (approximately 17%) of the triose phosphate made in the light-independent reaction (the net 'gain') is used to produce other organic molecules such as glucose, sucrose, starch, glycerol, fatty acids and amino acids (the latter using absorbed nitrate).

Note: Although called the light-independent stage as direct light is **not** required, the light-independent stage will usually only take place when light is present (as it requires products from the light-dependent stage). When the biochemistry of photosynthesis was first worked out, the two stages were referred to as the 'light reaction' and the 'dark reaction' – terms no longer used as they do not identify the requirement for light in the light-dependent stage, nor the fact that the light-independent stage takes place almost always in the light (and not in the dark).

The following two diagrams help demonstrate and explain the link between the light-dependent stage and the light-independent stage.

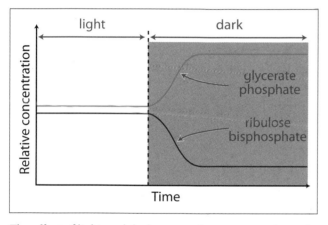

The effect of light and darkness on the concentrations of glycerate phosphate and ribulose bisphosphate

Explanation: When the light is removed (the plant is in darkness) the light-dependent reaction stops. Consequently ATP and NADPH will no longer be made and be available for the light-independent reaction. This means that glycerate phosphate cannot be converted into triose phosphate, leading to a buildup of glycerate phosphate and a reduction in ribulose bisphosphate (as the ribulose bisphosphate present in the stroma fixes CO_2 to form glycerate phosphate and no more can be regenerated from triose phosphate). The concentrations of each level off as the cycle grinds to a halt.

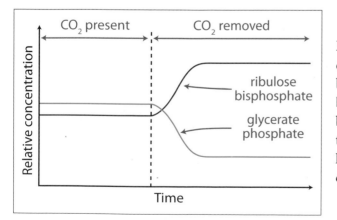

The effect of the presence and absence of carbon dioxide on the concentrations of glycerate phosphate and ribulose bisphosphate

Explanation: When CO_2 is no longer available it cannot be 'fixed' and combine with ribulose bisphosphate therefore glycerate phosphate cannot be formed. The ribulose bisphosphate therefore builds up and the glycerate phosphate already in the system gets converted to triose phosphate, leading to its rapid fall. As before the concentrations of each level off as the cycle stops.

Summary of the role of the chloroplast

The previous sections have described the reactions that take place in the different regions of the chloroplast. The following diagram outlines the role of the chloroplast in photosynthesis.

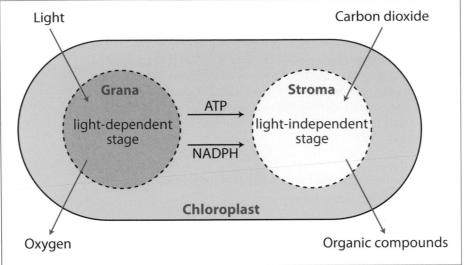

The chloroplast and photosynthesis

Case studies – two famous historical photosynthesis experiments

1. Engelmann (1880s) – was able to show that photosynthesis mainly used light from the blue and red parts of the spectrum. He used the filamentous alga *Spirogyra*, a genus that typically has its chloroplasts arranged in a spiral pattern that 'spiral' just inside the cell wall of each cell, analogous to the appearance of the spiral thickening of lignin in xylem. Engelmann also used motile, aerobic bacteria in his investigation, reasoning that the bacteria are likely to cluster in oxygen-rich regions. By passing light through a prism (and thus separating light into its spectral components) and then onto the *Spirogyra* in the presence of the bacteria, Engelmann observed that the motile bacteria clustered close to the algal chloroplasts in the cells that received blue and red light as shown in the diagram below.

Engelmann's conclusion was that the bacteria (being aerobic) accumulated in greater numbers around the parts of the chloroplasts that photosynthesised at the fastest rates and therefore produced most oxygen. The parts of the chloroplasts in the red and blue light (but not the green) were photosynthesising at the fastest rates showing that the alga could utilise the red and blue part of the spectrum but that green light was less readily absorbed.

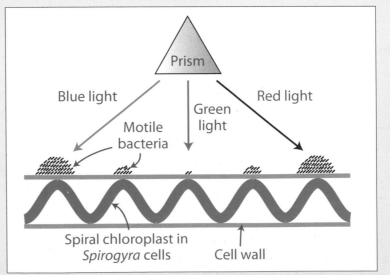

Engelmann's experiment showing that blue and red light was used in photosynthesis

2. Calvin – The light-independent reaction is also called the Calvin Cycle as it was worked out by Melvin Calvin and his co-workers just over 60 years ago. Calvin's experiment is referred to as the 'lollipop' experiment, as the apparatus he used resembled a lollipop, flattened from front to back.

In the experiment, Calvin added radioactive carbon dioxide ($^{14}CO_2$) to a suspension of the autotrophic protoctistan *Chlorella* in the 'lollipop' as shown in the diagram below.

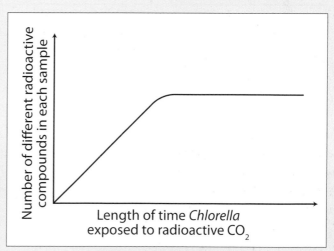

$^{14}CO_2$ injector

System for introducing *Chlorella*

System to control temperature, pH, amount of nutrients in suspension

Lollipop flask: flattened front to back, and illuminated front and back

Chlorella suspension

Hot methanol to kill *Chlorella* instantly

Tap that can be opened to remove sample of *Chlorella* at intervals

Calvin's lollipop apparatus used in working out the light-independent stage of photosynthesis

After a **very short interval of time** the tap was opened and the *Chlorella* was released into the hot methanol, killing it **immediately** and preventing any further reactions taking place. Following this, the *Chlorella* was homogenised and the compounds present identified by chromatography. Calvin deduced that any compounds present containing radioactive carbon must have been produced following the 'fixing' of the radioactive carbon dioxide in the light-independent stage of photosynthesis. Using this logic, he was able to identify **glycerate phosphate** as the first compound produced.

By very gradually increasing the time interval between adding the radioactive carbon dioxide and killing the *Chlorella*, he was able to identify the compounds produced at successive stages of the cycle. The graph on the right shows that the number of radioactive compounds identified increased as the time interval that the *Chlorella* was exposed to the radioactive carbon dioxide increased. This is consistent with successive compounds in the light-independent stage being labelled with increasing time. Eventually the number of different radioactively labelled compounds identified levelled off as all the compounds in the light-independent stage (and other compounds subsequently formed) were identified.

Number of different radioactive compounds in each sample

Length of time *Chlorella* exposed to radioactive CO_2

The relationship between the number of different radioactively labelled compounds formed and the length of time Chlorella was exposed to radioactive CO_2

External factors affecting the rate of photosynthesis

Limiting factors in photosynthesis

Light intensity, carbon dioxide concentration and **temperature** are the main factors that affect the rate of photosynthesis. The actual photosynthetic rate at any one time is determined by whichever of these factors is least favourable – the least favourable factor being the **limiting factor**.

Two key features of limiting factors:

- If a factor is limiting, increasing its amount will increase the rate of photosynthesis.

- Increasing the rate of the other (non-limiting) factors will not increase the rate of photosynthesis, if the rate of the limiting factor is left unchanged.

The following graph illustrates the effects of light intensity, carbon dioxide level and temperature on photosynthesis, demonstrating the principle of limiting factors.

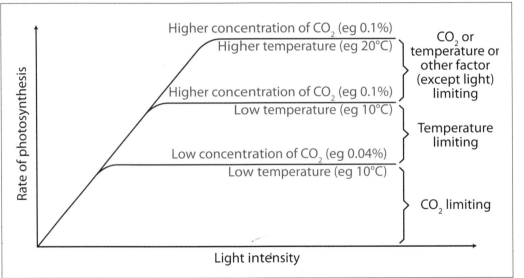

The effects of light intensity, carbon dioxide concentration and temperature on rates of photosynthesis

Light intensity and photosynthesis – The graph above shows that at low light intensities, light is the limiting factor, irrespective of the levels of carbon dioxide and temperature.

In most natural ecosystems, light tends to become limiting as dusk (nightfall) approaches, with photosynthesis unable to take place during the darkness of the night. In early morning (dawn) light usually ceases to be the limiting factor. However, light intensity can also become limiting for periods during very dark, cloudy days when temperature and carbon dioxide levels are high (or adequate).

If light intensity is limiting, it exerts its effect through there not being enough **ATP** and **NADPH** produced in the **light-dependent** stage of photosynthesis.

Carbon dioxide concentration and photosynthesis – The atmospheric level of carbon dioxide is around 390 ppm (approximately 0.04%); 0.04% is a sub-optimal level for most plants, so increasing atmospheric levels of carbon dioxide leads to higher rates of photosynthesis (the optimum level for many plant species is around 0.1% carbon dioxide). On a bright summer day, when light intensity and temperature levels are not limiting, carbon dioxide can be the limiting factor. Growers of glasshouse crops often artificially raise carbon dioxide levels to increase growth rates.

If carbon dioxide levels are increased, there is more available for the **carboxylation** of **RuBP** in the **light-independent** stage, allowing more glycerate phosphate to be formed.

Temperature and photosynthesis – Temperature can limit the rate of photosynthesis if light intensity and carbon dioxide levels are not limiting. In Britain, it is often the temperature that limits grass and other plant growth during the winter. Glasshouse growers can produce optimum growing conditions by increasing temperature (and light intensity and carbon dioxide levels) as necessary.

If temperature is increased (up to an optimum) the **enzyme-catalysed reactions** of the **light-independent** stage of photosynthesis occur at a faster rate.

Note 1: The optimum temperature for growth in many plants is around 25°C (not 37°C).

Note 2: Temperature is a limiting factor at low levels, but will also reduce photosynthesis rate if too high, due to enzymes being denatured.

A shortage of **water** can also affect photosynthesis. Unlike light intensity, carbon dioxide levels and temperature, shortage of water will not affect photosynthesis directly. However, if water is in short supply stomata will close as part of the plant's response in reducing water loss. Additionally, the plant will wilt and the orientation of the leaves will change, reducing incident solar radiation and many reactions will slow down. A dehydrated plant is likely to be dead long before there is not enough water available for the light-dependent stage.

Gross photosynthesis, net photosynthesis and the compensation point

We have come across the terms Gross Primary Productivity (GPP) and Net Primary Productivity (NPP) in Chapter 7.

The terms gross photosynthesis and net photosynthesis are very similar to GPP and NPP respectively, and are also an indication of the organic material (carbohydrate) produced and the carbohydrate gain when respiratory losses are taken into consideration.

Gross photosynthesis = net photosynthesis + respiration

Note: The terms gross (and net) primary productivity can be regarded as more ecological concepts, providing information on carbohydrate produced in a unit area of the ecosystem. Gross or net photosynthesis is often used to provide information on the carbohydrate produced by a single plant, or even part of a plant.

Gross and net photosynthesis can be considered in terms of **carbon dioxide** or **oxygen exchange** or even change in organic (carbohydrate) content in a plant.

The following graph shows the typical pattern of carbon dioxide exchange in plants in different light intensities.

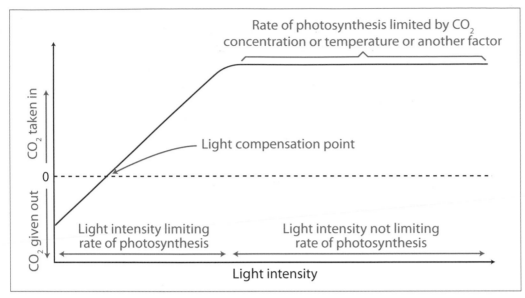

The effect of light intensity on the rate of photosynthesis with reference to rate of carbon dioxide exchange

At low light intensities carbon dioxide is given out (evolved) as the rate of respiration exceeds the rate of photosynthesis. The light **compensation point** is the point where there is no net intake or output of carbon dioxide (ie respiration and photosynthesis are taking place at the same rate).

The next diagram shows how carbon dioxide exchange takes place over a 24 hour period. For the plant to grow the area **X** (which represents net photosynthesis) must exceed the combined areas of **Y** (which represent respiratory losses).

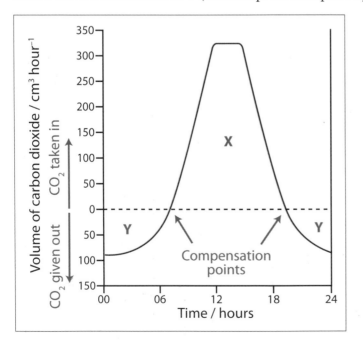

The net volume of carbon dioxide produced (and used) by a plant over a 24 hour period

Note 1: It is important to remember that respiration takes place throughout the 24 hour period – it is not restricted to the times where the line drops below 0. The line above the 0 shows the net intake of carbon dioxide, ie the carbon dioxide taken in by the plant above and beyond that produced in respiration (representing **net photosynthesis**).

Note 2: The same information can be easily demonstrated by measuring the relative levels of oxygen taken in and given out. The equivalent graph for oxygen demonstrating gas exchange in a typical plant over a 24 hour period will be an upside down mirror image of the carbon dioxide graph.

Practical work

Paper chromatography of plant pigments

The principle of paper chromatography is that some solutes are more soluble than others in the same solution. The more soluble substances will 'travel' further in a solvent that is moving through chromatography paper. Due to the separation of the different solutes by this process the different solutes present can be identified. The method is particularly useful in identifying the plant pigments present in a leaf. Unlike chromatography involving amino acids (see Chapter 1 in *Biology for CCEA AS Level 2nd Edition*, Colourpoint Educational) the plant pigments do not need developing using chemicals such as ninhydrin.

Paper chromatography of plant pigments does involve the following stages:

- Preparing the chromatogram
- Running the chromatogram
- Calculating R_f values

Preparing the chromatogram – The chromatography paper is cut to fit the tank/vessel used to hold it in a vertical position. The paper (chromatogram) should be long enough to allow attachment to the lid of the apparatus and to drop to just above the base of the tank. In due course solvent will be placed into the bottom of the tank – it is important that the chromatogram is long enough to extend into the volume of solvent being used.

A horizontal line should be drawn in pencil a few centimetres above the base of the chromatogram. The key thing is that the line should be drawn in a position that will lie above the level of the solvent when the chromatogram is placed in the solvent.

The solution containing the plant pigments to be tested needs to be 'spotted' on the pencil line. The solution is added to a pre-determined position (origin) by a micro-pipette. After adding a drop of the solution it is then dried before the process is repeated. This allows the solution to be concentrated. At this stage the chromatogram has been prepared and it is now ready to 'run'.

Preparing and running the chromatogram

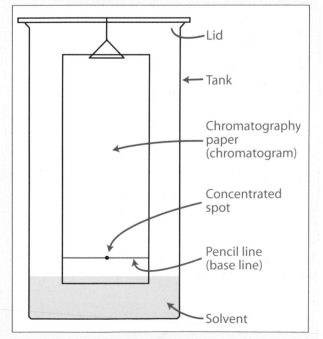

Lid

Tank

Chromatography paper (chromatogram)

Concentrated spot

Pencil line (base line)

Solvent

It is important to ensure that the concentrated spot forms as small an area as possible. This is aided by ensuring that the spot is dry before adding an additional drop of solution. In addition, it is important to avoid contamination of the chromatogram – only hold the chromatogram at the edges and avoid setting it on laboratory benches that could be contaminated with a range of chemicals. Before placing the prepared chromatogram in the tank the solvent should be added to allow the atmosphere to become saturated.

Running the chromatogram – The chromatogram is carefully suspended into the solvent and attached to the lid of the tank. This is a risky stage.

It is important to ensure that:

- the line (and concentrated spot(s)) does not make contact with the solvent.
- the chromatogram is securely attached.
- the chromatogram is not suspended at an angle.

As the solvent 'runs' up the chromatogram it carries the plant pigments that begin to become separated as the process continues. The 'run' of the solvent should be stopped when it is well up the chromatogram but **before** it reaches the top.

Developing the chromatogram – The chromatogram should then be dried – before the solvent is dry it is important to mark the 'solvent front' on the chromatogram with a pencil.

Calculating R_f values – A R_f value is the distance moved by a solute (in this case one of the pigments) divided by the distance moved by the solvent front.

It is calculated by measuring the distance from the origin (initial position of concentrated spot) to the position of the solvent front and measuring the distance from the origin to the position of the plant pigment being investigated. As each plant pigment will extend over an area of the chromatogram, it is essential that a consistent approach is taken to measuring the length from the origin. Either the distance from the origin to the leading edge of the spot is measured or from the origin to the centre of the spot.

The R_f value is then calculated (for example, X/Y in the diagram below for the plant pigment xanthophyll).

Note: A R_f value is always less than 1. So if you calculate a value greater than 1, you have probably got your two values the wrong way round.

As the leaves of most plants have the same pigments for trapping light energy, chromatograms of leaf tissue from most plants will be similar in that they will show the pigments chlorophyll b, chlorophyll a, xanthophyll and carotene in the order shown in the diagram below.

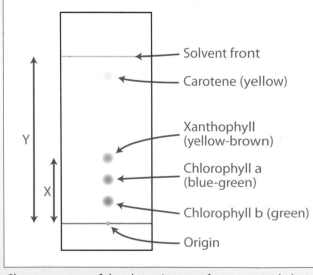

Chromatogram of the plant pigments from a typical plant

Tree leaves often appear yellow or yellow-brown in autumn as the green chlorophyll is broken down and valuable nutrients withdrawn into the tree, leaving other less valuable pigments and waste products

Demonstrating the role of hydrogen acceptors in photosynthesis using a redox indicator (for example, DCPIP)

In the light-dependent stage of photosynthesis, NADP is reduced by the electrons that have passed along the electron chain to form NADPH. A redox indicator such as DCPIP can also pick up electrons, but it serves as an indicator as it changes colour as it does so. Using the example of DCPIP, the colour changes from blue to colourless as the indicator becomes reduced.

This investigation is normally carried out using **isolated chloroplasts**. The chloroplasts are obtained by homogenising leaves and centrifuging the homogenate to precipitate out the chloroplasts. If DCPIP is added to a chloroplast suspension and the experimental tube strongly illuminated, the DCPIP will turn from blue to colourless. Comparison can be made with the chloroplasts placed in darkness and with the DCPIP added to water or buffer (rather than chloroplasts) as a control.

Note: It is important to use isolated chloroplasts for a number of reasons including maximising electron production but also to avoid contamination with mitochondria. Reactions in mitochondria are also capable of reducing the DCPIP.

Typical procedure:

1. Place about 5 g of chopped lettuce in a mortar. Add about 10 cm³ of buffer solution and grind with a pestle.

2. Pour the contents of the mortar through muslin or a similar 'rough' filter into a beaker.

3. Pour the suspension into centrifuge tubes, remembering the importance of counterbalancing counter tubes.

4. Centrifuge at high speed for 10–12 minutes.

5. Pour off and discard the supernatant of the centrifuge tubes. This should remove organelles smaller than chloroplasts.

6. The sedimented chloroplasts in the centrifuge tubes can be added to two experimental test tubes (**A** and **B**). To these tubes buffer is also added. One of these tubes with chloroplasts is covered with foil (tube **B**) to prevent light reaching the chloroplasts. A third tube (**C**) is set up with buffer but no chloroplasts.

7. DCPIP is added to each of the tubes and the tubes are placed in a beaker of crushed ice.

8. The beaker containing the tubes is placed under a very strong light source and the colour of each tube is examined every 5 minutes for 20 minutes.

Typical results are shown in the table below.

Time / minutes	Colour of test tube contents		
	A (chloroplasts and buffer)	B (chloroplasts and buffer; test tube covered with foil)	C (buffer only)
0	blue-green	blue-green	blue
5	blue-green	blue-green	blue
10	green	blue-green	blue
15	green	blue-green	blue
20	green	blue-green	blue

Note 1: Tube A changes from blue-green to green (not just blue to colourless) as the isolated chloroplasts are green.

Note 2: It is important that the speed of the centrifuge is set to the correct level and the centrifuge run for the appropriate length of time to ensure that chloroplasts, and not mitochondria, are spun down into the sediment.

Note 3: The DCPIP is not reduced in B as the chloroplasts are not illuminated, showing that the reduction of DCPIP in A is due to electrons/hydrogen produced in the light-dependent reaction.

Exam questions

1. The light-dependent stage of photosynthesis involves photosystems which are affected by both light intensity and wavelength.

   (a) State precisely where the light-dependent stage takes place in the chloroplast. [1]

   (b) With reference to the events within the photosystems, explain the effect of an increased light intensity. [2]

   (c) Explain the effect of different wavelengths of light on the activity of the pigment molecules within the photosystems. [2]

   Question taken from CCEA's Biology Assessment Unit A2 2, Biochemistry, Genetics and Evolutionary Trends, June 2013, © CCEA 2017

2. Photosynthesis involves a number of different plant pigments which absorb light energy.

   (a) Describe one advantage of plants having different pigments to absorb light energy. [1]

   (b) In deciduous trees the leaves emerge in spring and are lost in autumn. Suggest one advantage to trees of losing their leaves in autumn. [1]

   (c) Chromatography can be used to separate and identify the photosynthetic pigments present in a leaf. In an investigation, chromatography was used to compare and contrast the photosynthetic pigments present in the leaves of a particular species. This was done in May (at the start of the growing season) and in October (at the end of the growing season).

The results of the investigation are shown in the table below. Assume the technique used to extract the pigments was equally effective in both May and October.

Pigment	May (start of growing season)		October (end of growing season)	
	Colour of pigment	Intensity of colour	Colour of pigment	Intensity of colour
Carotene	yellow	4	yellow	5
Phaeophytin	yellow-grey	1	yellow-grey	2
Xanthophyll	yellow-brown	5	yellow-brown	4
Chlorophyll a	blue-green	5	blue-green	1
Chlorophyll b	green	5	green	2

Key

Intensity of pigment colour	
Dense colouration	5
Just visible	1

(i) Using the information provided, explain why the leaves of this species would be coloured green in May but would appear yellow-brown in October. [3]

(ii) In this investigation it is important to control as many variables as possible. Suggest one variable that should be controlled and explain the reason for controlling it. [2]

(d) The light-dependent reaction of photosynthesis is summarised in the diagram below. However, the process of photolysis is not included.

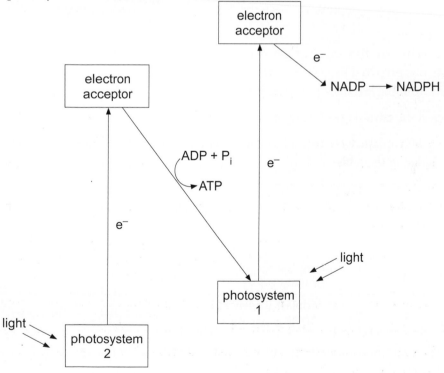

(i) Using the diagram and your knowledge, describe what happens to the products of photolysis (the splitting of water) in the above reaction. [3]

(ii) Describe precisely how the products of the light-dependent reaction are used in the light-independent reaction. [2]

Question taken from CCEA's Biology Assessment Unit A2 2, Biochemistry, Genetics and Evolutionary Trends, June 2015, © CCEA 2017

3. (a) The process of photosynthesis involves two stages which are distinct yet linked. These are known as the light-dependent and the light-independent stages.

   (i) State precisely where the light-independent stage takes place. [1]

   (ii) Explain the link between the two stages of photosynthesis. [2]

   (b) In the light-independent stage, glycerate phosphate is the first product formed following carbon fixation.

   (i) Name the compound which fixes carbon dioxide to produce glycerate phosphate. [1]

Cacti are plants which are adapted to very hot, sunny, and dry conditions. Their stomata only open during the relatively humid and cooler desert nights.

Carbon dioxide diffuses into the plants during the night and is fixed into a compound called malate, rather than glycerate phosphate.

The malate formed is then stored in the cell vacuole overnight. In the morning it is broken down, releasing high concentrations of carbon dioxide which then diffuses into the chloroplast. At this stage the light-independent reaction takes place.

   (ii) Using the information provided, explain how this variation of photosynthesis is advantageous to cacti. [3]

   (c) The redox indicator DCPIP is blue when oxidised but colourless when reduced, as shown below.

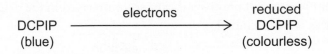

In an experiment investigating the light-dependent stage of photosynthesis, a suspension of chloroplasts was prepared by grinding fresh leaves in a buffer solution and then separating the chloroplasts from the leaf debris by centrifugation (spinning at high speeds).

   (i) Suggest the advantage of using isolated chloroplasts rather than ground-up leaf tissue. [1]

The isolated chloroplasts were treated as outlined in the table below. The results of the investigation are also included in the table.

Tube	Treatment	Colour	
		At start	After 30 minutes
A	water + DCPIP in bright light	blue	blue
B	chloroplast suspension + DCPIP in bright light	blue/green	green
C	chloroplast suspension + DCPIP in darkness	blue/green	blue/green

   (ii) Using the results for all three tubes, explain fully the result for tube B. [3]

Question taken from CCEA's Biology Assessment Unit A2 2, Biochemistry, Genetics and Evolutionary Trends, June 2014, © CCEA 2017

4. (a) An investigation into the biochemistry of photosynthesis was carried out using the simple water plant, *Spirogyra*. *Spirogyra* is characterised by having a spiral chloroplast, and the plant consists of long chains of cells, called filaments.

In the investigation, motile (mobile) aerobic bacteria were also present with the plant in the water.

The investigation was set up in darkness and then very narrow, bright beams of light were shone onto the *Spirogyra* at positions A and B for one hour as shown in the diagram below. (The nucleus and other cytoplasmic detail is not shown.)

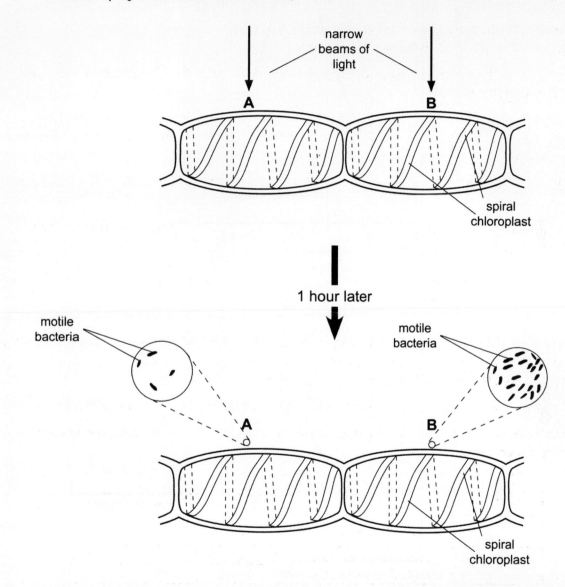

(i) Explain the difference in the numbers of bacteria found at positions A and B after one hour. [2]

(ii) State one factor (variable) that should have been controlled in the investigation design to ensure that valid results were obtained. [1]

(b) (i) The investigation could be extended to investigate the photosynthetic action spectrum of the *Spirogyra*. Briefly outline how this could be done. [1]

(ii) Briefly describe the results you would expect. [1]

(c) Photosynthesis can also be investigated at the whole organism level. The graphs below show the rates of carbon dioxide uptake in an evergreen tree in Northern Ireland over 24 hours in midsummer (July) and in midwinter (January).

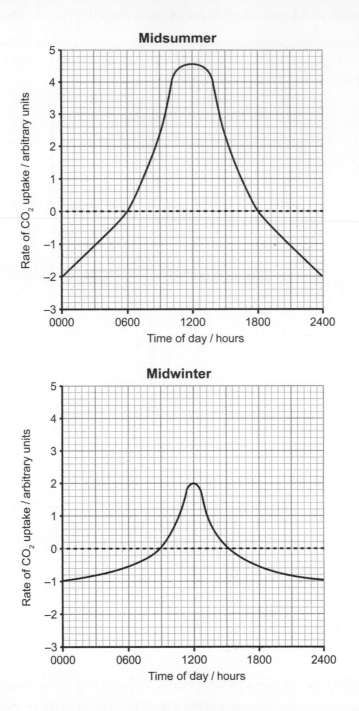

(i) The graphs provide information on changes in the rate of net photosynthesis, rather than gross photosynthesis. State and explain the evidence for this. [2]

(ii) Describe and explain the differences in the rate of uptake of carbon dioxide in midsummer and midwinter, as shown in the graphs. [4]

(d) In most evergreen trees, such as pine species (genus *Pinus*), an individual leaf (needle) does not remain throughout a tree's lifetime. Normally, leaves are replaced at staggered intervals in a way that allows the tree to have continuous leaf cover.

In a long-running investigation, the lifespan of leaves in one species of pine was monitored at each of five different soil fertility levels.

The graph below shows the relationship between mean leaf lifespan and soil fertility. Associated 95% confidence limits are also included.

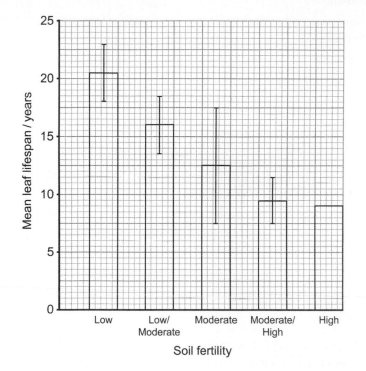

(i) The mean leaf lifespan for trees growing in soils with high fertility was nine years and the standard deviation (error) of the mean ($\hat{\sigma}_{\bar{x}}$) was 1.433 (n = 20).

Using the information given and the Statistics sheets provided, calculate the 95% confidence limits of the mean lifespan for the leaves sampled from trees growing in high fertility soils. [3]

(ii) Make a copy of the graph and complete it by adding the 95% confidence limits for the leaves sampled from trees growing in high fertility soils. [1]

(iii) The graph suggests that there is a negative correlation between leaf lifespan and soil fertility. Suggest one explanation for this trend. [1]

Question taken from CCEA's Biology Assessment Unit A2 2, Biochemistry, Genetics and Evolutionary Trends, June 2016, © CCEA 2017

Chapter 10 – DNA as the Genetic Code (Protein Synthesis)

Students should be able to:

5.3.1 Demonstrate knowledge and understanding of the nature of the genetic code.

5.3.2 Demonstrate knowledge and understanding of the process of transcription in synthesising proteins.

5.3.3 Demonstrate knowledge and understanding of the process of translation in synthesising proteins.

5.3.4 Demonstrate knowledge and understanding of the one gene one polypeptide theory.

5.3.5 Demonstrate knowledge and understanding of the concept of epigenetics.

The nature of the genetic code

Deoxyribonucleic acid (DNA) is the molecule of inheritance. DNA is the 'blueprint' that allows the characteristics of a species, or even a population or family, to pass through generations with limited change. An understanding of DNA also allows us to understand the genetic variation that exists among individuals. DNA carries out its role within cells by determining the polypeptides (and proteins), in particular the enzymes, that are produced by the cell. The enzymes in turn then control cell metabolism.

The nature of the genetic code

We already know that DNA contains repeating units of deoxyribose sugar and phosphate, with the two strands linked together by the nitrogenous bases adenine, guanine, cytosine and thymine, with adenine always linking with thymine and cytosine always linking with guanine through hydrogen bonding. It is the **linear order** of the nitrogenous bases along one of the two backbone strands, the **template strand**, which forms the **DNA code**.

Polypeptides and proteins are made up from 20 different types of amino acids. The **sequence of amino acids** (the primary structure) determines the overall polypeptide structure as the primary sequence influences the secondary and tertiary structures. Consequently, DNA works by controlling the **primary structure** of the polypeptides it codes for. The way in which the DNA codes for specific amino acids in specific positions in a polypeptide (protein) is described as the **genetic code**. In general, the length of DNA coding for a particular polypeptide is referred to as a **gene**.

The genetic code

As the DNA contains four different types of base then one base cannot simply code for one type of amino acid (as there are 20 different types of amino acids). Two consecutive bases operating as a code is not enough either – there are only 16 possible different combinations involving any two of the four bases ($4 \times 4 = 16$). The 16 possible combinations are:

AA, AC, AG, AT, CC, CA, CG, CT, GG, GA, GC, GT, TT, TA, TC, TG

However, if three consecutive bases are used, then there are 64 possible combinations (4 × 4 × 4 = 64). Around 50 years ago it was confirmed that the genetic code did indeed involve three consecutive bases coding for a particular amino acid – the **triplet code,** with each group of three bases coding for an amino acid called a **base triplet**.

The genetic code for each amino acid was subsequently worked out and the 3-base DNA code (base triplet) for each of the 20 amino acids is now known. For example, the DNA sequence of AAT codes for the amino acid leucine and GCG codes for the amino acid arginine.

Some key features of the genetic code include:

- The code is **non-overlapping**. This means that each base in the DNA sequence is read (counted) only once. Using the two examples in the previous paragraph, a DNA sequence of AATGCG codes for leucine and arginine in consecutive positions in the protein primary structure. The diagram below demonstrates the linear, but non-overlapping nature of the genetic code.

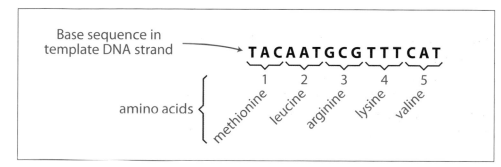

The non-overlapping nature of the genetic code

- The code is **degenerate**. This means that most amino acids have more than one possible code. With 64 possible sequences of three bases coding for 20 amino acids this allows a degree of duplication. For many amino acids it is the first two DNA bases in a triplet that are crucial in determining the amino acid produced. For example, **GG**A, **GG**C, **GG**G and **GG**T all code for the amino acid proline.

- Some base triplets do not code for an amino acid but terminate the coding sequence, much in the way a full stop ends a sentence. They are called **stop** base triplets. Similarly, the sequence **TAC** codes for methionine but also acts as a **start** triplet, starting a coding sequence.

- The DNA code is a **universal code**. With very few exceptions, and occasional modifications, the DNA code described above is present in all living organisms.

The chromosomes in the nucleus contain the genetic code. However, the process of protein synthesis takes place in the cytoplasm. Consequently, the 'code' has to pass from the nucleus to the cytoplasm. This is where **messenger RNA (mRNA)** comes into play. The copying of the code from the DNA in the nucleus to the mRNA is described as transcription and will be discussed in the next section. Once the code is transcribed it is then 'translated' into polypeptide (protein). Consequently protein synthesis consists of the two distinct, but closely related, stages of **transcription** followed by **translation**.

Transcription

Transcription is the process of forming complementary copies of mRNA from sequences of DNA that code for a particular polypeptide or protein.

Messenger RNA

Why use mRNA? – The use of mRNA, as opposed to the DNA in the chromosomes, leaving the nucleus to the sites of protein synthesis, has many advantages. The DNA is copied producing many complementary copies of mRNA that can each form the template for the production of many polypeptides or proteins. By remaining in the nucleus, the DNA is always available for 'copying' and is less likely to be damaged in the nucleus than in the metabolically more volatile cytoplasm.

Structure of mRNA – mRNA is a long strand organised as a **single** strand, unlike DNA which has a double helix arrangement. Other differences with DNA include the presence of a **ribose** pentose sugar in the backbone (as opposed to deoxyribose) and the presence of **uracil** as a nitrogenous base (which replaces the thymine of DNA).

Short section of an mRNA molecule

As an mRNA strand is a complementary copy of the template DNA strand, there are as many different arrangements of coding bases in the mRNA as there are in the DNA. As the mRNA is a facility for transporting the DNA code from the nucleus to the cytoplasm, the same principles concerning the nature of the code apply. This means that each sequence of three bases along the mRNA strand code for an amino acid as a **base triplet**.

As an mRNA molecule codes for a polypeptide (or protein) it will only be complementary to a relatively short section of DNA (as DNA runs the length of the chromosome it can code for many polypeptides). Therefore mRNA is usually a much **shorter** molecule than DNA. The main differences between mRNA and DNA are summarised in the following table.

Feature	DNA	mRNA
Relative size	Much longer than mRNA (millions of nucleotides – in humans range from 50 million – 250 million base pairs)	Much shorter than DNA (75–3000 nucleotides)
Polynucleotide arrangement	Double stranded (double helix)	Single stranded (single helix – not twisted)
Pentose sugar	Deoxyribose	Ribose
Nitrogenous bases	Adenine (A), guanine (G), cytosine (C) and thymine (T)	Adenine, guanine, cytosine and uracil (U)
Location	Found mostly in nucleus (some found in mitochondria and chloroplasts)	Produced in nucleus but found throughout cell (in particular in association with rough ER and ribosomes)

The process of transcription

The enzyme **DNA helicase** separates the two DNA strands of the relevant section of DNA to be copied. It does this by breaking the **hydrogen bonds** between the bases linking the two strands of the double helix, causing the DNA double helix to **unzip** (separate).

The enzyme **RNA polymerase** moves along the **template (coding) strand** linking the (now exposed) nucleotides in that strand with free complementary **RNA (ribo) nucleotides** from the nucleotide pool within the nucleus. The building up of the mRNA strand alongside its complementary DNA template strand follows the rules of **complementary base pairing** ensuring that the mRNA bases are aligned in sequence complementary to the template DNA strand. The RNA polymerase joins adjacent mRNA nucleotides to each other by **phosphodiester bonds** as the mRNA molecule extends.

> **Note:** During transcription normal C-G, G-C, T-A base pairing arrangements apply. The one exception is that an A base on the DNA template strand will be matched by a U (uracil) base on the mRNA strand.

As the mRNA strand is assembled, increasing in length one nucleotide at a time, the unzipped DNA rejoins behind the assembly area. As a result only around 20 base pairs of the DNA are exposed at the one time. When the RNA polymerase reaches a 'stop' triplet code on the DNA, it detaches and the copying of this particular section of DNA is completed. The process of transcription is summarised in the following diagram.

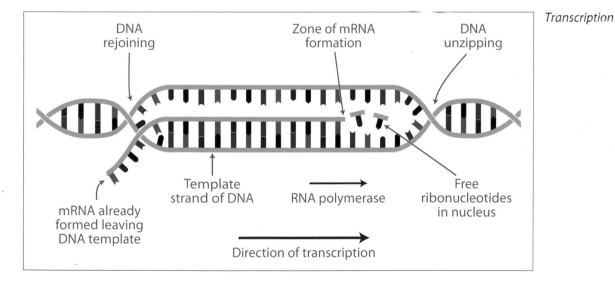

Transcription

Modification of the mRNA

DNA is made up of sections that code for polypeptide/protein (**exons**) and other sections (**introns**) that have a number of functions but do not code for polypeptide or protein directly. The introns are often (inaccurately) referred to as 'junk' DNA, but it has long been known that at least some of this has a regulatory role controlling the activity of the coding genes themselves. Recent research has confirmed that much of the non-coding DNA functions as gene switches or regulators that control the activity of the coding sections of DNA (the genes).

Note 1: Only around 2% of our DNA is in the form of exons – enough to code for around 21,000 different genes. The remaining 98% forms intron sections that exist both between and within genes. Some very large genes can have well over one hundred introns.

Note 2: Prokaryotic DNA does not have introns – all prokaryotic DNA is coding.

Irrespective of the exact function of the introns, it is clear that they do not directly code for specific polypeptides or protein. However, intron sections of DNA are often sited within the coding exon sections of DNA. How does transcription deal with this particular problem? There are two possibilities – either the transcription process is able to bypass introns as the mRNA is formed or the template DNA is copied as it is and the intron sections are subsequently removed.

In practice, it is the subsequent removal of introns following transcription that actually takes place. Adjacent exons and introns are copied in the formation of the mRNA from the DNA template strand. Following transcription, the introns are removed from the **pre-mRNA** and the exons are **spliced** back together again to produce the coding sequence that actually codes for the required polypeptide or protein.

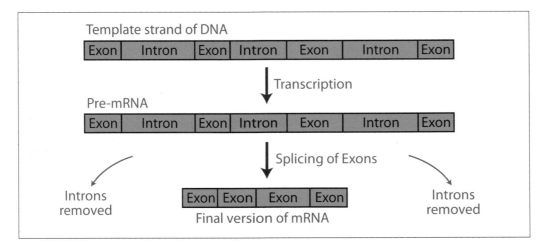

Exons and introns – the making of functional mRNA

Note: Following the removal of introns, the exons can be spliced back together in a range of different combinations. This flexibility allows a gene to code for a number of different polypeptides or proteins depending on the order in which the exons are recombined. It is likely that some of the non-coding DNA (part of the 98%) is involved in the regulation of this. This explains the fact that the 21,000 genes in humans can code for the 100,000 different proteins that occur in the body.

Following the removal of introns, the final version of the mRNA (**the functional mRNA**) moves out of the nucleus through a nuclear pore and into the cytoplasm where the actual formation of new proteins takes place, a process known as **translation**.

Translation

Translation involves the 'translation' of the mRNA code into the polypeptide **primary structure** (sequence of amino acids). Each sequence of three bases on the mRNA (the base triplet) that codes for a particular amino acid is referred to as a **codon**.

As well as the coding mRNA, very important components of the translation process are **transfer RNA (tRNA)** and **ribosomes**. These two structures will be discussed in more detail in the next section.

Transfer RNA and ribosomes

tRNA – is a small molecule consisting of around **70–80 nucleotides**. It is a single stranded molecule twisted into a clover leaf shape. The two key 'functional' parts of the tRNA molecule are a sequence of three bases (**anticodon**) at one end that form complementary base pairs with a mRNA codon and the 'exposed' nucleotide section (at the opposite end of the molecule) to which an amino acid can attach. Enzymes help attach amino acids in the cytoplasm to the appropriate tRNA molecule.

There is a different tRNA molecule for each of the 20 different types of amino acid, with each type being able to attach to only one type of amino acid. Similarly, each of the different types of tRNA has a particular anticodon code (for example AAA) that is unique to that type of tRNA, and also matches with a particular codon (in this case UUU) on the mRNA.

Consequently the role of the tRNA is to:

1. **transport** amino acids within the cytoplasm to the site of protein synthesis.

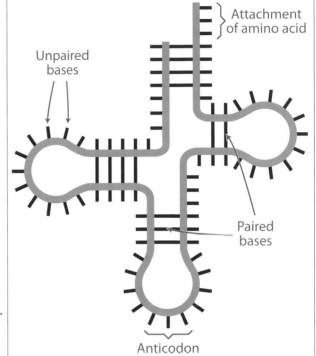

tRNA

2. ensure that each **mRNA codon codes for a particular amino acid**. In effect, this means that as the protein is being built up, each amino acid will be aligned in sequence adjacent to its matching codon on the mRNA.

Ribosomes – are small organelles (up to about 30 nm in diameter) that are found free in the cytoplasm or attached to endoplasmic reticulum. Each ribosome contains a **large** and a **small sub-unit**, and is made of **protein** and **ribosomal RNA**.

The sub-units are assembled in the **nucleolus** within the nucleus and subsequently transported into the cytoplasm. At the start of translation the two sub-units link together as they lock on to the start of the mRNA strand to be copied.

The ribosome contains two sites, each of which can cover a codon (analogous to a zip fastener covering six 'teeth' in a zip with the six 'teeth' representing the bases in two adjacent codons). The first codon-linking site is the **aminoacyl (A)** site and the second is the **peptidyl (P)** site. The A site, sometimes called the acceptor site, is where the tRNA molecules link together in the correct position on the mRNA strand through the linking of complementary anticodons and codons. The P site is where adjacent amino acids are linked together by peptide bonds.

> **Note:** In summary, the role of the ribosome is to hold the mRNA, the tRNA and the enzymes involved in protein synthesis in place.

Note 2: Many ribosomes can operate in concert, one immediately after the other along the same strand of mRNA. This is obviously a more efficient process, meaning that many polypeptides or proteins can be assembled in a very short time from the same section of mRNA. The complex of ribosomes involved is called a **polyribosome**.

The following table shows a **genetic dictionary** – the mRNA codons involved in translation and the amino acids or actions they code for. The degenerate nature of the genetic code can be clearly seen in the diagram.

The genetic dictionary (the mRNA codons)

Note: In an examination question you will not be expected to have memorised the opposite table in detail. However, you will be expected to understand it. You could be given either the genetic dictionary represented as the mRNA codons (as opposite) or as the original DNA base triplets. In either case, you need to be clear which you are working with.

Second base in codon

First base in codon		U	C	A	G	Third base in codon
U		phenylalanine	serine	tyrosine	cysteine	U
		phenylalanine	serine	tyrosine	cysteine	C
		leucine	serine	stop	stop	A
		leucine	serine	stop	tryptophan	G
C		leucine	proline	histidine	arginine	U
		leucine	proline	histidine	arginine	C
		leucine	proline	glutamine	arginine	A
		leucine	proline	glutamine	arginine	G
A		isoleucine	threonine	asparagine	serine	U
		isoleucine	threonine	asparagine	serine	C
		isoleucine	threonine	lysine	arginine	A
		methionine and start	threonine	lysine	arginine	G
G		valine	alanine	aspartate	glycine	U
		valine	alanine	aspartate	glycine	C
		valine	alanine	glutamate	glycine	A
		valine	alanine	glutamate	glycine	G

In this section on the translation phase of protein synthesis, the two nucleic acids most involved are mRNA and tRNA (although ribosomal RNA has a role in the formation of ribosomes). The main similarities and differences between mRNA and tRNA are summarised in the following table.

Feature	mRNA	tRNA
Relative size	Larger molecule (75–3000 nucleotides)	Smaller molecule (70–80 nucleotides)
Polynucleotide arrangement	Single stranded (not twisted)	Clover shaped molecule
Pentose sugar	Ribose	Ribose
Nitrogenous bases	A, G, C, U	A, G, C, U
Location	Produced in nucleus but found throughout cell (in particular in association with rough ER and ribosomes)	Produced in nucleus but found throughout cell

Once the newly synthesised polypeptides are formed by translation, they are normally transported to the Golgi apparatus in vesicles. Here they fuse with the convex (formative or forming) face. In the Golgi apparatus the polypeptides are processed to produce the final functional proteins before being pinched off from the concave (maturing) face and transported by vesicles for use either within the cell or to be secreted.

The one gene one polypeptide theory

Francis Crick and James Watson worked out the structure of DNA around 60 years ago following earlier work by Chargaff and then by Franklin and Wilkins.

Crick produced what he described as the 'central dogma of molecular biology' in which he and others built up the key link between DNA, RNA and protein as described in this chapter. Crick's 'central dogma' can be summarised as:

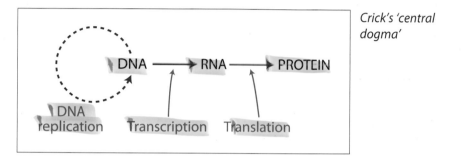

Crick's 'central dogma'

Current understanding shows that the above diagram is somewhat simplified. Retroviruses such as HIV have **reverse transcriptase** enzymes which can use a mRNA template to make complementary DNA (normal transcription in reverse). Taking account of current understanding, Crick's original summary would now be written as:

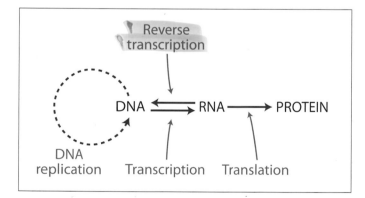

Current understanding of the link between DNA and protein synthesis

Throughout this chapter we have usually described the DNA as coding for a **polypeptide** (an exception being the short section above relating to Crick's work). This is accurate as a coding sequence of DNA (the gene) codes for a particular polypeptide. The polypeptide is formed as the amino acids are linked together during translation in a particular sequence (the primary structure).

However, before the term 'one gene one polypeptide' was widely used, the terms 'one gene one protein' or 'one gene one enzyme' were used to describe the essential role of DNA.

The term 'one gene one protein' is appropriate when the protein concerned has only one polypeptide. However, it is a less suitable term for those proteins that are formed of more than one polypeptide, for example haemoglobin, a protein that has a quaternary structure. For proteins formed of more than one polypeptide, there is often a different gene that codes for each polypeptide (and the genes involved may not even be on the same chromosome).

Similarly, the term 'one gene one enzyme' may be regarded as a simplification for the reason noted above (enzymes may be formed of more than one polypeptide) but also because not all proteins are enzymes. For example, haemoglobin and insulin are not enzymes and proteins can also be channel proteins in membranes, antibodies and have many other roles, including structural roles such as collagen.

However, although the term 'one gene one polypeptide' may be the most accurate in terms of the link between the DNA and its products, the DNA is able to control overall development in organisms through its control of enzyme activity. As enzymes control all metabolic pathways in cells, DNA through controlling enzyme synthesis, ultimately controls cell (and the organism's) development.

Epigenetics

Epigenetics is the study of heritable modifications of the genome that do not involve changes to the DNA base sequence. Epigenetics affects **gene activity** (expression) without changing the DNA sequence. It can enhance expression, ie the gene is more active, or it can shut down genes, both permanently and temporarily. These changes are referred to as **epigenetic modifications**.

> **Note 1:** Epigenetic modification does not change the DNA sequence itself, ie what a gene codes for. It increases or decreases the likelihood of a gene making a protein.

> **Note 2:** Mutations are **not** epigenetic modifications; mutations (permanently) alter the DNA sequence.

Two important ways in which epigenetic modification occurs are DNA methylation and histone modification.

DNA methylation – The chemical group methyl (CH_3) can be added to cytosine (C) bases in the DNA in places where the C base is immediately followed by a G base; these sequences are known as CpG sequences. Typically many of these CpG sequences are grouped together in CpG 'islands'. If a critical number of CpG 'islands' are methylated, the DNA is switched off in that region and **transcription cannot take place**. Often the DNA that is methylated is the 'switch' (regulator or promoter) at the start of a particular gene, rather than part of the coding sequence itself; in effect, the gene is switched off. DNA methylation is **long term** and it is **stable**.

> **Note:** The CG bases involved in methylation are in **sequence** along the coding strand – this is not referring to C-G bases linked through pairing.

DNA methylation can explain why proteins associated with, for example, liver function are only produced in the liver and not in other parts of the body. In all other parts of the body, the genes involved in coding for liver proteins are methylated and therefore 'switched off'. As DNA methylation is a long term (permanent) change to DNA, epigenetic modifications involving DNA methylation can pass from cell to cell as **mitosis** takes place. Again, this helps explain why liver cells undergoing mitosis produce other liver cells rather than skin cells or neurones.

Histone modification – DNA is wrapped around bundles of eight histone proteins. The histones can be modified by adding chemical groups to them. Epigenetic modification involving histone modification is **relatively short term** and is important for both increasing and decreasing the expression levels of particular genes. Histone modification is more complex than DNA methylation and can occur in many different ways, each affecting the **frequency or likelihood of transcription** in a particular gene.

Many epigenetic modifications remain in sequences of DNA that pass from cell to cell during **mitosis** as stated above and some (for example many of those involving DNA methylation) can pass from parent to offspring (and often through many generations).

In general, epigenetics allows the environment in the wider sense, for example nutrition, hormones and age, to influence gene activity.

Case Study – Holland in the winter of 1944–1945

The winter of 1944–1945 was the last winter of the Second World War. The people living in Holland were in near starvation conditions as a consequence of a Nazi blockade preventing food reaching the country (and with the Germans transferring any food that there was back to Germany).

Subsequent scientific research investigated the effects of the near starvation conditions on the birthweights of children to mothers who were pregnant during this period.

Analysis showed that:

- if the onset of near starvation conditions coincided with the mother's last few months of pregnancy, then the baby was likely to be born with a lower birthweight than normal (as most of the foetus's growth takes place in the last few months).

- if the mother suffered malnutrition only for the first few months and was subsequently well fed (due to the removal of the blockade at the end of the war), the baby was likely to have a normal birthweight.

Further research showed that the babies that were malnourished (due to the mother's malnourishment) in the **early months of pregnancy** were very likely to be overweight or obese as adults but this did not happen with the babies that were undernourished only during the later months of pregnancy.

Explanation – Research has shown that many of the genes normally switched off (by DNA methylation) very early in development were **not** switched off in those children who were malnourished in the first few months of pregnancy. These genes remained on through life and maximised the conversion of available nutrients to body tissues and fat. When these individuals did have a 'normal' diet they were more effective at building up body fat than others not deprived in early development. Consequently, very many became overweight or obese. Children of these overweight and obese individuals also became overweight or obese as they retained the epigenetic modifications of their parents.

Note: This example shows how the environment can influence gene expression and that the genome can be controlled to some extent by life experience. In this example the 'environment' was nutrition in the womb. It also shows how conditions very early in development can have lifelong consequences.

Epigenetic modifications also occur in **plants**. For example, in some species that are adapted to growing in low light intensities there is increased gene expression in those genes linked with light harvesting. They also have decreased expression (due to genes being switched off through DNA methylation and/or histone modification) in genes associated with reproduction (due to reproduction being sacrificed in favour of growth in low light intensities).

Note 1: Epigenetic modification significantly increases the flexibility of the genome. It controls which genes are active (can be expressed) and enables gene expression to be graduated, rather than a simple on or off situation.

Note 2: Epigenetic modifications can change as an individual ages, can be different between tissues (see liver example on page 187) and between cells of the same tissue.

Exam questions

1. (a) The diagram below represents the process of transcription.

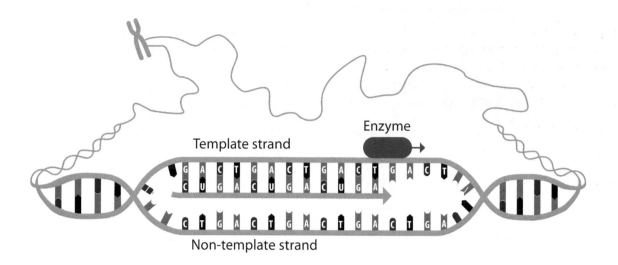

Note: For copyright reasons, this diagram has replaced the one that appeared in the CCEA past paper.

   (i) Using the information provided, describe the process of transcription. [4]

   (ii) Using only the information in the diagram, state two structural differences between DNA and RNA. [2]

(b) It has long been known that genes are sections of chromosomes which control specific aspects of an organism's characteristics. Early research suggested that each gene coded for a protein or even for an enzyme: hence the *'one gene one protein'* and the *'one gene one enzyme'* hypotheses that were promoted several decades ago.

Current understanding of gene action suggests that the *'one gene one polypeptide'* hypothesis is a more accurate description.

   (i) Using your understanding of protein structure, suggest why the *'one gene one polypeptide'* hypothesis is a more accurate description than each of the two earlier hypotheses. [2]

   (ii) Explain precisely what is meant by the term *'one gene one polypeptide'*. [1]

(c) DNA length is measured in base pairs. Analysis of a particular polypeptide shows that the gene involved in its synthesis is 330 base pairs long yet the polypeptide itself has only 84 amino acids in its primary sequence.

   (i) How many base pairs would be required to code for 84 amino acids? [1]

   (ii) Suggest why the gene contains 330 base pairs. [1]

Question taken from CCEA's Biology Assessment Unit A2 2, Biochemistry, Genetics and Evolutionary Trends, May 2012, © CCEA 2017

Chapter 11 – Gene Technology

Gene technology is at the forefront of current biologically-related research. Once the structure and function of DNA had been worked out, it was only a short step to try to manipulate the functioning of DNA in organisms or even to transfer DNA from one organism to another.

DNA technology has huge potential in many areas including food production, drug development and medicine. However, it is an area where progress should always be considered within the wider ethical framework.

Key advances in gene technology include the ability to extract sections of DNA of interest from a cell and then copy this DNA to make large quantities available for analysis.

Gene transfer – obtaining the required section of DNA (gene)

DNA sections of interest (for example, genes) require the correct sequences to be identified and then removed. Processes enabling this to take place are described in the following sections.

Restriction endonucleases

Restriction endonucleases (restriction enzymes) occur naturally as defensive bacterial enzymes that cut up foreign DNA injected by bacteriophages.

Many restriction endonucleases have been isolated and are used in gene technology to cut specific sections of DNA. Each restriction endonuclease cuts the DNA double strand, by a hydrolysis reaction, at a specific sequence of bases called a **recognition**

sequence. Sometimes the enzyme cuts straight across the two strands (ie between opposite adjacent bases) to leave the cut section of DNA with **blunt ends**. Some restriction enzymes make a staggered cut to leave **sticky ends**. This happens when the cuts in each DNA strand (within the recognition sequence) are between adjacent bases that do not lie opposite each other (due to the nature of base pairing). Two examples of how restriction endonucleases work are shown below.

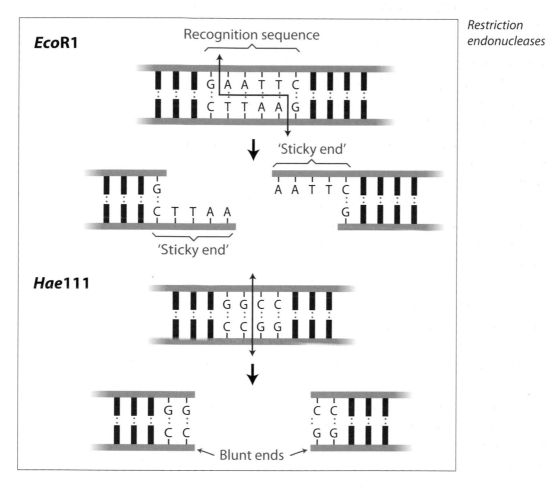

Restriction endonucleases

In **EcoR1** the recognition sequence is **GAATTC** and the cut is made between the adjacent bases **G and A** (or A and G) that lie beside each other on the same DNA strand. As the complementary base pairs of G and A on the opposite DNA strand will be C and T (and not G and A) the *Eco*R1 will not cut directly across the DNA – instead the cut is deflected along the DNA to where the bases G and A do lie beside each other on the opposite strand.

In the **Hae111** the recognition sequence is **GGCC** with the cut taking place between adjacent **G and C** (or C and G) bases.

In this example G and C bases lie opposite C and G bases due to base pairing rules, therefore a straight cut will take place.

Sticky ends are in fact short sections of DNA where there is only one strand and the bases in that section are unpaired and therefore exposed. The advantage in using restriction enzymes that produce sticky ends is that DNA with sticky ends will easily join with another section of DNA if it has complementary sticky ends. This knowledge has been widely used by genetic engineers when inserting DNA sections into the DNA of other organisms.

Reverse transcriptase

During the AS course and in the previous chapter there have been references to how retroviruses, which store genetic information in the form of RNA, use enzymes to make DNA from the RNA. The enzyme involved is **reverse transcriptase**.

In gene technology, reverse transcriptase is used to make a desired section of DNA (gene) from the gene's mRNA.

The technique involves:

- Isolating and extracting the **mRNA** of the desired gene. The search can be made easier by analysing those cells in which there is likely to be a lot of the relevant mRNA (ie a cell in which the desired gene is very active). For example, the mRNA of the genes that produce digestive proteases, lipases and amylases, will be found in certain secretory cells in the pancreas, whereas the mRNA of insulin will be found in the pancreatic endocrine regions.

- **Reverse transcriptase** can be used to make a single strand of DNA (**complementary DNA** or **cDNA**) using the mRNA as a template and following normal base pairing rules.

- The enzyme **DNA polymerase** is then used to make the double stranded DNA (gene) from the single strand of cDNA.

It is obviously important to check that the correct section of DNA (or mRNA) is being targeted when using the technologies described above. One way of checking a section of DNA (or mRNA) is to use a gene probe.

DNA (gene) probes

DNA probes can be used to identify sections of DNA that contain a **specific sequence of bases**. If a section of DNA can be identified, then restriction endonucleases can be used to cut out the desired section by cutting the DNA immediately outside the desired section.

A probe is a **short single strand of DNA** (for example, 20 nucleotides in length). This short section will be complementary to the target section of DNA so that its bases will bind (**hybridise**) to the target section if it is present.

It is also important to be able to identify exactly where this target section is on the targeted DNA, therefore the DNA probe is usually 'labelled' in such a way that it can be identified. The two most common types of labelling are **radioactive** labelling (that can be detected using **X-ray film**) or **fluorescent** labelling (detected using **UV light**).

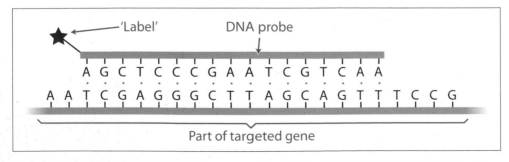

Targeting a specific gene with a DNA probe

Note: A DNA probe can be made **radioactive** by labelling the 5' end with ^{32}P.

Using DNA probes – The following section is an example of how fluorescently labelled DNA probes can be used to identify specific DNA sequences.

DNA that is expected to contain the target sequence is hydrolysed into sections using **restriction endonucleases** with the DNA fragments being subsequently separated by **gel electrophoresis**.

The DNA sections, now separated by gel electrophoresis, are transferred to a **nylon membrane**. At this stage the fluorescently labelled DNA probe is added. If the target sequence is present, the DNA probe will hybridise (bind) with it; if not it will then be 'washed off' and removed. If the nylon membrane is then exposed to UV light, the DNA probe (and target sequence) will appear as a **fluorescent band**.

Note 1: In most types of contemporary gel electrophoresis, the transferring to another membrane stage is bypassed, ie the gel itself is subjected to UV light. With this, the probes are added earlier and the target sequences are visible *in situ*.

Using a fluorescent DNA probe

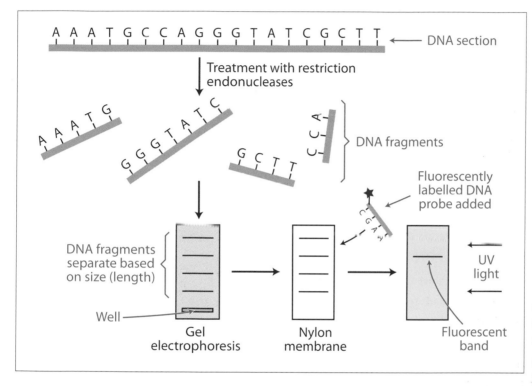

Gel electrophoresis and fluorescent labelling in action

© Simon Fraser / Science Photo Library / G210/0581

Note 2: It is important to 'wash off' any DNA probes that do not attach to their target sections – fluorescently labelled probes will show up whether they have hybridised with their target sequences or not! (This stage is not necessary in most contemporary gel electrophoresis set ups – see Note 1 above.)

Note 3: The gel electrophoresis separates the DNA sections on the basis of size (length). Shorter sections of DNA travel further (and faster) through the gel. The series of bands on the gel will represent a series of sections of DNA of different lengths, with shortest sections closest to the positive electrode (anode at the top of diagram), longest sections closest to the negative electrode (cathode) and the well (origin) at the bottom of the diagram.

Note 4: In the diagram above the fluorescent band is the second from the top, as the sequence GCTT is the second smallest and also is the sequence that is complementary to the fluorescent probe CGAA.

Note 5: DNA probes will attach to single strands of DNA, not the normal double stranded form. Therefore when using DNA probes it is usually necessary to treat the DNA in a way that splits the two strands along its length.

Note 6: If a radioactively labelled probe is used (instead of a fluorescent one), the nylon membrane is exposed to an X-ray film. If the probe and target sequence combine, this will cause the fogging of the X-ray film.

The Polymerase Chain Reaction (PCR)

Often in forensic science (genetic fingerprinting) or in medical research (researching a disease-causing allele) it is necessary to make many copies of the DNA that is available. The PCR can produce many copies of the selected section of DNA in a very short time.

The PCR technique is a modified version of the process of DNA replication that takes place in cells naturally.

1. The DNA section to be amplified is **heated to around 95°C**. This breaks the hydrogen bonds holding the two strands together.

2. The DNA is **cooled to 40–60°C**. This is necessary to allow **primers** to bind (anneal) to each strand at specific points – they could not form bonds if it remained at 95°C. The primers are short chains, approximately 20 nucleotides long, which are complementary to the bases in the part of the DNA strand selected. The primers have a number of functions:
   - they stop the two DNA strands rejoining.
   - they 'bracket' the section of DNA to be copied.
   - DNA replication can only start within a double stranded region.

   In addition to primers being added, **free nucleotides** and **DNA polymerase** must be introduced to complete the rest of the copying process.

3. The mixture is **heated again**, this time to around **70°C**. **DNA polymerase** copies each strand, starting at the primers. At temperatures of around 70°C normal DNA polymerase would be denatured. The DNA polymerase used must be **thermostable**. Thermostable DNA polymerase has been isolated from the *Thermus aquaticus* bacterium found in hot springs. This *Taq* polymerase allows the process to occur rapidly at the higher temperatures involved. Other thermostable DNA polymerase enzymes have been isolated and a trade off appears to exist between speed of replication and the ability to proofread and correct mistakes in the DNA being copied. The particular DNA polymerase used in a given situation will depend on whether the emphasis is on accuracy or speed of replication.

4. The two DNA molecules formed following the PCR process can be used as templates as the process is repeated. Millions of copies of the original DNA can be produced in a very short time.

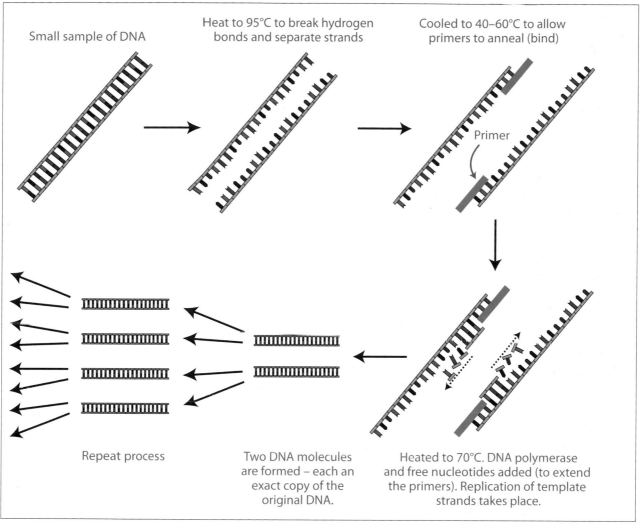

Small sample of DNA

Heat to 95°C to break hydrogen bonds and separate strands

Cooled to 40–60°C to allow primers to anneal (bind)

Primer

Repeat process

Two DNA molecules are formed – each an exact copy of the original DNA.

Heated to 70°C. DNA polymerase and free nucleotides added (to extend the primers). Replication of template strands takes place.

The Polymerase Chain Reaction

Note: The exact temperatures involved (and the length of time the sample is kept in each temperature) depend on the type of DNA being amplified (for example, the species and even the chromosomes involved).

Role of PCR

Often a crime scene may contain as little as a speck of blood or a fragment of a hair from a suspect. PCR allows the DNA to be amplified to produce sufficient quantities for forensic analysis. PCR is also widely used in medical and scientific research. For example, investigating the DNA of extinct organisms to elucidate relationships with living species, genetic screening and research involving many genetic diseases all rely heavily on the PCR process. The Human Genome Project was also very dependent on PCR producing the quantities of DNA necessary.

In all these examples a key requirement is avoiding contamination of the DNA – contaminated DNA will copy every bit as well as the original uncontaminated DNA sample! DNA evidence in many famous legal cases involving genetic fingerprinting has been disallowed because of possible contamination.

A PCR machine

Image courtesy of Dr Catherine Napier

The following diagram shows how it is possible to identify the transformed bacteria (the assumption is made that none of the bacteria have the R-plasmid initially).

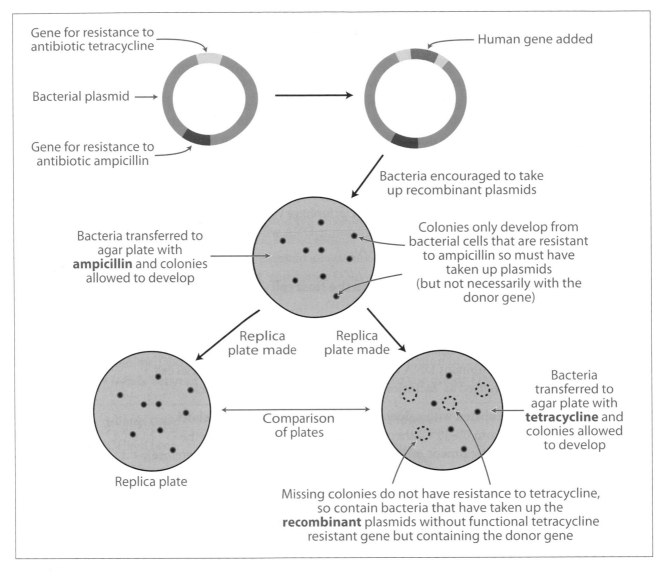

Gene for resistance to antibiotic tetracycline

Bacterial plasmid

Gene for resistance to antibiotic ampicillin

Human gene added

Bacteria encouraged to take up recombinant plasmids

Bacteria transferred to agar plate with **ampicillin** and colonies allowed to develop

Colonies only develop from bacterial cells that are resistant to ampicillin so must have taken up plasmids (but not necessarily with the donor gene)

Replica plate made

Replica plate made

Comparison of plates

Replica plate

Bacteria transferred to agar plate with **tetracycline** and colonies allowed to develop

Missing colonies do not have resistance to tetracycline, so contain bacteria that have taken up the **recombinant** plasmids without functional tetracycline resistant gene but containing the donor gene

Detecting the transformed bacteria by replica plating

In the diagram above, the colonies that do not survive in the tetracycline (missing in bottom right diagram) are formed of transformed bacteria with the human gene – ie the bacteria required. These transformed bacteria will be present on the plate in the bottom left hand corner (not treated with tetracycline) and can be identified and subsequently cultured.

Replica plating involves 'blotting' the original plate carefully with an absorbent pad and then pressing this against the surface of a fresh plate allowing some of the cells of each colony to be transferred. The key thing is that colonies will form (or not) on equivalent positions on the new plate.

Note: Other markers are now available that are quicker and more straightforward than replica plating. For example, a gene that produces protein that fluoresces in certain conditions can be incorporated into a plasmid. The donor DNA can be added to the 'already' recombinant plasmid by using a restriction enzyme to cut the plasmid in the centre of the gene that codes for the fluorescent protein (similar principle to the tetracycline above). When tested, the host cells that have taken up the donor DNA will not be able to fluoresce.

Using DNA probes – DNA probes can be used to identify if host DNA is recombinant. The principle of using DNA probes is discussed on page 194.

Once it has been confirmed that a colony of bacteria contain recombinant DNA, the next phase is usually to clone the bacteria to ensure that large numbers are produced. They are typically grown in large fermenters where conditions are ideal for rapid growth and the production of the desired product.

Transformed bacteria as described in the previous sections are examples of **genetically modified organisms (GMOs)** in general, and specifically **genetically engineered microorganisms (GEMs)**. Some of the benefits, and potential hazards, in using GMOs are reviewed in the following sections.

Genetically Modified Organisms (GMOs)

It is convenient for explanatory purposes to split genetically modified organisms into genetically modified microorganisms and other genetically modified organisms (plants and animals).

Genetically Engineered Microorganisms (GEMs)

Bacteria have proved to be the ideal (but not the only) microorganisms suitable for genetic modification. Unlike most other organisms, it is relatively straightforward to insert donor DNA into the bacterial DNA (aided by the presence of plasmids).

The bacterium *Escherichia coli* has been widely used in genetic engineering, as have a range of other microorganisms including the yeast *Saccharomyces cerevisiae*.

The general public is more accepting of the use of GEMs including bacteria than they are about the genetic modification of crop plants and animals. For this reason, and as it is less complex, scientific research and commercial development in the field of GEMs is at a more advanced stage of development.

Many important chemicals and other products have been produced by GEMs over the last 40 years. Examples include:

A modern insulin 'pen' containing genetically engineered human insulin for the treatment of diabetes

- **Insulin** – Insulin produced by transformed bacteria can be produced in sufficient quantities to meet the needs of the growing numbers of people who have diabetes. Additionally, as the bacteria use the 'human' insulin gene to produce the insulin, it is identical to the hormone naturally produced by humans. Previously, insulin had to be extracted from the bodies of dead domestic animals (for example, pigs and cattle) in abattoirs, a time-consuming and ineffective process, by comparison. Furthermore, non-human insulin is slightly different to human insulin and therefore has the potential to cause allergic reactions – cow insulin differs from human insulin by three amino acids and pig insulin differs by one amino acid.

- Other important products produced by GEMs include the **human growth hormone**, **enzymes**, **adhesives**, **lung surfactant protein** and **interferon** (a drug used in the treatment of certain cancers).

Research is currently ongoing into using genetically modified viruses to target and kill cancer cells and to treat bacterial infections. The viruses targeting **cancer cells** are genetically modified in ways that prevent them from harming normal healthy cells and also in ways to encourage a stronger immune response against the cancer cells. This can involve genetic modifications that prevent the viruses replicating in healthy cells (therefore not harming them) and also through them containing cytokines to help stimulate an immune response.

The viruses used to help treat **bacterial infections** are modified to be more effective than traditional antibiotic use on its own. Bacteria become resistant to antibiotics for many reasons but these may involve them breaking down the antibiotic or using alternative metabolic pathways to the pathways normally disrupted by antibiotic action. The genetically modified viruses can support antibiotic action by disrupting these evolving defensive strategies in antibiotic resistant bacteria.

Note: For classification purposes viruses are described as being non-living and not placed in any kingdom. However, in the context of genetically modified organisms they can be classified as a GEM.

Note: Although we have used the term transformed bacteria in the sections above, a more recent term used to describe an organism (or type of organism) that has had its DNA deliberately altered is '**transgenic**'. In the next section we will cover examples of transgenic plants and animals – the term transgenic is generally used when referring to plants or animals that have had their DNA altered by recombinant DNA technology.

Other Genetically Modified Organisms

Transgenic plants

Transgenic crop plants have enormous potential commercial, health and other benefits. Before reviewing some of the benefits we will review the methods that can be used to insert donor (foreign) DNA into plants.

The soil bacterium ***Agrobacterium tumefaciens*** causes the growth of tumour-like plant galls in plants that it infects. The bacteria enter the plant at a point where it has been damaged in some way and then integrate bacterial DNA (from a plasmid) into the DNA of the plant. The bacterial DNA causes the very rapid cell growth that leads to the formation of the galls.

In genetic engineering, the gall-forming genes are removed from the bacterial plasmids and replaced with donor DNA using the techniques already described in this chapter. Recipient plant cells are specially treated so that they will readily take up the recombinant plasmid.

Note 1: The recombinant plasmids retain the ability to become integrated into the host (plant) DNA but will not cause the galls.

Note 2: Rather than introduce the donor DNA into mature plants (where its effect would be localised and therefore limited), the donor DNA can be added to a small number of cells in tissue culture – the result being that as the cells in the culture grow into mature plants, all the cells in the plant will contain the recombinant DNA.

'Gene guns' can also be used to insert the donor DNA into the host cells. By coating microscopic (tungsten or gold) pellets with the donor DNA it can be fired (using compressed air) into the host cell – it is a bit 'hit or miss' whether the donor DNA will actually become incorporated into the host DNA. Although much less reliable than using *Agrobacterium*, it can be used with species that are resistant to infection by the bacterium.

Most transgenic plants are more commonly known as **Genetically Modified (GM) Crops**. Up to now GM crops have had a bad press in Europe but is this really a fair assessment of their potential?

Case study – GM Crops

Transgenic crops have been used to try and address the issues of crop quantity and quality. The benefits of producing more crops and crops with less wastage are obvious at a time when there is a world shortage of food.

The benefits

GM crops have been produced that have:

- **Herbicide resistance** – GM plants that are resistant to herbicides will be unaffected by herbicide applications, therefore allowing more effective applications without the need to avoid spraying near the crops. Maize (corn) and soybeans are examples of species that have GM varieties resistant to herbicides.

- **Pesticide properties** – The bacterium *Bacillus thuringiensis* (Bt) produces a protein that is toxic to insect pests (it has an additional advantage in that it is not toxic to other types of animals). Many species of crop plants now have varieties with the Bt gene incorporated into their DNA; examples include maize, potato and cotton. Advantages include a reduction in losses to insect pests and a reduction in the use of insecticides with benefits including less expense, less harm caused to non-pest insects and less pollution.

- **Disease resistance** – GM crops can be produced that are resistant to fungal and viral pathogens.

- **A greater ecological range** – For example, plant varieties have been produced that are more drought resistant. Ryegrass plants have been developed that have a drought tolerance gene added from another species.

- **Nutritional enhancement** – Many GM programmes have improved nutritional composition and content as their goal. One of the best examples is the genetic manipulation of rice ('Golden rice') to provide enhanced levels of vitamin A and iron. The 'Golden rice' has been genetically engineered to contain up to 30 micrograms of beta-carotene per gram (ordinary rice has none).

Note: Several billion people across the world are at risk of iron deficiency and nearly half a million people each year have suffered blindness as a result of vitamin A deficiency (the effects of both deficiencies are greater in the developing world). Of those that go blind in the developing world, a very significant number die within months.

Research published in the journal *Science* at the end of 2016 showed that genetic engineering of tobacco plants produced an increase yield of up to 20%. In this research a number of genes were altered to increase the efficiency of photosynthesis in the plants. There is real hope that similar changes in the genomes of major crop plants can lead to an increase in global food production.

GM crops have also been developed that produce compounds beneficial to man, for example, **vaccines** and **drugs**. Transgenic plants can produce vaccines, drugs and other chemicals that are difficult or very costly to produce.

The ethical issues and potential risks

There are many benefits to using GM crops, only some of which are outlined on the previous page. However, there are also some potential risks:

GM maize – can you tell the difference?

1. **GM crops are 'not natural'** – GM crops contain DNA from other species that would not occur through natural reproduction. There are concerns that the implications of this 'unnatural' engineering have not been sufficiently examined. However, crop species (and their DNA indirectly) have been manipulated by man for around 10,000 years by selective breeding. Transgenic manipulation differs in extent but not principle. Also the insulin produced by transgenic bacteria involves the same principles as GM crops and saves millions of lives each year, yet it does not have the same level of opposition.

2. **The creation of 'superweeds'** – Genes can be transferred from GM crops to other species by cross-pollination. However, this is no more likely than between other plant species. The possibility of toxic 'weeds' gaining a herbicide resistant gene would almost certainly lead to these weeds increasing in number. Rigorous risk assessments and safety precautions ensure that the risk is kept as low as possible.

3. **GM crops have a greater ecological range than non-GM crops** – Some species of GM crops can grow in a wider range of habitats and may therefore outcompete non-crop species in certain ecological situations. This risk has to be weighed against producing more food (particularly in developing countries where there may be food shortages).

4. **Some insects are becoming resistant to the toxic effects of GM crops with the Bt gene** – This means that the crops are no longer protected against insect attack by resistant populations (the very reason the gene is added). However, the GM crops are still protected against many other insect species.

5. **Compounds produced by GM crops could cause allergies** – There are concerns that genetic engineering could increase existing or produce new allergens. However, this is no more likely than allergies being caused by the production of other 'new' products. Also the majority of allergies are caused by non-GM foods such as peanuts, eggs, milk and wheat.

GM crops are extensively used in many countries including the USA (in 2011, 94% of the soybean planted was genetically modified) and Argentina. However, the focus for much of the resistance to GM crops has been in Europe.

The benefits that GM crops can provide are so great that the scientific community is firmly of the opinion that opposition is political and driven by public opinion, which is not always based on the latest scientific understanding.

Transgenic animals

As with transgenic plants there are several techniques for inserting donor DNA into animal cells. These include encapsulating the donor DNA in lipid vesicles called **liposomes**. The use of a lipid carrier makes it easier for the DNA to cross the lipid bilayer of the cell surface membrane.

Another method involves the technique of electroporation. **Electroporation** involves disrupting the cell membrane (and making it more permeable) by the use of high voltage treatment. **Viruses** can also be used to insert donor DNA into animal cells – we will review the potential of viruses as vectors in the next section on gene therapy. By inserting the donor genes directly into the **fertilised eggs** of the animal this will ensure that all the cells in the animal will contain recombinant DNA. This technique has been used to produce many valuable products listed in the following table.

The mouse is probably the animal that has been genetically engineered to the greatest extent; transgenic mice are produced for many reasons including disease modelling – see later sections.

However, many transgenic animals produce products of value to man as summarised in the following table. In general, the donor gene (**transgene**) can be added to the fertilised egg at the one-cell stage. This ensures that the donor gene will be present in all the daughter cells of the developing organism.

Transgenic organism	Genetic modification and consequence
Chicken	Human gene for the production of the antibody miR-24 inserted. The miR-24 antibody is obtained from eggs and used in the treatment of skin cancer.
Cow	Human gene added that codes for the protein alpha-lactalbumin, leading to milk that is more similar in composition to human milk. Other genes can be added to increase milk production or milk with reduced lactose content (for individuals with lactose intolerance).
Sheep	Have the human gene that codes for Factor VIII (blood clotting factor). Factor VIII can be purified from ewes' milk and used to treat haemophilia. Transgenic sheep can also produce the serum protein alpha-1-antitrypsin, important in regulating the activity of proteases and used in the treatment of individuals with cystic fibrosis.
Goat	Human gene added to produce the anticoagulant anti-thrombin. Can be given to individuals deficient in anti-thrombin due to a defective allele.

Knowledge of gene transfer technologies raised the prospect of tampering with the human DNA complement. The most obvious place to start was to look at the possibility of inserting functional donor alleles (genes) into human cells that are not functioning as well as they should due to the presence of a single defective allele. This is **gene therapy**.

Gene therapy

Human conditions such as **cystic fibrosis** and **muscular dystrophy** are caused by the presence of a single defective gene. In these examples the defective alleles are recessive so the condition is only fully expressed when the individual has both recessive alleles at the relevant gene locus (cystic fibrosis) or is present as a single allele on the (single) X chromosome present in males (muscular dystrophy).

If a functional allele can be inserted into the cells affected by the condition, theoretically the cells will function as normal – this is the principle behind **gene therapy**.

There are two distinct approaches to gene therapy as outlined below:

1. **Somatic-cell gene therapy** – This is where the gene therapy only targets the affected tissues. This technique can be used when a condition caused by a defective gene(s) affects specific and easily reached parts of the body, for example lungs. Additionally, somatic-cell gene therapy can be used at any stage of an individual's life.

2. **Germ-line gene therapy** – This approach involves replacing the defective gene(s) in the fertilised egg (or theoretically in a defective gamete). In germ-line gene therapy, all the cells of the developing individual are normal (in terms of the defective gene under consideration) and there is no issue with targeting affected tissues in the body, which is a problem with somatic-cell gene therapy. Additionally, with germ-line gene therapy the defective gene will not pass on to future offspring as the gametes produced will not contain the defective gene.

Currently it is only somatic-cell gene therapy that is used. Germ-line gene therapy is (probably) beyond current technological capability and raises so many moral and ethical issues that it is presently not permitted.

Therefore, the remainder of this section on gene therapy is focused on the progress and limitations of somatic-cell gene therapy. As with any aspect of gene technology, a good place to start is to review how the donor (functional) DNA can be inserted into recipient cells.

Getting the functional allele into recipient cells

A range of different methods have been used as vectors to transfer functional DNA into recipient cells. These include:

- **Adenoviruses** – are viruses that cause respiratory infections. They are ideal for gene therapy involving lung tissue as adenoviruses are able to inject their DNA into lung epithelial cells. However, before adenoviruses can be used in gene therapy they have to have their 'harmful' disease-causing genes removed as well as the donor DNA being spliced in. Adenoviruses are not without problems though, as it is difficult to remove the disease-causing genes without dismantling the genes that allow the virus to enter cells and insert their genetic material. They may cause **infection**. Additionally, some individuals may be immune to adenoviruses and they are **unable to penetrate** the respiratory cells.

- **Retroviruses** – can be used to target host cells. When the host cells are affected by the retrovirus, its RNA and any additional donor RNA is converted by reverse transcriptase into DNA in the host cell. If the donor DNA replaces or supplements the defective DNA in the host cell, then gene therapy is possible.

- **Liposomes** – are artificial lipid vesicles containing the donor DNA. The lipid coating of the vesicle protects against degradation and helps the donor DNA bind to the appropriate target cells. This process can be aided by using specific markers, for example, monoclonal antibodies, that help the liposome target the appropriate recipient cells. Having a lipid coat means that the liposome can pass relatively easily through the lipid part of the phospholipid cell surface membrane.

Note: Liposomes are less effective at getting the donor DNA into the host cell nucleus compared to viruses but they are often safer in that they do not have some of the problems associated with deliberately inserting viruses into human cells (for example, infection, allergies and other immune responses).

When the donor DNA is in the appropriate host cells it can function in two distinct ways – the donor DNA can become incorporated into the host DNA or can function as independent DNA units (**episomes**) in the nucleus that are **not** incorporated into the main nuclear DNA.

Although still at the early stages of its development, gene therapy has huge potential in replacing (or supplementing as with episomes) defective DNA that causes many of the major genetic diseases today. Major difficulties still surround the ability to target all the affected areas of the body for a particular condition; the fact that treatment is often short-lived as any new and replacement cells will not have the donor DNA; and also that offspring of treated individuals may still be affected, depending on the genetics involved. Additionally, the defensive strategies employed by cells may destroy the introduced DNA or prevent it being 'switched on'.

Another problem is that as many genetic disorders (or disorders with a genetic pre-disposition) involve many genes across a range of chromosomes (for example, Type 1 diabetes), it can be very difficult to both identify the genes involved and effectively incorporate all the donor DNA necessary into host cells.

A good way to review progress to date is to use one particular example as a case study.

Case study – gene therapy and cystic fibrosis

Cystic fibrosis, the condition – Cystic fibrosis (CF) is the most common inherited genetic condition in the western world. In Europe approximately 1 in 2500 people are affected. The condition is due to the malfunctioning of a protein of around 1500 amino acids in length. The protein malfunction is caused by a mutant recessive allele – in the dominant or heterozygous state the individual concerned functions normally, but if both recessive alleles are present cystic fibrosis will be the result.

The affected protein is the **trans-membrane-conductance regulator (CFTR)** protein. This protein is responsible for keeping epithelial membranes in good condition. In an individual with cystic fibrosis, the protein will not function as normal and the membranes become covered with thick sticky mucus. This affects several parts of the body including:

- The buildup of mucus in the **lungs** affects **gaseous exchange** and leads to a much higher risk of **lung infection**.

- The buildup of mucus in the **pancreatic duct** prevents the pancreatic enzymes reaching the duodenum leading to problems with **food digestion**.

Delivering the donor DNA – The use of gene therapy to improve lung function in patients with cystic fibrosis has an obvious advantage – it is relatively straightforward to target and get access to the cells affected.

The main vectors in delivering the functional CFTR gene are **adenoviruses** and **liposomes**. In more recent research trials liposomes are used rather than adenoviruses as these are less likely to produce an immune response.

Recent research has shown that liposomes are proving more successful than viruses as vehicles for delivering the functional gene as a gene therapy treatment for CF, largely because of the body's immune system destroying the viruses before they enter lung cells.

The benefits and drawbacks – If the donor DNA enters enough host respiratory cells and is expressed (works!) in producing functional protein, then the debilitating lung symptoms associated with cystic fibrosis can be reduced and the quality of life for the patient improved.

However, there are many reasons why the process is less effective than hoped for in many patients. While lung function may improve, this technique does not affect the **other parts** of the body, for example the pancreas, also affected by cystic fibrosis. Adenoviruses may cause **infections**, **immune responses** or **allergies**. Patients may develop **immunity** to the adenoviruses (therefore they are unable to enter the respiratory cells or are destroyed when they do) and the aerosol may **not reach all parts** of the lung (making its effect localised).

A major problem of course is that the donor DNA functions as an episome. It reaches the nucleus but **does not become incorporated into the host DNA** – the donor DNA masks the effect of the defective allele but does not replace it – therefore is only effective for the life of the cell. With lung epithelial cells being very short-lived, this means the functional donor gene is not passed on to new cells (and is certainly not passed on to offspring); therefore regular **repeat treatments** are necessary.

> **Note:** The example of cystic fibrosis highlights a key feature of DNA. The same DNA (same 46 chromosomes) is present in all the cells of an individual human (excepting sex cells). However, in different parts of the body different genes are active or expressed. This explains that although the defective CFTR gene is present in all the cells, it has its major effect in those parts of the body where the gene is particularly important and is expressed.

Gene therapy is used to treat a range of disorders and many more gene therapy based treatments are coming on-stream. Gene therapy is a fast-changing area of gene technology with both huge medical potential and almost certainly complex underlying ethical issues, particularly as the boundaries between addressing genetic malfunction and genetic enhancement become blurred. In a recent development in this field, there has been success in the treatment of **haemophilia B** using gene therapy.

> **Note 1:** Haemophilia B is one of two major variants of haemophilia in which the gene for clotting factor IX is mutated.

> **Note 2:** Part of the reason for the successful treatment of this variant of haemophilia by gene therapy is due to the use of viruses that were easy to manipulate to the extent that they did not lead to a significant immune response in patients.

The potential of gene therapy can only be realised when there is an excellent knowledge of the total DNA complement with all relevant genes being effectively mapped.

Genome sequencing and genetic mapping

Throughout this chapter we have referred to all the DNA in an organism being the total DNA complement, or used similar terms. The **complete DNA (base or nucleotide) sequence** is its **genome**. In very simple terms, the genome is a 'map' of the DNA in an organism. Precisely, the definition of the genome is the complete DNA sequence (on one set of chromosomes in diploid, eukaryotic organisms).

> **Note:** The genome includes **all** the DNA, ie exons and introns.

There is a subtle distinction between genome sequencing and genetic mapping. **Genome sequencing** is working out the base sequence in an organism, ie the order of bases along each chromosome. Genome sequencing has many applications including its use in DNA fingerprinting in forensic analysis and the analysis of ancestral relationships between organisms.

Note: If the sequence of bases can be worked out along one chromosome in a homologous pair, it will be possible to work out the majority of bases in its partner chromosome by assuming that they will be the same. The exceptions will be in the relatively small number of cases where the alleles at a particular gene locus are different (heterozygous). We are familiar with heterozygous genes from genetics at GCSE; however, it is important to understand that heterozygosity is relatively rare with most genes being homozygous.

Genetic mapping is identifying exactly where particular genes are on chromosomes (without necessarily knowing the base sequence within the genes). Genetic mapping has been important for many reasons, including the location of defective genes and the identification of 'useful' genes that could be used in recombinant DNA technology.

Genome sequencing – key steps

While the genome sequencing of man was the ultimate target, it is not surprising that in the early stages of genome sequencing scientists targeted more straightforward organisms. Key early stages in identifying the complete DNA nucleotide sequence in organisms included:

- **Yeast** was the first eukaryotic organism to be fully sequenced – it has approximately 16,000 genes and 16 chromosomes.

- The **roundworm** (nematode) was the first multicellular organism to be sequenced – it has 20,000 genes but only 6 chromosomes.

- Other organisms that have been sequenced include the virus phage λ, the bacterium *Escherichia coli*, the plant *Arabidopsis thaliana* and the fruit fly *Drosophila melanogaster*. In recent years the number of species being sequenced has increased exponentially.

- It is also possible to sequence the genome of extinct species. For example the genome of 'Neanderthal Man' (*Homo neanderthalensis*) has been sequenced in recent years. This species (closely related to *Homo sapiens* but not a direct ancestor) became extinct around 30,000 years.

- DNA sequencing has become both **faster** and **cheaper**. It is now possible to sequence the human genome in a few hours at a cost of several hundred pounds. We are now in the era where individuals can pay to get their genome sequenced.

The **Human Genome Project** was a massive multinational project, started in 1990 and largely completed by 2003. This project took over a decade and billions of pounds to work out the DNA nucleotide sequence in the human genome.

The Human Genome Project showed that the human genome is just over **three billion base pairs** in length. Further analysis showed that the human genome contains around **21,000 genes**, very similar to the number in other mammals. Furthermore, only around 2% of this DNA actually codes for polypeptides or protein with the remainder having a regulatory role through acting as gene switches or having no known function as yet (commonly, although not entirely accurately, referred to as 'junk' DNA).

211

Microarray technology

Microarrays (DNA 'chips') consist of a solid base such as glass or silicon onto which is attached a grid of thousands of microscopic spots or 'wells'. To each of these spots is added a different sequence of DNA, each of which can act as a DNA probe; typically each spot can contain multiple copies of the identical DNA sequence. The setting-up process is completed robotically and the identity of the DNA in each well is stored digitally. As thousands of spots are present in each microarray, a single microarray can be used to analyse many genes simultaneously.

Single stranded DNA (or mRNA) of interest is washed over the array. Any DNA (or mRNA) in the added sample that is complementary to one or more of the DNA sequences in the array will hybridise with it. If the added sample is labelled with, for example, a fluorescent or chemiluminescent tag, then the wells containing hybridised DNA can be identified. (Unhybridised DNA in the sample will have been washed off.)

Note: A chemiluminescent tag involves emission of light as a consequence of a particular reaction (for example, a reaction in the hybridisation process).

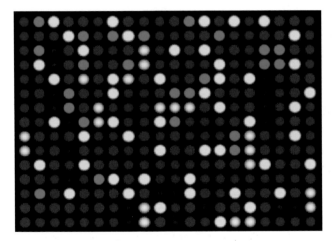

Note: The different colours in a microarray can identify the level of hybridisation. For example, high levels of hybridisation show as one colour and lower levels as a different colour.

Microarray technology – The different colours can show where hybridisation has taken place (and where it has not) and as a consequence can identify unknown DNA or RNA sections or mutations. The data provided can also be used to compare gene expression across many genes.

© Alfred Pasieka / Science Photo Library / G210/0907

Microarrays have many uses. They can **identify mutations**, **SNPs** or provide information on the **expression level of genes**. When investigating the expression level of genes mRNA transcribed from a gene of interest can be used directly or used to make cDNA. The degree of cDNA or mRNA hybridisation with probes in the array can be used to compare gene expression between different genes or between patients of certain medical conditions, such as cancer, and unaffected individuals.

Note 1: Microarray technology is not gene sequencing as such. It can compare how sample DNA (for example, in someone with cancer) is different from 'normal' DNA and can compare the expression of genes between different groups.

Note 2: As there are many identical probes in each spot the number of hybridisation events can be used to compare levels of gene expression.

The benefits of genome sequencing (the Human Genome Project) and the creation of 'genome libraries'

Some of the benefits of the Human Genome Project (and genome sequencing in general) are summarised in the following bullet points.

- More detailed **mapping of genes** is possible as are the benefits this can bring in terms of the diagnosis and treatment of genetic disorders. Sections of DNA or genes can be identified and compared using the **microarray technology** described in the previous section. This technology can be used to identify harmful alleles in carriers and also DNA sequences or SNPs associated with particular medical conditions.

Note: DNA 'chips' can also be used to identify specific sections of mRNA (rather than DNA). This can identify if genes are being **expressed** (are working) in a particular cell, ie if the gene is actually functioning, as the mRNA is only produced by functioning genes.

- **Drug development** can be matched to the genomes of individuals (or groups of people) so that drug treatments can be more effective in the individual(s) concerned, and importantly be modified to reduce side effects and allergies. The development of drugs and medicines to match the genetic profile of individuals is known as **pharmacogenetics** and the drugs are commonly referred to as **'designer drugs'**. While there is huge potential for the use of 'designer drugs', the realisation of their potential is likely to be an uneasy compromise between scientific capability and the economics of **'personalised medicine'**.

Note: Medicine has been 'personalised' to some extent for a very long time. For example, the mass of some drugs given to a patient has been calibrated to match the body mass of the patient and the treatment options for cancer patients has depended on how advanced the cancer is in that particular patient. However, what is new (and the context in which 'personalised medicine' is used) is the matching of the treatment to the patient's genome.

Nonetheless, there has been significant progress in linking drug therapy to the actual genome mutation(s) involved in some forms of cancer, for example, breast cancer.

Personalised medicine is not restricted to cancer treatment. Individuals can respond differently to some drugs that are in relatively common usage. One such drug is **codeine** (see the case study on the following page).

Note 1: Pharmacogenetics can be defined as the study of how genetic differences in humans affects how particular drugs are metabolised by the body, which in turn affect both the effectiveness (efficacy) of a drug and also the side effects arising.

Note 2: Pharmacogenetics reduces the 'trial and error' application in terms of drug dosage in treatment. Essentially it allows medical staff to get it right first time.

Case study – personalised medicine and codeine

Codeine is not active as a painkiller until it is metabolised into the opiate morphine by the body. Morphine can be very toxic or even fatal if present in high concentrations, a risk for someone who can metabolise codeine into morphine very quickly.

Individuals may be genetically classified as 'poor', 'intermediate', 'extensive' or 'ultra-rapid' metabolisers of codeine, depending on their particular genotypes. Similar dosages may have little therapeutic painkilling effect on a 'poor' metaboliser yet could be an overdose for an 'ultra-rapid' metaboliser as high levels of morphine can be produced quickly. Consequently it is very beneficial if medical staff are aware of the grouping of a patient before administering codeine.

Case study – treating cystic fibrosis

Cystic fibrosis is caused by having two recessive alleles for a particular gene. However, there are many variants of the recessive allele.

About 7% of CF patients in Ireland have the **G551D ('Celtic')** gene mutation. The drug **Ivacaftor** can be used to help treat this sub-set of patients.

Whereas, a combination of **Lumacaftor and Ivacaftor** is used to help treat individuals homozygous for the **delta F508** mutation – which is the most common mutation, with a frequency of around 70% of all CF gene mutations.

Unlike earlier drug applications, both these 'personalised' genome-linked treatments target and help improve function in affected cells in CF sufferers rather than just symptoms linked to the condition.

- The development of genome sequencing increases the potential of **gene therapy**. An understanding of the difference between functional and defective genes in terms of base pairs is important in identifying exactly what donor DNA is required and also with the possibility of artificially making donor DNA in 'gene machines'.

- DNA (genetic) profiling or **fingerprinting** is essentially comparing genetic sequences in people. DNA fingerprinting is dependent on the differences in repeat DNA sequences – microsatellite repeat sequences (MRSs) or short tandem repeats (STRs). Different individuals have different numbers of repeat sequences. These repeat sequences occur in introns and probably form a part of the DNA that does not have a (known) function, ie 'junk' DNA.

- Knowledge of gene sequence allows the **primary structure** of **proteins** to be worked out. For example, if a certain sequence of DNA has been mapped to show that a particular gene lies between two specific points, then knowledge of the bases between those points will allow the mRNA codons and amino acid sequence to be determined. Molecular modelling software can then be used to predict secondary, tertiary and quaternary protein structure based on predicted bonding and folding arrangements.

- A greater knowledge of the DNA sequences in different species has led to a better understanding of the **ancestral links** between organisms and their **evolutionary development**. Prior to the arrival of genome sequencing, similarities in morphology, anatomy, biochemistry and even ecology have been used to work out ancestral relationships. Genome sequencing has been able to confirm, or even modify, these relationships.

Case study – the evolutionary development of Man

The relationship between the different species of primate and the relationship between man and other primates has been advanced through genome sequencing and related investigations. At the DNA level, humans and chimpanzees are 98–99% similar, with a slightly greater divergence between humans and the other great apes such as the gorilla. There is even less genetic divergence between humans and 'Neanderthal Man' (*Homo neanderthalensis*), our closest relative, that became extinct around 30,000 years ago.

It has long been known that modern man evolved in Africa and subsequently (perhaps as recently as 50,000 years ago) migrated from there to other parts of the world. Genomic analysis shows that there is much more genetic divergence in Africa than in more distant areas, for example, Arctic Europe and Australasia – exactly the pattern expected to fit the migration 'out of Africa' theory.

As already noted, one consequence of the Human Genome Project is that it is apparent that we have many fewer genes that have more than **one type of allele** (can be heterozygous) than we thought. In reality, most of our genes have two identical alleles. Additionally, **humans are 99.9% similar** in terms of DNA sequences. Much of the variation (the 0.1%) involves differences in single nucleotides. These are referred to as **single nucleotide polymorphisms** (**SNPs**). Assuming the frequency of these variants reaches 1% in the population and they are not just very isolated mutations in small groups, there are as many as **10 million SNPs** in human populations.

Note: It is the other 0.1% that provides much of the variation among different humans. Much of this is provided by the small number of genes that have more than one type of allele, with different people having different combinations of alleles, but this is not the whole story – mutations (and we all have at least some mutated genes) also contribute to variation.

The **HapMap Project** involved an international consortium that analysed the genomes of nearly 300 people across the world with the intention of mapping the locations of SNPs. The aim of the researchers was to identify a set of genetic markers that can be used to screen genetic data. Obvious examples include the use of **genetic screening** to match specific DNA sequences with the risk of genetic disease.

Note: While some medical conditions such as cystic fibrosis can be clearly attributed to the inheritance of two defective alleles of one gene, the genetic basis of many medical conditions is much more complex. Conditions such as Type 1 diabetes, heart disease, many forms of mental illness and many others are linked to a 'genetic pre-disposition' in individuals, involving many genes across a number of chromosomes. Gene sequencing and its many spin-off projects offer the possibility of progress with these more complex conditions.

Considerable genetic data has been generated by genome sequencing projects and stored in **biobanks**. This data is used for many purposes including, but not only, medical research. For example, the data in some biobanks is being used to work out human migration patterns in our distant past.

Inactivation or replacement of genes (knockin and knockout technology)

The deliberate removal or addition of a gene (or other sequence of DNA) can enable the organisms concerned to function as model organisms for the study of genetic disease or drug therapies.

A **gene knockout** is a transgenic organism in which a gene (or genes) has been removed or made inoperative.

With gene knockouts, the principle is that the effect of loss of gene function can be modelled in non-human living organisms. This technology has obvious potential in furthering progress in the understanding of genetic diseases such as cystic fibrosis, Huntington's disease and muscular dystrophy. Most vertebrate knockout technology has involved the mouse. The mouse has many advantages in this setting: it is a mammal and biochemically and physiologically very similar to humans; it has a short life cycle and can easily be kept in laboratory conditions. The International Mouse Knockout Consortium was established in 2007 with the aim of making data available from the knockout of all the protein-coding genes available to the scientific and medical community. Another advantage with using mice is that many people are not as ethically opposed to using mice as they would be to using larger mammals.

A **gene knockin** is where a particular gene has been added. Knockin technology has been used to deliberately add a defective gene in order to study in detail disease progression.

As with many aspects of gene technology, progress is underpinned by ethical considerations.

The benefits and risks of gene technology – the ethical imperative

Reference to ethical issues has often been made in this chapter. With gene technology the benefits and risks must always be considered in tandem.

GMOs

GMOs (or more specifically **GEMs**) were developed around 40 years ago with the use of transformed (transgenic) bacteria in the development of products, for example insulin, useful to man. For many, the benefits of this technology far outweigh any potential risks. Nonetheless, there are very strict regulations concerning the containment of transgenic microorganisms with considerable resources used to prevent their escape into the wild. The level of containment required has a positive correlation with the perceived risk.

These containment measures include:

- Appropriately licensed and **purpose-built laboratories** that have very effective **air filters** including 'negative – pressure' atmospheric gradients that 'suck' air back into the laboratory.

- Very tightly controlled procedures for staff in terms of access and cleaning.

- Special disinfectant procedures.

- Using bacterial strains that are **poorly adapted** to survive outside controlled laboratory conditions, and in particular, poorly equipped to survive in humans. These strains will typically have optimum temperature ranges very different to human body temperature.

- Using strains that have '**suicide genes**' that are activated if conditions do not remain within specific pH or temperature limits.

However, no matter how good the containment measures are or how tight the legislation is, there is always the *possibility* that genetically engineered microorganisms could escape and survive beyond the confines of the laboratory.

GM crops

GM crops are another matter in the public consciousness. There is a much greater opposition to GM crops in Europe compared to GEMs. Perhaps this is because they are more visible or that people have to consider eating a GM crop. We have already noted the arguments (see page 206) that they are not natural or that the escape of their pollen or seeds could create superweeds. Superweeds can also be created through normal natural selection processes, so while it cannot be discounted, GM technology is no more likely to cause the development of 'superweeds' than could occur naturally – particularly if appropriate legislative controls are in place.

Nonetheless, field trials with GM crops are held in the open and not in closed containers as with GEMs. Legislation does require that appropriate controls are in place such as the completion of the trials (and the removal of the crop) before flowering takes place.

With the potential of producing disease-resistant, more nutritious and more productive crops in a greater range of habitats (including in arid and salty soils that currently cannot be used without considerable treatment and investment), many believe the benefits outweigh the disadvantages. This is particularly important at a time when nearly a billion people worldwide go hungry because they cannot produce or buy food. This world food shortage can only get worse as the human population continues to grow out of control, climate change renders more land each year unsuitable for agriculture and pesticide resistance is increasing.

Genetic screening

Genetic screening is another technology with huge potential. It can take place before birth or after a child is born. Genetic screening before birth raises huge ethical issues for some people. It is possible to screen for many conditions including Down's Syndrome but what if the screening provides a positive result? The decision of whether to have an abortion or not is a complex ethical issue. Individuals concerned have to weigh up the possibility of bringing up a child with a medical disability and the quality of life the child would have against the possibility of destroying the foetus, a very difficult choice for many.

Usually (but not always) genetic screening **after** birth has fewer ethical implications. All newborn children in Britain are tested for the presence of **phenylketonuria** (**PKU**). PKU is a recessive inherited condition that affects about 1 in 10,000 people. Affected individuals lack an enzyme, a consequence of which is that the amino acid phenylalanine accumulates in the blood which, if allowed to continue, will lead to severe mental handicap. The advantage of early screening ensures that children with the condition are given a diet low in phenylalanine and PKU does not develop.

Some types of genetic screening are less straightforward. Take the case of Huntington's disease.

Case study – Huntington's disease

Huntington's disease is caused by a single defective allele. In DNA a base sequence of CAG is repeated many more times in a particular gene (Huntingtin gene) in individuals with Huntington's disease than in unaffected individuals. The condition causes progressive brain deterioration in middle age with complete neurological dysfunction and death the inevitable outcome.

Note: We have come across repeating sequences of DNA before – the **MRSs** (STRs) in non-coding ('junk') DNA that can be used in DNA fingerprinting. The repeating sequences in Huntington's disease are certainly not 'junk' DNA as they have a very significant effect in controlling metabolism in individuals affected.

The defective allele in Huntington's disease is unusual compared to some of the other genetic diseases we have reviewed (for example, cystic fibrosis and Duchenne muscular dystrophy); the Huntingtin allele is **dominant** not recessive – there are no carriers. Therefore if even one parent is heterozygous for Huntington's disease, each child has a 50% chance of inheriting the condition.

Individuals who suspect that they might be affected can get a test to confirm, or otherwise, the presence of the defective allele (ie whether or not the individual tested will develop the condition). Suppose that in a particular family an elderly grandparent has the condition but his/her 40 year old son/daughter does not want to take the test – he/she prefers not to know. However, the 20 year old grandchild does want to know and opts for the test. If the grandchild is shown not to have the defective allele, this is obviously a huge relief to the grandchild but does not tell whether the 40 year old parent has the allele. However, if the Huntingtin allele is confirmed in the grandchild, his/her parent will then know that he/she will develop the condition, as the Huntingtin's allele must be present. The option of ignorance was removed by the grandchild taking the test.

With genome sequencing now much faster (hours rather than a decade as with the Human Genome Project) and much less expensive, the possibility of individuals being routinely screened for a wide range of genetic conditions is feasible. It is possible that in a generation each 'newborn' will have his/her genome as just another part of their medical notes. But as genetic screening becomes more common, other ethical issues arise. Should information gleaned through genetic screening be made available to insurance companies? How easy would it be to get life insurance if a genetic condition was confirmed that could affect quality or length of life? Yet another point for consideration is the huge gap in our ability to identify the presence of a genetic defect and our ability to do anything about it, as is the case with Duchenne muscular dystrophy and Huntington's disease. Also what if as a consequence of screening for a particular disease, the alleles that predispose for another totally unrelated disease were discovered – should the individual be informed?

However, **pre-implantation genetic diagnosis** (PGD) is an effective screening method at the embryo stage for potential parents in 'at risk' groups. In PGD, conception is by IVF and a number of embryos are screened for genetic abnormality. Only 'healthy' embryos are implanted in the uterus. In the UK over 60 inherited conditions are licensed for PGD. This takes us back to gene therapy.

Gene therapy

Issues specific with gene therapy for cystic fibrosis were reviewed earlier but there are other more general issues. Gene therapy is expensive; would the money used be better spent in reducing hospital waiting lists or even spent on antibiotics and vaccines for developing countries – decisions that would save many lives?

The introduction of donor DNA into human cells is not without risk. The deliberate introduction of viruses into cells and the introduction of donor DNA has the potential to disrupt the host DNA. In the French trial of gene therapy for **SCID** (severe combined immunodeficiency disease) in 2002, two of the eleven babies in the clinical trial died from **leukaemia** – the assumption being that the gene therapy disrupted the host DNA leading to the leukaemia. Following the death of the children, all research in this area was stopped for nearly ten years. In recent years, research into the application of gene therapy has started again and been much more positive, partially due to the avoidance of the pitfalls of the earlier trials. With the use of 'new' viruses that are unlikely to cause immune responses by the patient and pre-treatment of the patient with drugs to minimise any immune response, there is genuine progress being made.

Although germ-line gene therapy is banned, the potential and probably the technological know-how of creating designer babies, or even human clones, exists. Not surprisingly, strict legislation regulates the whole area of reproductive biology.

Other possibilities with gene technology

Detailed knowledge of the human genome and progress in drug development raises the possibility of **personalised medicine**. Personalised medicine is already in use, with very specific drug treatments being tailored to the genome of the individual and even the genome of specific cancer tumours caused by the presence of specific genes. While one aim of personalised medicine is a more effective targeting of the problem, another aim is to reduce side effects of treatment – the same drug or treatment can affect different individuals in very different ways. Again the potential is enormous but often the more specific the treatment, the greater the expense.

The development of **biobanks** that store genetic data for some (or all) in a population is a step on the way to personalised medicine but it is not without its problems. If the gathering of data is mandatory (for example, through the collection of blood, urine or even tissue samples) there are issues with consent. If it is not mandatory but an opt-in arrangement, certain ethnic minority groups and the less well educated may be under-represented. Either way there are issues with data security.

The biggest obstacle to developing biobanks is probably the complexity, as the conditions that can have a genetic pre-disposition that affect large groups in the population often involve many genes, with each one contributing only a very small factor towards the pre-disposition. Additionally, the genetic pre-disposition can often be a small part of the picture, with environmental influences being more important. For example, most would acknowledge that diet, obesity and lack of exercise are major factors in the development of coronary heart disease (CHD), with genetic pre-disposition playing a relatively minor role in individuals who are very obese, have fat-rich diets and do not exercise regularly. Most people would agree that attention to obesity, diet and exercise would have a far greater effect than focusing on the genetics of this condition. Nonetheless, it is thought that there are as many as 100 genes involved in the degree of genetic pre-disposition involved – too many to make personalised medicine in this area anything other than very complicated.

The complex nature of many apparently 'straightforward' genetic diseases also complicates matters. 70% of cystic fibrosis sufferers have the same mutation (the same three bases missing – the delta F508 mutation) but the other 30% of cases are caused by up to a thousand different mutations.

There is no doubt that gene technology is a very fast moving part of biology, with huge potential benefits: nor is there any doubt that it is steeped in increasingly more complex ethical issues.

Practical work

Gel electrophoresis of DNA

Sections of DNA of different sizes can be separated using the process of gel electrophoresis. In gel electrophoresis a small electric current flows in a buffer solution, through an agarose gel, between the cathode and an anode that are connected to a 'power-pack'.

Fragments of DNA travel at different speeds (and different distances) through the agarose, depending on their size (and electric charge).

When setting up the apparatus, 'wells' are sunk into the agarose gel at one end of the gel. These are formed by placing a 'comb' in situ in the gel and allowing molten agarose to set (harden) around it. When the comb is removed after the agarose has set, the wells remain. The DNA samples to undergo electrophoresis are placed in the wells. Typically each well contains DNA that has been treated with different restriction enzymes.

Gel electrophoresis

After a period of time, when the DNA sections have migrated partially across the agarose, the electric current is stopped. Depending on the set-up, a dye may need to be added to make the DNA fragments visible or a visualising dye may already be present within the agarose. UV light is often used to pick out the fluorescing DNA 'bands' on the agarose.

Note 1: The agarose gel contains tiny pores which allow small DNA fragments through more easily than larger fragments. This is why the smaller fragments travel further through the gel.

Note 2: DNA molecules have a small negative charge (due to the presence of the phosphate). This explains their migration towards the anode during gel electrophoresis.

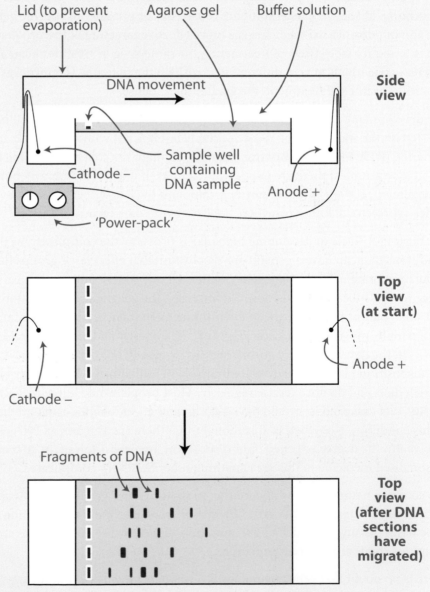

Extraction of DNA

DNA can be extracted from a range of plant or animal material in a number of ways. For example, it can be extracted from plant tissue by carrying out the following procedure.

Procedure:

1. Add a pinch of salt and a small amount of cold water to the plant material, for example, spinach.

2. Use a blender to break up the plant material; alternatively grind using a mortar and pestle.

3. Strain off the larger pieces of plant material and mix the resulting macerate with detergent (or liquid soap) to break down the cell membranes. Leave for 5–10 minutes.

4. Add protease enzyme (or pineapple juice or meat tenderiser) to separate the DNA from the chromosomes (histone proteins).

5. Gently add a layer of very cold ethanol. This causes the DNA to precipitate out of the solution. The DNA can be seen as a series of white strands.

Note: There are many different methods of extracting DNA from plant and animal tissue and these can be found on the Internet.

Exam questions

1. An understanding of the structure of DNA has led to the development of gene technology. One application of gene technology is the production of transgenic organisms.

   (a) Explain precisely the term 'transgenic organism'. [1]

   (b) Molecules, such as human growth hormone, can be produced via genetic engineering.

   Describe the role of the following in genetic engineering:

   • reverse transcriptase
   • DNA polymerase
   • plasmids [3]

   Question taken from CCEA's Biology Assessment Unit A2 2, Biochemistry, Genetics and Evolutionary Trends, June 2015, © CCEA 2017

2. Bacterial plasmids may carry genes that provide resistance to naturally occurring antibiotics.

   (a) (i) What is a plasmid? [1]

   (ii) In recombinant DNA technology, plasmids are often used as vectors. Explain what is meant by the term 'vector' in this context. [1]

Continued overleaf...

Diagram 1 illustrates a naturally occurring plasmid that contains genes for resistance to two antibiotics. When this plasmid is not present in a particular bacterium, the bacterium would be killed in the presence of either of these antibiotics.

Diagram 2 illustrates a recombinant plasmid, which has had a human gene inserted at the point shown.

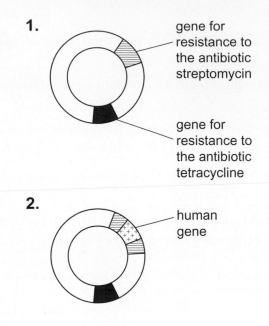

1.
gene for resistance to the antibiotic streptomycin

gene for resistance to the antibiotic tetracycline

2.
human gene

(b) (i) Describe two methods by which a specific gene could have been obtained from human cells. [4]

(ii) Describe how the human gene could then have been inserted into the original plasmid (diagram 1) to produce the recombinant plasmid (diagram 2). [3]

The human gene, referred to previously, codes for the production of a medically important hormone. In order to mass produce the hormone, E. coli cells (lacking any plasmids providing antibiotic resistance) are encouraged to take up plasmids. Those E. coli cells which have taken up the recombinant plasmids are identified and cloned in a nutrient medium and the hormone then separated and purified.

(c) (i) Explain how the E. coli bacteria might be encouraged to take up the recombinant plasmids. [1]

(ii) Outline the procedure by which the bacteria that have taken up the recombinant plasmid (diagram 2), might be identified. [2]

(iii) Explain how the elimination of other bacteria would increase the efficiency of the production of hormone. [1]

Using bacteria to manufacture hormones has many advantages. For example, an increasing number of people with diabetes has increased the demand for the hormone insulin. This increased demand is met by producing insulin from genetically modified bacteria rather than extraction from the pancreas of cattle or pigs.

(d) Suggest one health and one ethical advantage of using bacteria to produce insulin. [2]

Question taken from CCEA's Biology Assessment Unit A2 2, Biochemistry, Genetics and Evolutionary Trends, May 2012, © CCEA 2017

3. Cystic fibrosis is a condition caused by a fault in the CFTR protein, a trans-membrane protein responsible for pumping chloride ions out of cells.

If the CFTR protein is faulty, chloride ions may not be pumped out of cells. This results in the mucus immediately outside some cells (for example, cells lining the airways in the lungs) becoming thick and viscous as a consequence of reduced water content.

The symptoms of cystic fibrosis include clogged airways in the lungs and blocked enzyme ducts in the pancreas.

(a) Using the information provided, suggest the role of chloride ions in maintaining a normal thin, watery mucus in the lung airways. [2]

Around 70% of people with cystic fibrosis in northern Europe have the same gene mutation: three base pairs are missing, with the loss of a phenylalanine amino acid in the protein. The other 30% can have any of up to a thousand different types of mutations, some with only a single base being affected.

The severity of the condition in individuals varies and depends on the degree of protein malformation, which in turn depends on the type and extent of mutation involved.

(b) In relation to protein structure, explain the link between the type and extent of mutation and the severity of the cystic fibrosis. [3]

(c) Gene therapy is a potential procedure for reducing symptoms in individuals with cystic fibrosis. This involves inserting donor DNA, that codes for the functional CFTR protein, into the cells of affected individuals.

Genetically Modified (GM) crops are developed using the similar process of inserting donor DNA into the cells of crops such as maize and rice. GM crops have many advantages. For example, varieties have been developed that:

- provide nutritional enhancement, eg rice rich in beta-carotene (precursor of vitamin A necessary for visual photopigments)
- produce compounds that are toxic to insects
- have an increased ecological range, eg are able to grow in more arid conditions than the original variety

(i) Using the information provided, explain the economic and health advantages of using GM crops. [4]

Nonetheless, the use of GM crops (unlike gene therapy) has significant public opposition and is banned in many European countries.

(ii) Give two reasons why there is significant public opposition to GM crops. [2]

Question adapted from CCEA's Biology Assessment Unit A2 2, Biochemistry, Genetics and Evolutionary Trends, June 2014, © CCEA 2017

4. Ash 'dieback' is a fungal disease which has caused the destruction of many ash *(Fraxinus excelsior)* woodlands in Europe, including well over half of the ash trees in Denmark.

In March 2012, the first case of this infection in Britain was reported. By 2013, the disease had spread across native woodlands in south east England and was also found in other isolated pockets in England, Scotland and Wales.

It is thought that the fungus responsible, *Chalara fraxinea,* was carried to Britain from mainland Europe in infected seedlings and young trees. Once in Britain the infection spread rapidly from tree to tree by wind-borne spores, with a typical dispersal range of up to ten miles.

In early 2013, the only examples of infected ash trees in Northern Ireland were in sites which had been recently planted with commercially grown seedlings. There were no reported cases in native woodland.

(a) Suggest why the first cases of *Chalara fraxinea* infection in Northern Ireland were in new plantations, but not in native woodland. [2]

(b) Several strategies are being used to control the spread of the disease. One strategy involves developing an understanding of the genome of the ash. In 2013 its genome was sequenced for the first time.

  (i) Explain fully the term 'genome sequencing'. [2]

  (ii) A strain of ash (referred to as 'tree-35') resistant to the fungus has been identified in Denmark. This strain originated around 100 years ago and currently makes up two percent of Danish ash trees.

  Suggest how knowledge of the genomes of both the native British ash and 'tree-35' could be used to help conserve native British ash woodland. [3]

(c) The human genome has also been sequenced. As a result, it is now possible to test an individual for the presence of alleles that increase susceptibility to certain medical conditions, such as some cancers and heart disease.

  (i) There has been limited progress in directly linking alleles to conditions such as cancer and heart disease. Suggest two reasons for this limited progress. [2]

  (ii) In terms of treatment, continued research into the link between alleles and disease is likely to be beneficial.

  In this context, explain the term 'designer drug' and suggest one advantage of developing such drugs. [2]

Question taken from CCEA's Biology Assessment Unit A2 2, Biochemistry,
Genetics and Evolutionary Trends, June 2015, © CCEA 2017

5. (a) Addison's Disease (AAD) affects hormone production in the adrenal glands, which are found just above the kidneys.

It is a genetic condition, and research has shown that many genes are involved.

A single nucleotide polymorphism (SNP), which is found in a gene on the X chromosome, appears to be involved in the condition.

During medical research, DNA from the blood of a number of patients with AAD, and a control group (unaffected individuals), was analysed to compare the incidence of this SNP in each group.

  (i) Suggest one component of the blood from which DNA could be obtained. [1]

Gene probes were used to determine the bases present at the SNP under investigation. The results are shown in the following table. (T = thymine, C = cytosine)

Group	Bases found at SNP / %		
	TT (females) T (Males)	TC	CC (females) C (males)
AAD Males (n = 71)	58	–	42
Control Males (n = 224)	43	–	57
AAD Females (n = 215)	19	50	31
Control Females (n = 84)	17	38	45

Source: Adapted from C Napier et al, J Clin Endocrinol Metab, January 2015

(ii) Explain why there were no TC results for males. [1]

(iii) Summarise the results in the table, by comparing both male and female sufferers with their respective control groups. [3]

(iv) This data comparing AAD patients and control individuals was statistically analysed, using a test similar to the t-test. Following statistical analysis of these two groups, the probability value (p) was found to be $p < 0.03$.

In terms of probability and significance, describe and explain what is meant by a probability value of $p < 0.03$. [2]

(b) Gene therapy is increasingly being used to treat patients who have a faulty gene. This involves identifying the gene involved, isolating the appropriate gene from human DNA, and inserting it into patients in the appropriate organs or tissues.

Using the information provided, suggest two reasons why gene therapy is not, as yet, an option in the treatment of Addison's Disease. [2]

(c) The mouse is a commonly used organism for genetic studies. For example, 'knockout' and 'knockin' mice are often used in investigations into the study of human genetic disorders.

(i) Describe the difference between a 'knockout' and a 'knockin' mouse. [1]

(ii) Suggest two reasons why the mouse is widely used as a model organism in genetic studies. [2]

Question taken from CCEA's Biology Assessment Unit A2 2, Biochemistry, Genetics and Evolutionary Trends, June 2016, © CCEA 2017

6. *Quality of written communication is awarded a maximum of 2 marks in this section.*

Gene technology is opening up many medical and commercial opportunities through the production of transgenic organisms and in gene therapy.

(a) Describe the processes of obtaining desired genes and their subsequent transfer into the cells of organisms. [8]

(b) Discuss the benefits and potential problems arising from the production of transgenic organisms and from gene therapy. [8]

Quality of written communication. [2]

Question taken from CCEA's Biology Assessment Unit A2 2, Biochemistry, Genetics and Evolutionary Trends, June 2013, © CCEA 2017

result. However, if only one (or neither) of the genes is present in its dominant state (C_pp or ccP_ or ccpp) then the flowers are white. The ratio of offspring produced when crossing two double heterozygotes is shown in the diagram on the right.

The ratio shown (**9 : 7**) is a variation on the normal 9 : 3 : 3 : 1 dihybrid theme and is explained below.

Gene interaction, in general, normally arises when two or more genes are involved in the control of a metabolic

Parental	Phenotypes	purple flowers ✕ purple flowers	
	Genotypes	CcPp	CcPp

Gametes: CP Cp cP cp   CP Cp cP cp

	CP	Cp	cP	cp
CP	CCPP	CCPp	CcPP	CcPp
Cp	CCPp	CCpp	CcPp	Ccpp
cP	CcPP	CcPp	ccPP	ccPp
cp	CcPp	Ccpp	ccPp	ccpp

F₁ Genotypes

F₁ Phenotypes

purple (coloured) flowers : white flowers

9 : 7

Flower colour in sweet pea (a 9 : 7 epistatic ratio)

pathway leading to a particular phenotype. Each gene may code for an enzyme important at a particular stage of the pathway; consequently both (or all if more than two) genes need to be functional to achieve the 'normal' phenotype. In the above example of colour in sweet pea, at least one dominant allele in each gene must be present to make the gene functional and able to metabolise the two steps in the process (if either gene is homozygous recessive, the enzyme is not produced by that gene and therefore the metabolic pathway cannot be completed).

The metabolic pathway involved is summarised in the following diagram.

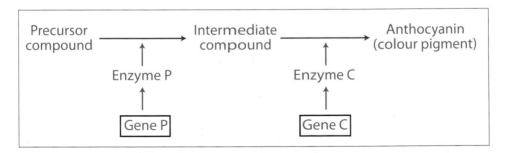

The **9 : 7** ratio can be explained by the requirement for at least one **dominant allele** to be present in **each gene**. This ensures that each of the steps in the metabolic pathway can be completed as both the P and C genes will produce the necessary enzymes.

These are only two examples of epistasis. In comb type in chickens, two loci **interact** to create a new phenotype (for example walnut) and in flower colour in sweet pea, the two loci also interact to produce the purple flower colour. In other examples, for example wheat kernel colour, two (or more) genes can **duplicate** (substitute for) the work of each other producing a **15 : 1** phenotypic ratio, with the '1/16' representing the double homozygous recessive.

Additionally, an allele at one locus could **mask** an allele (or alleles) at another locus. Squash can be yellow, green or white with colour controlled by two genes (1 and 2) with alleles (W and w) and (Y and y) respectively. If there is at least one dominant W allele present (W–) the squash will be white irrespective of the genotype of gene 2.

If gene 1 has only recessive alleles (ww) then the squash fruit will be coloured, but the actual colour produced depends on gene 2. Genotypes of wwY– give a yellow colour and wwyy gives a green colour. A cross between two plants producing white squashes, but both heterozygous for each gene, produces an offspring phenotypic ratio of **12 : 3 : 1** as shown in the following diagram. In this example, gene 1, if homozygous dominant or heterozygous, **masks** the effect of gene 2.

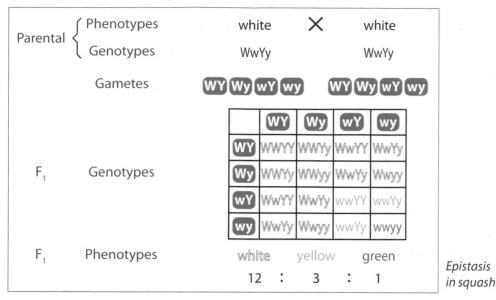

Epistasis in squash

The effect of the environment

Most of the examples we have covered in this chapter involve phenotypes that are directly dependent on their genotypes. In effect, this means that particular genotypes produce particular phenotypes irrespective of environmental influences. An individual with two recessive alleles for cystic fibrosis will have the condition irrespective of environmental influences.

But in truth, in complex living organisms (and certainly in humans) most traits are not inherited in typical Mendelian fashion as demonstrated by monohybrid or dihybrid crosses or any of their variations. Most traits are polygenic and controlled by many genes. In the last chapter we have already noted that pre-disposition to coronary heart disease (CHD) can be affected by as many as 100 genes. Similar numbers have an influence on human height. The polygenic picture is further complicated by the fact that many traits are also influenced by the environment. For example, a particular individual may have a suite of alleles that predispose towards 'tallness', but the actual height reached will be influenced by many environmental factors including diet.

If we look at overall development of many traits in a human (and many other species), for example personality, the actual trait produced is a result of the complex interactions between genetics (nature) and the environment (nurture).

At the cellular level, it is relatively straightforward to understand how the environment may have an influence on genetic expression. Certainly DNA in the nucleus controls cell development (and ultimately the development of the organism) through the production of the proteins (enzymes) that control metabolic pathways. However, it is the cell (sometimes through environmental influences) that determines which genes are switched on in the first place. The role of the environment in affecting gene expression (**epigenetics**) is a branch of biology that is currently attracting considerable interest.

Mendel revisited

It is nearly 150 years since Mendel published his conclusions on the inheritance of characters in peas. In his investigations he analysed the inheritance of seven traits (length of stem, shape of seed, colour of seed, shape of pod, colour of pod, colour of flower and position of flower). Since that time our understanding of genetics has developed, but this understanding has built on, rather than contradicted, his original ideas. At the time of his research he did not know about chromosomes or genes, referring to 'factors' inside the plant.

Nonetheless, his work was meticulously planned and he spent over ten years carrying out his research. He also used many replicates, allowing him to produce offspring in the numbers to calculate ratios (the same argument holds true today with genetic investigations: a large number of offspring is often required to identify ratios due to the random nature of gamete production and fertilisation).

He also had the wisdom (or luck) to choose the pea. The pea has a range of easily observable traits (including the seven traits he studied) that are subject to straightforward monohybrid or dihybrid inheritance patterns.

Exam questions

1. Haemophiliacs possess a non-functional form of the gene responsible for the production of blood clotting factors.

   The pedigree diagram below shows the incidence of haemophilia in an affected family.

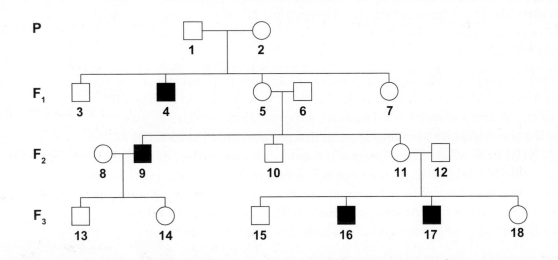

   Individuals within the pedigree are numbered. Males are represented by squares and females by circles. Those who have haemophilia are represented by solid symbols.

   (a) On the basis of the information provided, is the inheritance of haemophilia:

       (i) autosomal or sex-linked? Justify your answer. [1]

       (ii) dominant or recessive? Justify your answer. [1]

(b) Using the symbols h to represent the allele for haemophilia and H for the normal allele, state the genotype of each of the following:

- individual 2
- individual 4 [2]

(c) Individual 14 carries a recessive allele for albinism (lack of normal body pigment) which is not sex-linked. She marries a man who is also a carrier for albinism but who does not carry the haemophilia allele. The genes exhibit independent inheritance.

Using the symbol a for albinism and A for normal pigmentation, show, by means of a suitable genetic diagram, the probability of this couple producing a male child who has both haemophilia and albinism. [5]

(d) There is no evidence of haemophilia in previous generations of this family. State the most likely reason for the condition appearing in the family pedigree shown. [1]

Question taken from CCEA's Biology Assessment Unit A2 2, Biochemistry, Genetics and Evolutionary Trends, May 2012, © CCEA 2017

2. (a) In a species of small mammal, fur length is genetically controlled. One gene for fur length has alleles A and a. The genotype aa results in a fur length denoted as F. The genotype AA results in a fur length of F +10%, while the genotype Aa results in a fur length of F + 5%.

   (i) Using a genetic diagram, determine the possible offspring genotypes and phenotypes of the following cross: Aa × Aa [2]

Another gene (located on a different chromosome), with alleles B and b, also contributes to fur length. The genotype bb produces no further increase in fur length. However, the genotype BB results in a further 10% increase in fur length in addition to the effect produced by the A gene. The genotype Bb results in an additional 5% increase in fur length.

Therefore a genotype of aabb produces the baseline fur length F and the genotype AABB produces a fur length of F + 20%.

   (ii) State the possible genotype(s) of individuals with the F + 15% phenotypes. [1]

   (iii) Two of these mammals are crossed. One is a double heterozygote and the other is heterozygous at the A/a locus, with two b alleles at the B/b locus. Using a genetic diagram, determine the possible offspring genotypes and phenotypes of the cross. [4]

   (iv) In this species of mammal, fur length is discontinuous and, with careful observation, the different phenotypes can be distinguished from each other.

   In a second species, variation in fur length is continuous. Suggest one possible explanation for the continuous variation in fur length in the second species. [1]

(b) Fur colour in the species described in part (a)(i) is also controlled by two genes, D/d and E/e, as shown in the diagram on the right.

State all the genotypes that produce:

- white fur
- black fur [2]

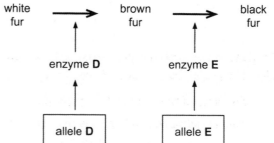

Question taken from CCEA's Biology Assessment Unit A2 2, Biochemistry, Genetics and Evolutionary Trends, June 2016, © CCEA 2017

3. The fruit fly, *Drosophila melanogaster,* is ideally suited for genetic investigations and has been widely used for this purpose for many years.

   The normal eye colour in *Drosophila* is red but a white-eyed form exists. In the genetics of eye colour, red eye (R) is dominant to white eye (r) and the inheritance of eye colour is sex-linked (in a similar way to sex-linked conditions in humans).

   (a) State the genotypes of:
       - a male with red eyes
       - a female with white eyes [2]

   (b) In a particular cross, a red-eyed female was crossed with a red-eyed male. The offspring produced are shown in the following table.

	Red eyes	White eyes
Males	48	53
Females	102	0

   (i) Using a genetic diagram, explain the outcome of this cross. [3]

   (ii) As with most genetic crosses, the numbers of offspring in this cross do not fit exactly with the predicted ratio. State the name of the statistical test that can be used to identify if observed offspring numbers are significantly different from expected numbers. [1]

   (c) In *Drosophila,* the genes for wing type and body colour are located on separate autosomes and so are independently inherited. Normal wing is dominant to vestigial wing and normal body colour is dominant to ebony body colour.

   A cross between a fruit fly with normal wings and normal body colour and one with vestigial wings and ebony body colour produced offspring displaying four different phenotypes.

   Using a genetic diagram, explain these results.

   (Let A = normal wing and B = normal body colour) [4]

   (d) Suggest two reasons why *Drosophila melanogaster* is ideally suited for genetic investigations. [2]

   Question taken from CCEA's Biology Assessment Unit A2 2, Biochemistry,
   Genetics and Evolutionary Trends, June 2015, © CCEA 2017

4. (a) Distinguish between the terms 'dominance' and 'epistasis'. [2]

   (b) The colour of squash fruit is controlled by two genes that have the alleles A/a and B/b. The B/b gene is suppressed (not expressed) in the presence of the A allele. If the B/b gene is expressed, the presence of the B allele codes for a yellow squash and absence of the B allele codes for green. If the B/b gene is suppressed the squash are white.

   A cross between two squash plants, each heterozygous for both genes, produced 126 white squash, 26 yellow squash and 8 green squash, approximating to a ratio of 12:3:1.

   Complete a genetic diagram to show the genotypes and phenotypes of the offspring. [5]

(c) The chi-squared test can be used to check if the results of the cross statistically fit a ratio of 12:3:1.

(i) Complete the table below and calculate the x^2 for these results. [2]

Category	Observed (O)	Expected (E)	(O–E)	(O–E)²	$\frac{(O-E)^2}{E}$
white	126				
yellow	26				
green	8				

(ii) On the basis of your calculated x^2 value, state the following:
- the degrees of freedom for the test
- the probability value [2]

(iii) Explain fully the outcome of your statistical test. [2]

Question taken from CCEA's Biology Assessment Unit A2 2, Biochemistry, Genetics and Evolutionary Trends, June 2014, © CCEA 2017

Chapter 13 – Population Genetics

Students should be able to:

5.6.1   Demonstrate knowledge and understanding of the concept of the gene pool.

5.6.2   Demonstrate knowledge and understanding of the Hardy-Weinberg equation.

5.6.3   Demonstrate knowledge and understanding of the source and maintenance of genetic variation.

5.6.4   Demonstrate knowledge and understanding of selection and its contribution to maintaining polymorphic populations and evolutionary change in populations.

5.6.5   Demonstrate knowledge and understanding of the concept of species and the process of speciation.

In the previous chapter the effect of gene and allelic combinations in individuals was studied. Inheritance, as studied in the last chapter, involves analysis of how genes and alleles pass through the generations producing the classic genetic offspring ratios generated.

Population genetics involves genetic analysis at the **population** level, ie the distribution of particular genes across entire populations rather than just at an individual or family grouping level. Some important terms are listed below:

- The **gene pool** is the term used to describe the sum **total** of all the **genes** (and alleles) in a **population** (or species) at a particular time.

- The **allele frequency** is the proportion of a particular allele in a population (or species) at a particular time.

- The **genome** refers to **all** the DNA in an individual – it is the entire genetic complement in any one organism.

Population geneticists are interested in the ways in which allele frequency changes within populations and over time. To investigate these changes it is important to be able to work out the allelic frequencies in populations. One way of doing this is by using the **Hardy-Weinberg equation**.

The Hardy-Weinberg equation

The Hardy-Weinberg equation can be used to calculate allele and/or genotype frequencies in a population with respect to a trait that shows Mendelian inheritance patterns.

Suppose that alleles **A** and **a** represent alternative alleles of a particular trait with **A** representing the dominant allele and **a** representing the recessive allele. Across the population under consideration, **A** and **a alleles** have frequencies represented as **p** and **q** respectively (with **p** representing the frequency of the dominant allele and **q** the frequency of the recessive allele).

Therefore the frequency of the alleles in the population can be represented as:

$$p + q = 1 \text{ (frequency of alleles)}$$

In the above equation, 1 represents 100% of the population meaning that each individual in the population will have two alleles which can be two dominant alleles, two recessive alleles, or one of each, for a particular trait.

Note: Some textbooks refer to the genome as being the total of all the DNA in a haploid set of chromosomes (as the alleles for most, but not all, genes will be identical in homologous chromosomes).

In terms of the **individuals** in the population, they can only be homozygous for the dominant allele (**AA**), homozygous for the recessive allele (**aa**), or heterozygous (**Aa**).

The frequency of homozygous dominant individuals (genotype **AA**) is represented as p^2 with the frequency of homozygous recessive individuals (genotype **aa**) being represented as q^2. Heterozygous individuals (**Aa**) have a frequency of **2 pq**.

	A_p	a_q
A_p	AA_{p^2}	Aa_{pq}
a_q	Aa_{pq}	aa_{q^2}

Therefore the frequency of individuals with the different genotypes can be represented as:

$$p^2 + 2pq + q^2 = 1 \text{ (frequency of individuals)}$$

In the above equation, 1 represents 100% of the population meaning that each individual in the population can only have a genotype that is homozygous dominant, homozygous recessive, or heterozygous, for a particular trait.

Therefore, if some of the population information is available in terms of either the frequency of a particular allele or genotype, or the frequency of a particular phenotype, the two equations above allow the allele and genotypic frequencies to be calculated.

Worked example

In the fruit fly (*Drosophila melanogaster*) wings can either be normal or vestigial (dramatically reduced). Wing type is inherited in typical monohybrid fashion with normal dominant to the recessive vestigial. In a particular population, 16% of the flies have vestigial wings.

Question

In a population of 200, calculate how many flies are heterozygous for wing type and also the frequency of the normal (W) and vestigial (w) alleles.

Note 1: In this question, as in many calculations involving the Hardy-Weinberg equation, you are given the number of individuals that are homozygous recessive – they can be identified by phenotype, but the homozygous dominant and heterozygous individuals cannot be identified by phenotype as they have the same phenotype.

Note 2: Although given percentages in the stem of the question, the Hardy-Weinberg calculations are based on proportions of 1.

Solution

16% represent the homozygous recessive individuals, so must have a **ww** genotype.

Therefore $q^2 = 0.16$

$\qquad q = 0.4$

Using $p + q = 1$ $\quad p = 0.6$

Therefore the frequency of the W allele = 0.6 (60%) and the frequency of the w allele = 0.4 (40%).

Using $p^2 + 2pq + q^2 = 1$

$0.36 + 2pq + 0.16 = 1$

Therefore $2pq = 0.48$ (48% of the population are heterozygotes).

In a population of 200 this represents **96** flies.

Although the Hardy-Weinberg equation can be used for calculating genotype and allele frequencies in populations, this only applies if the population is in Hardy-Weinberg equilibrium. To be in equilibrium certain assumptions are made. These include:

- **The population is large** – In small populations random variations can skew the distribution of alleles and genotypes in the same way that genotypic offspring ratios only hold true if large numbers of progeny are considered.

- **Mating is random** – This means that there is an equal chance of an individual of any one genotype mating with an individual of the same or any other genotype. Obviously, if there was increased frequency of mating within a particular genotype group (or between specific genotype groups) then the population would not be in equilibrium.

- **Individuals are diploid** – and the trait in question is inherited in typical Mendelian pattern.

- **Differential selection is not taking place based on the three genotypes under consideration** – In other words, no particular genotype is more likely to survive (or reproduce) than any other genotype; all genotypes (and alleles) are equally 'favoured'.

- **Mutation is not taking place** – Although mutation rates vary in different genes, under normal circumstances the rate is so low at a particular locus, that it can usually be discounted when investigating allele frequencies at a particular point in time.

- **There is no migration** – Loss of individuals from a population or the gain of individuals from other populations will affect the Hardy-Weinberg equilibrium of populations. For this reason, many studies of population genetics involving the Hardy-Weinberg equation have involved isolated populations (for example island populations).

The many assumptions surrounding the Hardy-Weinberg equation do **not** apply to the populations of many species. Migrations and mutation do happen. Differential selection is a fact of life in most species in that some individuals will be better adapted than others and therefore more likely to survive and pass on their alleles to offspring. However, selection only happens if there is variation across the population for certain phenotypes (and genotypes) to be favoured over others. Before looking at the process of selection, it is important to review the range of mechanisms that contribute to the variation that exists among the individuals of a population.

1. Sources of genetic variation (meiosis and fertilisation)

Meiosis as a source of variation

Meiosis (see Chapter 5 of *Biology for CCEA AS Level 2nd Edition,* Colourpoint Educational) is a major source of variation in sexually reproducing organisms and it contributes to variation in a number of very important ways.

Independent assortment is a crucial source. Remember that the golden rules in meiosis are that only one chromosome from each homologous pair enters a gamete and which of the two chromosomes from each pair enters a particular gamete is dependent on how the homologous pairs line up at the equator of the cell at the start of metaphase I. As the way in which a homologous pair lines up at the equator in meiosis is random and independent of how any other pair aligns, there are 2^{23} potential chromosome arrangements in a gamete in humans – obviously huge potential for variation.

Crossing over, which occurs in prophase I of meiosis, is another source of variation as it facilitates the exchange of genetic material between homologous chromosomes.

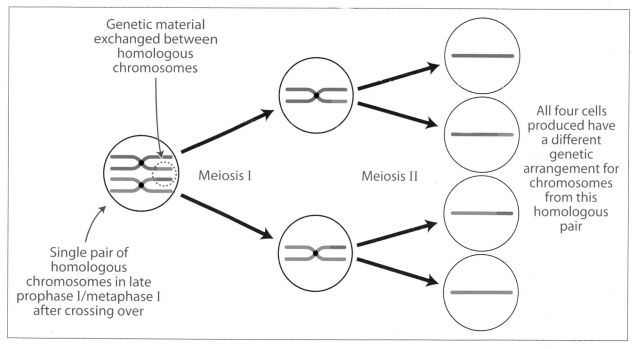

Crossing over in meiosis

Crossing over can produce entirely new allele (but not gene) arrangements along the length of the chromosomes and it produces allelic combinations that were not present in either parental chromosome.

Cross-fertilisation

Meiosis ensures that there is considerable variation in the gametes produced by any one individual. However, the process of cross-fertilisation provides further opportunity for variation.

Normally the male (whether producing sperm in animals or pollen in flowering plants) produces very large numbers (often millions) of gametes, each with different chromosome and allele arrangements, for the reasons described earlier. Females are usually more frugal with egg production, as each egg is larger and usually requires more investment but also because the female can only provide support and nourishment for a small number of developing young. Nonetheless, the fusion of male and female gametes is an entirely random process, further shuffling the possibilities, so the actual genetic material that recombines together in the new individual during cross-fertilisation (fertilisation involving two parents) will further add to the variation produced.

Independent assortment and crossing over during meiosis, and the random nature of fertilisation, mixes up allelic combination possibilities but does not produce genetic novelty in the sense that there are no new alleles produced in the process.

Mutation can produce genetic novelty and is therefore a very important source of variation in living organisms.

2. Sources of genetic variation (mutation)

Mutation is a permanent change to the DNA in an organism. There are many different types of mutation. Mutation can affect chromosome number or structure, or can be more localised (and smaller) in scale affecting a gene or even a single base pair.

The significance of mutations not only depends on the type of mutation but also when and where they occur. A mutation in a skin cell in an adult will only affect that cell or any daughter cells produced should the affected cell divide mitotically. A mutation in a gamete will affect all the cells in any offspring produced should that gamete remain viable and be involved in fertilisation.

Types of mutation

Gene mutations

These are mutations that are restricted to a single gene. Many affect only one base – these are **point mutations**. Point mutations can involve **substitution** and **deletion** of single bases.

Substitution is when one base is **replaced** by another as represented by the diagram on the right.

Clearly the consequence of a point mutation involving substitution will be limited to one amino acid (taking account of base triplet rules and the non-overlapping nature of the DNA code). If the substitution occurs in the third base of the triplet it may produce no effect at all due to the **degenerate** nature of the DNA code. In these circumstances the mutation is described as **neutral**.

Sickle cell anaemia is an autosomal recessive condition caused by the presence of two recessive alleles. The sickle cell allele is an example of a gene

Substitution

DNA before substitution of base	DNA after substitution of base
T A C } amino acid 1	T A C } amino acid 1
A T A } amino acid 2	A T A } amino acid 2
G C G } amino acid 3	G G G } amino acid 5 — base substitution
T T A } amino acid 4	T T A } amino acid 4
G G G } amino acid 5	G G G } amino acid 5

(point) mutation caused by substitution. The normal allele contains the DNA base triplet CTC, which codes for the amino acid glutamate at a particular position. In contrast, the mutated sickle cell anaemia allele has the DNA sequence CAC, which codes for valine.

Deletion is a second example of point mutation. With deletions, one base is **removed** (deleted) from the DNA sequence. The consequences of this can be very significant as they cause **'frameshift' mutations**. As the DNA sequence is read in threes, the deletion of one base changes the base triplet template along the rest of the gene, after the point of mutation, as shown in the following diagram.

This means that all the **amino acids** after the point of mutation may be changed or that the protein can be shortened if a 'stop' codon is produced earlier in the sequence than intended.

Note 1: Substitution (gene) mutations may still produce the original or (largely) functional protein but mutations caused by base deletions can lead to changes so large that a non-functional protein is produced.

Note 2: Many of the genetic conditions discussed in the last two chapters are caused by gene mutations and in some cases point mutations.

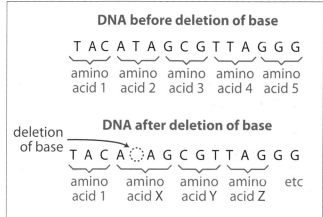

Deletion

Note 3: Point mutations (or gene mutations involving a small number of bases) are relatively common. It is estimated that each human embryo may have as many as between 50 to 100 new mutations in its genome. The vast majority will be neutral or have very little effect.

Chromosome mutations

Chromosome mutations involve change to large sections of DNA containing several genes or even whole chromosomes. Large sections of a chromosome can break off (possibly during cell division) and attach to another chromosome or even get lost.

A relatively common mutation affecting chromosome number, rather than structure, is the mutation that gives rise to Down's Syndrome. If one of the parental homologous pairs (chromosome 21) fails to segregate properly during gamete formation, this results in some gametes being produced with 24 rather than 23 chromosomes. If an affected gamete is involved in fertilisation, a zygote (first cell of new individual) will be produced with 47 chromosomes, resulting in Down's Syndrome.

Failure of chromosomes to segregate can also lead to affected individuals having a missing chromosome (for example, Turner's syndrome in humans is caused by the presence of only one sex chromosome [an X], giving the genotype XO; affected individuals are female but sexually underdeveloped and sterile).

Some other features of mutations are listed below:

- **What causes mutations?** Mutations can occur spontaneously for no obvious reason. However, the rate at which they occur can be accelerated if the individual is exposed to particular environmental stimuli. An example seldom out of the headlines is the link between **UV light** and the mutations that give rise to the uncontrolled cell division that leads to **skin cancer**.

- **How often do they happen?** Rates of mutation vary from species to species and within the genome of a particular species. The mutation rate in humans has been estimated at one error every 100 million base pairs per generation. However, some types are much more common. The errors that give rise to Down's Syndrome occur much more frequently.

- **Are all mutations harmful?** As mutation involves a change to the DNA it will most often have harmful (and often fatal) consequences – revisit the genetic diseases over the last two chapters. As noted earlier, some mutations can be neutral (for example, some substitutions in the third base of a base triplet) in that they have no effect on the phenotype. Variation in human blood groups (the ABO system) and in eye colour has been caused by mutation and appears to be neutral. A very small number of mutations can be beneficial. Although very rare, these beneficial mutations can be very important as seen later in this chapter.

Selection

As we have seen with genetic diseases, the alternative forms of a particular trait may not be equally beneficial to the organism concerned. In nature, **variation** is subject to **selection** pressure, with beneficial variations increasing the chances of survival and harmful variations harming the chances of survival of the individual concerned.

In any given environmental situation, the better adapted individuals will **survive** at the expense of the less well adapted individuals (the *survival of the fittest*). This is particularly likely to happen if there is competition for resources (the *struggle for existence*). The 'struggle for existence' and 'survival of the fittest' summarise key tenets of Charles Darwin's theory of **natural selection**.

While selection can act on any type of variation, whether caused by genetic or environmental factors, it is only the genetic variation that can contribute to change in allele frequencies over time. Some key points about selection are listed in the points below:

- Selection acts on **populations** of organisms through its effect on **individuals**. Individuals may survive or die because they are more or less well adapted in a particular environment. Over time, the genetic makeup of the populations may change as particular alleles increase in frequency and others reduce in frequency.

- Selection is **environmentally dependent**. The thick white fur of the polar bear only gives a selective advantage in the Arctic.

- For selection to lead to change in a population or species over time, the basis of the variation must be **genetic** (not just environmental).

- Selection is the editing of genetically inheritable features in a population, increasing the frequency of some while decreasing the frequency of others over time.

Note: Natural selection will act against (eliminate) individuals that are poorly adapted, irrespective of whether the decreased fitness is due to environmental or genetic variation. However, if it is to lead to **evolutionary change** in a population over time, it is only the **genetic variation** that is significant, allowing the favourable traits to pass to future generations.

- Fitness is a term that describes how well an organism is adapted for its environment. Selection favours those organisms that are most fit and acts against those that are less fit.

- If selection leads to a change in a population or species over time (a change in **allelic** frequencies), it does so through **differential reproductive success**. If the better adapted individuals are more likely to survive, it is also very likely that they will produce more offspring (and perpetuate their beneficial alleles).

- Selection is an **ongoing process**. It is always taking place although not always obvious.

Note: The perpetuation of beneficial alleles in populations usually involves both differential survival and **differential reproductive success**.

In a constant (unchanging) environment, natural selection will tend to favour the status quo. This type of selection tends to maintain constancy in the genetic makeup of a population and is called **stabilising selection.**

In a changing environment it may be that one of the extremes is better adapted (fitter) than the average individuals. The type of selection in this situation is **directional selection**.

Stabilising and directional selection are discussed in the following sections.

Stabilising selection

Many traits in living organisms show **normal distribution.** In humans, height and mass are two obvious examples of traits that are normally distributed, with most individuals being close to average and fewer individuals approaching the extremes.

In **stabilising selection,** the **average phenotypes (individuals)** are best adapted in terms of the trait under consideration (ie selection favours the modal variants). The 'extremes' are less well adapted and likely to be selected against; consequently it is the average individuals that are more likely to survive and pass on their genes to their offspring.

Stabilising selection

The analysis of births in a London hospital in the 1930s showed that the babies with the best chance of survival were those close to average mass. Mortality rates were higher for the babies with low birth masses (they were often premature) and those with the highest birth masses (their large size often led to complications at birth). In this example the selection pressure was much greater at the extremes of body mass, as babies with very low or very high body masses at birth were less well adapted.

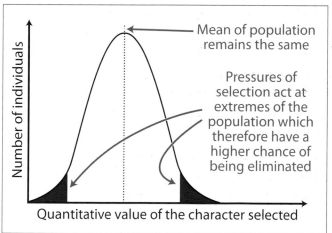

This example of stabilising selection also shows that selection pressures can change over time. As a consequence of modern medical advances, very small and very large babies are now much more likely to survive; therefore the selection pressures contributing to the stabilising selection are much reduced.

In **highly adapted populations** in **stable ecosystems**, almost all the selection taking place will be stabilising. Over many years, organisms in an ecosystem have become highly adapted as a consequence of selection. In this situation, there will be no obvious change in phenotype over time, therefore it appears as if selection is not taking place! Stabilising selection is **not** a force for evolutionary change.

Directional selection

With directional selection the average individuals are not those most highly adapted. The best adapted individuals have **phenotypes** that lie **closer to** (or at) **one** of the **extremes** of variation.

Directional selection is most likely to take place in one of the following two scenarios:

- The environment is changing.
- A population (or species) colonises a new habitat.

There are many examples of directional selection in nature. Most GCSE textbooks use the example of the **peppered moth** (*Biston betularia*) with which you are probably already familiar.

Another example is the development of **pesticide resistance** in insects – the resistance is caused by mutation. In insect populations not subject to pesticide control, insects that have the resistance mutation are selected against (the metabolic 'cost' of the mutation may cause the insects to grow slower and be less 'fit' in other respects) and therefore the frequency of the mutated allele(s) in the population will be low. However, in insect populations subject to pesticide applications, the presence of alleles that confer resistance to pesticide is a significant adaptive advantage. These insects will be selected for – they will be the ones that survive and pass their (resistant) alleles on to their offspring, ensuring that the frequency of the resistant alleles rapidly spreads through the population.

A very contemporary example is the earlier flowering times of some populations of plants subject to climate change. Although climate change in Britain appears to mean more storms, wetter weather and more flooding, in much of the world, areas that already have a shortage of rain are becoming even drier (ie increased 'desertification'). The populations of many species of flowering plants are flowering earlier in these increasingly dry habitats, ensuring that they reproduce in the increasingly short window where growth is possible. In this example, aridity is the **selection pressure** and those plants able to flower at an earlier stage in their growth are more highly adapted than those that exhibit later flowering times.

Note: This example is an interesting one as the scientists involved in collecting the data had to check that it wasn't just the change in environment (and nothing to do with genetic change) that caused the plants to flower earlier (as will happen with many plant species). To confirm that **genetic change** was taking place, plants of the same species, but from different populations, were grown in the **same environmental conditions**. When grown in the same conditions, plants from populations from the more arid habitats still flowered earlier, showing that flowering times were under genetic control.

Antibiotic resistance in **bacteria** is yet another very common example of directional selection.

Case study – antibiotic resistance in bacteria

The antibiotic **penicillin** was first produced in commercial quantities in the early 1940s. Penicillin's anti-bacterial properties are due to its ability to disrupt bacterial cell wall formation. When it was first used to combat bacterial infections, less than 5% of the strains (varieties) of ***Staphylococcus aureus*** (a common bacterium responsible for many types of infection) were resistant. Now over 95% of strains are resistant to penicillin.

Resistance to penicillin (or related antibiotics) is caused by random mutation in the bacterial genome. Resistance can come in many ways. Some mutations lead to the production of enzymes that break down the penicillin, others lead to changes in cell wall structure that prevents the penicillin gaining entry and even new metabolic pathways in cell wall formation that bypass the effects of the antibiotics.

When a new generation of antibiotics was produced, including **methicillin**, these initially proved successful against penicillin-resistant strains. However, as could have been anticipated, some strains became resistant to the methicillin, hence **methicillin-resistant *Staphylococcus aureus*** (**MRSA**). MRSA is now resistant to a range of antibiotics and other drugs, and it and other similarly resistant bacteria (for example *Clostridium difficile*) are widely referred to as 'superbugs'.

Antibiotic resistance in bacteria is an example of directional selection with the use of antibiotics as the selection pressure. Evolutionary change in the *Staphylococcus aureus* species has occurred over time. The change in phenotype (resistance) is underpinned by genetic change.

Note: The examples of pesticide resistance in insects and antibiotic resistance in bacteria are very obvious in the populations concerned – insects and bacteria will either survive or not when subject to pesticide or antibiotics respectively. Most examples of directional selection, such as the development of slightly earlier flowering times of some plant species in drought conditions or changes in fur thickness in mammals in response to changing climate, are much more subtle and gradual. Nonetheless, directional selection leads to evolutionary change over time.

A key feature of all of the examples used in this section is that the directional selection is associated with **environmental change** (change including introduction of pesticides and antibiotics). Unlike with stabilising selection, directional selection does tend to lead to **evolutionary change** in populations.

Polymorphism

In many examples of directional selection there are two or more discrete genotypes that produce distinct phenotypes (for example, black or light coloured peppered moths or bacteria that are resistant or not to antibiotics). Populations where there is more than one alternative for a particular trait are described as being **polymorphic**.

A typical definition for polymorphism is the presence of two or more genotypes, the rarest of which exceeds 1%.

Other examples of polymorphism include human blood groups and eye colour, and banding in snails – polymorphism in living organisms is very common with no shortage of examples. However, polymorphic populations are effective tools for the study of natural selection. One example is the incidence of sickle cell anaemia in different human populations.

Case study – sickle cell anaemia

Sickle cell anaemia is a blood disorder that affects many people in parts of Africa and a number of Mediterranean countries. The allele that codes for sickle cell anaemia leads to red blood cells that are sickle shaped and less well adapted to flow through narrow capillaries.

The condition is caused by a point (gene) mutation where the normal DNA base triplet CTC, which codes for the amino acid glutamate, is replaced by the base triplet CAC, which codes for the amino acid valine.

Individuals who are heterozygous for sickle cell anaemia (one normal allele and one allele that codes for sickle cell anaemia) do not have sickle cell anaemia but are described as having sickle cell trait. Individuals heterozygous for the sickle cell allele have haemoglobin that is less efficient than normal haemoglobin, but is more efficient than that in individuals with two sickle cell alleles. The genotypes and phenotypes are summarised in the following table.

Phenotype	Genotype
normal	$Hb^A Hb^A$
sickle cell trait	$Hb^A Hb^S$
sickle cell anaemia	$Hb^S Hb^S$

In most human populations, the sickle cell allele (whether homozygous or heterozygous) is selected against and its frequency in the population is very low. However, it has been found that in those regions where the incidence of sickle cell anaemia (and the sickle cell allele) is high, malaria is also common. This can be explained by the fact that the malformed red blood cells, formed as a consequence of sickle cell anaemia (or sickle cell trait in heterozygotes), offer a degree of protection against malaria. The protection is due to the malarial parasite being less able to complete its life cycle in the sickle shaped red blood cells.

Consequently, while the homozygote sickle cell condition ($Hb^S Hb^S$) can lead to ill health and often death at an early age, in Africa the presence of the sickle cell allele in the heterozygous condition ($Hb^A Hb^S$), due to its protective effects against malaria, gives a selective advantage over the 'normal' genotype ($Hb^A H^A$). In areas of Africa affected by malaria, the relative fitness of the three genotypes has been estimated as $Hb^A Hb^A = 0.90$; $Hb^A Hb^S = 1.00$; and $Hb^S Hb^S = 0.20$. In effect, 'normal' individuals are only 90% as likely to survive and pass on their genes compared to an individual heterozygous for sickle cell anaemia.

This is an example of **balanced polymorphism** as the adaptive advantage of the heterozygote (**heterozygosity**) ensures that in the African populations the relative proportion of the three different genotypes remains stable.

Note: Although the homozygous sickle cell condition is strongly selected against, there will still be a high proportion of individuals born with sickle cell anaemia as a consequence of the offspring ratios produced by unions between the more favourably adapted heterozygotes.

Species and speciation

Selection in a particular population of a species can cause this population to diverge to an extent that it is very different genetically from the ancestral (original) species (ie all the other populations). A point could be reached where the population concerned actually forms a new species – the process of speciation.

The species

But what exactly is a species? There are many definitions of a species but most are broadly similar to the following.

A species is a group of individuals of common ancestry that are normally capable of interbreeding to produce fertile offspring. Each species is **reproductively isolated** from other species.

> **Note: Reproductive isolation** means unable to interbreed.

Using this definition we can see why horses and donkeys are classified as different species even though they can interbreed but produce sterile mules. Similarly, a number of large cat species have been able to interbreed in captivity (for example, male tigers and lionesses) and a number of their offspring (for example, the tiglon) have proved to be fertile. However, tigers and lions are still classified as separate species as the hybrids tend not to occur in the wild.

There can be a blurring at the edges when determining if a particular species has split into two (or more) species as separate populations diverge. For example the dog (*Canis canis*) is still regarded as being one species but there are over 300 different breeds, many of them very different in physical appearance and character. As divergence continues to increase, a point may be reached where 'natural' interbreeding between some breeds becomes increasingly unlikely.

> **Note:** The domestic dog and the wolf share a common ancestor. Unlike the other examples of directional selection used in this chapter, the selection (and continued divergence) of particular traits in dogs has been accelerated by selective breeding by man – **artificial selection** rather than natural selection.

Speciation

Speciation is the formation of new species that are reproductively isolated from other species.

Speciation can occur in a number of ways, but in most cases there are two distinct processes:

- The original species becomes separated into two or more populations that become reproductively isolated from each other (ie breeding is restricted to **within** each isolated population).

- Different forms of directional selection take place in each of the isolated populations with the result that, over time, the populations become so different that they remain reproductively isolated from each other even if they subsequently come into contact.

The initial isolation is usually **geographical**. For example, populations can get isolated on oceanic or even small offshore islands or by mountains or rivers. Many species of small, and relatively sedentary invertebrates, have been effectively isolated by the building of motorway networks.

> **Note:** In the initial geographical isolation the key feature is not the mechanism of separation, or the distances involved, but the **effectiveness** of the barrier in preventing gene exchange between the different populations.

Once separation occurs there will almost certainly be **genetic divergence** between the different populations, as even slightly different environmental conditions will encourage natural selection to act in different ways in the isolated areas. In time, as a consequence of directional selection and genetic divergence, a number of reproductive isolating **mechanisms** develop that prevents interbreeding and gene exchange should the isolated populations overlap. At the stage when interbreeding between the formerly isolated populations becomes impossible, **speciation** will have occurred.

Reproductive isolating mechanisms that can develop include:

- **Barriers to the reproductive process** – including mechanical barriers to mating/ fertilisation, offspring infertility and reproductive cycles no longer synchronised.

- **Behavioural isolation** – Different populations can develop different courtship rituals (important in speciation in birds).

- **Ecological isolation** – Different populations can become ecologically isolated. Examples include different habitat or food preferences (for example, the different types of leaf (tree) used by leaf mining insects).

> **Note 1:** The term sub-species is often used to classify separate populations that have not quite diverged enough to become separate species but may do so in the future. Sub-species usually differ from each other in several significant aspects (although they are potentially capable of interbreeding and producing fertile young).

> **Note 2: Reproductive isolation** can have slightly different meanings depending on the context used. If populations are separated geographically, the separation (the fact that two or more populations are reproductively isolated) means that each of the separated populations can evolve independently due to natural selection acting in different ways in different environments due to the populations being **reproductively isolated** (ie no breeding between *populations* for geographic reasons).
>
> Different species are **reproductively isolated** from each other. In this context, individuals from different species cannot interbreed to produce fertile offspring as they have developed **reproductive isolating mechanisms** (ie no breeding between species for physical or other reasons).
>
> Therefore, reproductive isolation can be both a necessary step prior to speciation or a consequence of speciation.

Speciation that involves initial geographical separation followed by genetic divergence is described as **allopatric speciation**.

The most studied and most widely known example of allopatric speciation is the finches of the Galapagos Islands, first studied by Charles Darwin.

Case Study – The Galapagos Finches ('Darwin's finches')

The Galapagos Islands are a group of volcanic islands, 600 miles to the west of Ecuador in the South Pacific Ocean. The islands formed relatively late in geological history. Initially the islands were barren of life but a primary succession developed as plant seeds and other terrestrial organisms were carried to the islands by strong currents, winds or driftwood.

Eventually a number of finches (probably of one species) reached the islands from the South American mainland. In time populations of finches developed on most of the islands. Very occasionally the birds travelled between the islands but it was very rare due to the strong currents and winds in the area – in effect, the finches on each island were reproductively isolated from the finches on other islands.

Over time, the finches on the different islands diverged from the finches on the other islands (and from the South American mainland) to become different species. One key area of divergence is in beak size and shape as the finch beaks on the different islands evolved as they became adapted to the food sources available on each specific island.

There are two factors that have been critical in allowing the finches to evolve into a number of different species on the islands:

- There were very few other species of birds on the islands. This reduced competition and any adaptations in terms of beak shape had a greater chance of being advantageous in manipulating new food sources.

- Finches are poor fliers. Although this makes their initial arrival on the islands the more remarkable (they must have travelled the 600 miles from the South American mainland on driftwood or were supported by very favourable winds), it meant that the finches on the different islands were more effectively reproductively isolated.

The evolution of the finches on Galapagos is an excellent example of **adaptive radiation**. This describes the process of a range of species rapidly evolving to fill the abundant **ecological niches** available. Adaptive radiation is most likely to occur when there is little competition from other species and when there is a range of (uncolonised) habitats available to be exploited.

Exam questions

1. A consequence of sexual reproduction is variation in offspring.

    (a) Apart from mutations, identify three processes that contribute to variation in a sexually-reproducing organism. [3]

    (b) Babies produce the enzyme lactase to digest lactose, the disaccharide in milk. However, as they grow into adulthood some people lose the ability to produce lactase and so cannot digest lactose.

    The ability to produce lactase into adulthood varies in different populations and is linked with milk consumption. In populations which do not keep cows to produce milk (for example in Asia) it is rare for adults to produce lactase. Conversely, in populations which keep dairy cattle (for example in Europe) there are high frequencies of adults capable of producing lactase.

    Lactase production is determined by a single gene with two alleles, one allele coding for lactase production while the other allele fails to code for an effective enzyme. DNA analysis of human skeletal remains shows that the allele for lactase production was absent in adults until 3000 to

Chapter 14 – The Plant and Animal Kingdoms

Kingdom Plantae (The Plant Kingdom)

The Kingdom Plantae ('true' plants) encompasses species that are **multicellular**, have **eukaryotic cells** with **cellulose cell walls** and **photosynthesise** using **chlorophyll** contained in **chloroplasts**. Additionally, species in the kingdom Plantae show distinct **differentiation** with the cells in the different parts of the plant specialised for specific functions, for example, leaf cells specialised for photosynthesis.

The two major plant groups are the **bryophytes** and the **tracheophytes**.

Division Bryophyta (Mosses)

This division is represented by the **mosses**.

Structure – Mosses **lack true roots**, **stems** and **leaves** and they **do not possess vascular tissue** (xylem and phloem) – support is by **turgor**. However, the cells in the moss plant are organised into structures that have a superficial similarity to stems and leaves and there are filamentous-like structures called **rhizoids** that anchor the moss to the ground. Not being true roots, the rhizoids are unable to penetrate the substratum to any great degree and have no specific role in water uptake. Water and minerals can be gained (or lost) over the entire surface of the moss plant. Additionally, the leaf-like structures **do not possess** a **cuticle** or **stomata**.

As a consequence of the absence of true roots and vascular tissue, and a very restricted ability in reducing water loss, moss plants seldom reach a significant size and are usually restricted to damp habitats.

Moss growing in the crevices in a wall

Note 1: In the photograph above right, note the leaf-like appearance of the visible parts of the moss.

Note 2: By growing on the stone walls and the roof in the photograph above left, the mosses avoid competition from grasses and other plants, and avoid damage by trampling. This upland area in the Yorkshire Dales has high annual rainfall levels so forms an ideal habitat for the moisture-requiring mosses.

Mosses produce spores in a capsule at the end of a stalk that lifts the spore-producing capsule above the ground. This enables the spores to be dispersed by wind currents.

Moss growing on a wall – both the main plant and the elevated spore-producing structure are visible

Note: The spore-producing structure possesses stomata and a cuticle which provide a degree of protection as this part of the moss plant extends above the main plant into the drier air.

The spores germinate in moist conditions and are only partially resistant to desiccation (another feature that tends to restrict mosses to damp habitats). This means they would dry out and not remain viable if away from moisture for too long.

Division Tracheophyta

The tracheophytes are **vascular plants**. They have a vascular system (xylem and phloem). There are two major sub-divisions, the **ferns** (pteridophytes) and **flowering plants** (spermatophytes).

Sub-division Pteridophyta (ferns)

Structure – Ferns have **true roots**, **stems** and **leaves** (the leaves are typically subdivided into leaflets called pinnae).

Ferns possess **vascular tissue** in the roots, stems and leaves. The presence of **xylem** and **phloem** ensures that there are well developed systems for water and ion transport and organic nutrients respectively. The presence of vascular tissue is a very important factor in ferns being able to grow to considerable sizes. Support is both by turgor within the cells and by the presence of xylem cells thickened by lignin.

The presence of a **waterproof cuticle** and **stomata** (with fine control allowing the stomata to be closed if the plant is subject to water stress) in the leaves, in addition to true roots and stems with vascular tissue, allow ferns to colonise drier areas than mosses characteristically do.

In many ferns, the stem (rhizome) runs horizontally underground with the leaves being the only part that extends above ground as shown in the diagram below.

Ferns also disperse spores that germinate in damp conditions. As with moss spores, they are not highly resistant to desiccation.

Note: The production of spores that are not very resistant to desiccation is an important factor in restricting ferns to relatively damp habitats.

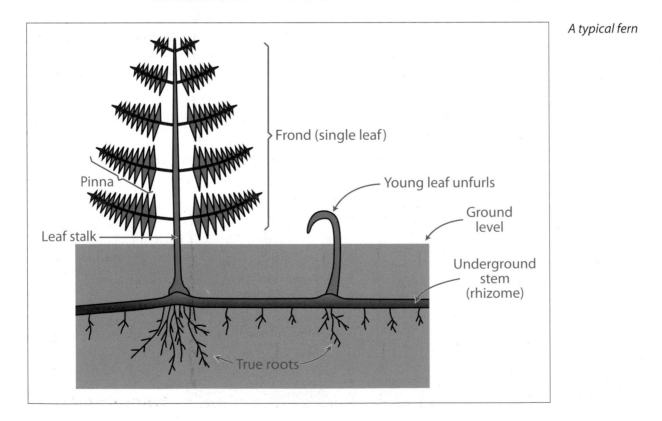

A typical fern

Ferns in a dark and damp hedgerow – a typical habitat

Lower side of a single fern leaf (frond) showing pinnae which are further subdivided into pinnules. The small brown dots on the pinnules are the spore-producing structures.

Sub-division Spermatophyta (flowering plants)

Flowering plants (**angiosperms**) have flowers as reproductive structures and produce seeds instead of spores.

Flowering plants are very variable in form and include small herbaceous herbs and large trees.

As with ferns (the other sub-division of the tracheophytes) angiosperms have **true roots**, **stems** and **leaves** with a **waterproofed cuticle** and **stomata** that are subject to fine control.

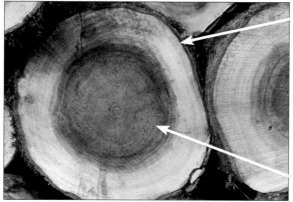

Section through the stem of a tree

Most of the living tissue (for example, phloem and unspecialised cells) are found in a thin rim around the edge of the stem. The main water-conducting xylem vessels are also located near the outer rim.

Most of the stem is xylem (wood) which has a purely supporting role.

Vascular tissue is also highly developed and, as with ferns, the roots are able to penetrate deep into the ground to absorb water and minerals.

In terms of adaptations to life on land (terrestrial habitats), flowering plants are more highly adapted in a number of ways:

- Many of the adaptations evident in ferns are even more highly adapted for life on land in angiosperms than in the ferns. For example, root systems are often more complex and the xylem is usually much more extensive and capable of providing much more support.

Note: Trees are usually over 95% xylem (wood). In older trees, most of this wood no longer transports water and has a purely supportive role. This allow trees to reach great heights and obtain more light than other plants when growing in woodland.

Trees are almost all wood!

- **Seeds** have a tough outer coat which provides protection against drying out (desiccation) in addition to enclosed 'food' reserves that provide energy during the germination process. Many seeds can be dispersed into hostile environments and remain dormant but viable for decades or longer and eventually germinate if conditions become suitable.

Many seeds (or their surrounding fruits) are highly adapted for dispersal whether by wind, animal (including birds) or explosive mechanism.

Fruits on a hawthorn tree are attractive to birds

The great diversity of flowering plants has resulted in different species being adapted for virtually all the habitats available on Earth and they can be highly adapted for anything between very moist environments (or even life in water – hydrophytes) to extremely dry environments (xerophytes) as seen in the photographs.

Marsh marigold – adapted for wet or very damp habitats

Prickly Pear cactus in La Gomera – a true xerophyte, highly adapted to storing water and minimising its loss

Samphire – although found on UK rocky shores, this species has xerophytic adaptations such as succulent leaves that have a small surface area to volume ratio

Kingdom Animalia

Animals are **eukaryotic multicellular** organisms that do **not** possess a **cell wall**. They are **heterotrophs** feeding on organic food that they can **digest internally**. Most animals are capable of **locomotion**.

The major groupings within the animal kingdom are the various phyla. In this specification students are required to know the body form of the phyla Cnidaria, Platyhelminthes, Annelida, Arthropoda and Chordata.

Phylum Cnidaria

Cnidarians include the marine jellyfish and freshwater *Hydra*. Cnidarians are **radially symmetrical** and they are restricted to an aqueous medium for support – they have a **hydrostatic skeleton** formed by the **fluid-filled enteron** (gut cavity). They are also restricted to an aqueous medium as they have no means of restricting water loss across their body surface.

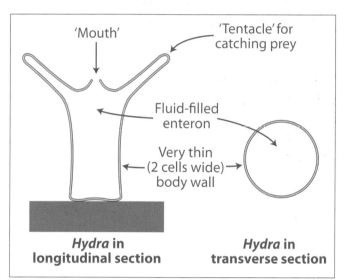

The body structure of a typical cnidarian (Hydra)

Phylum Platyhelminthes

Platyhelminthes are flatworms. Examples include the planarians and liver flukes. Platyhelminthes are **bilaterally symmetrical** and flattened **dorso-ventrally**.

An advantage with **bilateral symmetry** is that the animals have a 'front' where sensory receptors can be positioned, allowing them to 'test' the environment into which they are entering. The streamlined bilaterally symmetrical shape makes movement much easier compared to the radial symmetry of the cnidarians.

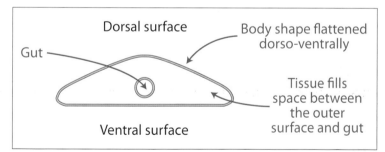

A generalised platyhelminth

Platyhelminthes have much more tissue than cnidarians – they have a tube-like gut rather than a gut cavity (enteron) as in cnidarians. This means that solid tissue fills the space between the outer surface and the gut. While all this tissue allows specialisation to take place, it also means that there are many cells per unit volume involved in metabolic activity. This means that there are high demands for oxygen and other metabolites. The **dorso-ventral flattening** of flatworms increases the **surface area to volume ratio**. The dorso-ventral flattening has two major advantages:

- It increases the uptake of oxygen (due to the high SA : V ratio).
- It decreases the diffusion distance from the body surface to body cells.

Platyhelminthes have a **single opening to the gut**. This means that the remains of food are passed out through the same body opening through which it enters.

Note 1: Most platyhelminthes are aquatic free-living flatworms (for example Planaria) but some are highly adapted parasites (for example the liver fluke).

Note 2: Although the surrounding aqueous medium provides support for most platyhelminthes, the cells between the outer surface and the gut provide support through acting as 'packing' tissue.

Note 3: It can be difficult to explain the difference between radial and bilateral symmetry. **Radial symmetry** means there is symmetry around a central axis – there is no left or right 'side'. The body can be divided into two halves **by any plane** that goes through the central axis, ie the organism is round in cross-section. **Bilateral symmetry** means that the body can be divided into two **identical halves / mirror images** on each side of a single central axis – there are **left** and **right** 'sides'. The two halves are mirror images of each other (but only on either side of the central axis).

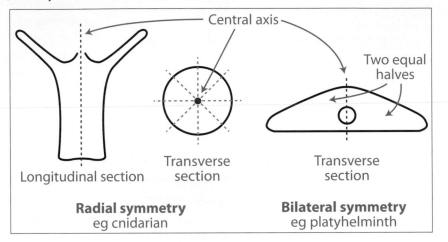

Radial and bilateral symmetry

Phylum Annelida

Annelids include the earthworm and the lugworm. They are also known as round worms as they are much more **rounded in cross-section** compared to the platyhelminthes and are **bilaterally symmetrical**.

Annelids have **spaces** within the tissue that lies between the body surface and the gut. These spaces are collectively called a coelom.

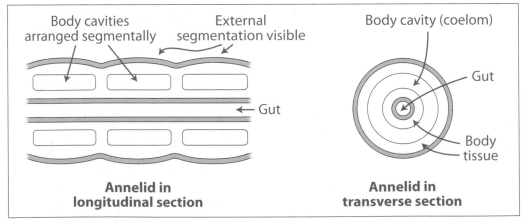

Annelid in longitudinal and transverse section

Note: The cross-section on the right (transverse section) has been taken through a section of the worm where there is a body cavity present.

There are a number of advantages in possessing a coelom (spaces) within the body:

- **The ratio of surface area to metabolically active tissue is increased**. This is largely why annelids can be round in TS – there is not the same requirement to maximise surface area to volume ratio for respiratory purposes.

- As the spaces are fluid-filled, it can function as a very effective **hydrostatic skeleton**.

- The muscles involved with **locomotion** are separated from the **gut muscles**. This allows movement of the organism and peristaltic gut movements to occur independently.

- It provides room for the development of **organs**.

Annelids are **metamerically segmented** meaning that the body is divided into (usually) a large number of structurally similar segments, each with its own body cavity. Most of the segments are similar in structure with their own cavities. As the photograph below shows, annelids have a blood system and a simple nerve system.

Earthworm, transverse section

© Dr Keith Wheeler / Science Photo Library / Z195/0131

Annelids have a **one-way gut** with a **separate mouth** and **anus.** This allows **regional specialisation** and prevents food waste following digestion being mixed up with incoming food. Within the gut there is a muscular pharynx (adjacent to the mouth), an oesophagus, a crop (storage area), a muscular gizzard (for mechanical digestion) and an intestine for absorption.

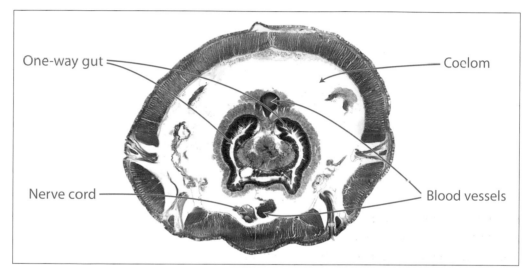

One-way gut — Coelom

Nerve cord — Blood vessels

Note 1: The earthworm is on the left of the photograph.

Note 2: If you look carefully you will see evidence of (metameric) segmentation in several of the worms.

Note 3: The annelid second from left has been partially dissected showing the specialisation of gut regions.

Note 4: The smaller oval worm (sea mouse) on the top right does not look worm-like in appearance but is an annelid as it has the diagnostic characteristics of the phylum (some of which have been covered in this section).

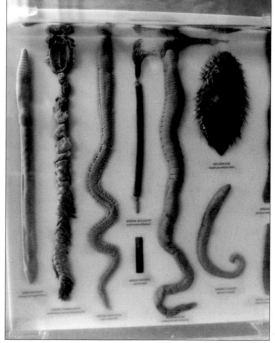

Some preserved annelids

Phylum Arthropoda

Arthropods such as insects and spiders are **bilaterally symmetrical** and typically have a **fixed number of metameric segments** in each region of the body (for example, the head, thorax and abdomen of insects). Typically insects have three segments in the thorax and 10–11 in the abdomen. They also have **jointed limbs**, typically three pairs, one pair on each segment of the thorax and an **exoskeleton**.

As with the annelids there is both a mouth and an anus and the gut shows regional specialisation.

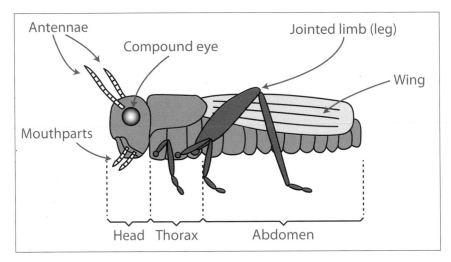

A 'typical' insect

Arachnids (spiders), as with insects, are bilaterally symmetrical and have a fixed number of metameric segments. However, they have four pairs of legs rather than three and their body has two main sections (rather than the three in insects). In spiders, the head and thorax are combined to form the cephalothorax.

Arthropods, and in particular insects, are the most successful animal group on Earth. There are more species of insects and more insects in total than any other group. This is largely because the basic insect body plan can, in evolutionary terms, be easily adapted (modified) to fill a wide range of niches.

Spiders are arachnids
Image courtesy of
Ronnie Irvine

For example, insect mouthparts have evolved for chewing (eg locusts), piercing skin (eg mosquitoes) or plant material (eg aphids), sucking fluids (eg houseflies) and many variations of these themes. Many insects have wings for flight and many species have separate distinct body forms, such as larval (eg caterpillars) and adult forms that have separate food sources.

Caterpillars feeding on ragwort plants

The photographs below show some of the many themes that have evolved in insects.

Variation in insects
Images courtesy of
Ronnie Irvine

Phylum Chordata

Vertebrates (animals with backbones) are chordates. The main groups within the Chordata are the fish, amphibians, reptiles, birds and mammals.

Chordates are **bilaterally symmetrical** and **segmented**.

Note: Segmentation can be described as a linear series of repeating units. While segmentation is obvious in the annelids and arthropods, it is much more subtle in the chordates. It is most obvious in the chordates in the vertebrae and rib bones.

The body cavity is much greater in extent proportionally and more continuous than in annelids and contains much more extensively developed and complex organs which are usually organised into complex systems, for example digestive, circulatory, excretory and reproductive.

In vertebrates there is a **vertebral (spinal) column** with **segmented muscle blocks**, with the skeleton consisting of an **internal jointed system of calcified bones**.

Note: In non-vertebrate chordates (a very small group of relatively rare animals), which in terms of evolutionary development are a bridge between the invertebrates and the vertebrates, there is a stiff dorsal rod (notochord) instead of a true backbone (vertebrate column).

Chordates have a **one-way gut** with both a mouth and an anus. There is a high degree of regional specialisation along the length of the gut.

Evolutionary trends in the Kingdom Animalia

The sequence from the Cnidarians, through the Platyhelminthes, Annelida and Arthropoda to the Chordata shows a number of evolutionary trends including:

- The gradation from **radial symmetry** (cnidarians) to **bilateral symmetry** (other phyla). Radial symmetry gives sessile organisms living in the open the opportunity to obtain food from all directions but it has many limitations. Bilateral symmetry allows streamlining to develop and the development of an anterior (and posterior) end that is more suitable for movement and allows for the concentration of sensory receptors (sense organs) that can test out the environment in front of the organism.

- The gradation from solid tissue between the body surface and the gut lining to the **presence of cavities** that reduce the amount of metabolically active tissue per unit volume.

- The development of **metameric segmentation** in annelids, arthropods and chordates.

- The development of a **one-way gut** as opposed to a gut cavity (cnidarians) or a gut with only one opening (platyhelminthes).

Practical work

Use living examples, preserved specimens, preserved slides and photographs to study the groups covered in this chapter.

One of the designated practical tasks for A2 is a dissection. This could be one or two systems in a small mammal or a fish, for example, a mouse or dogfish. Insect mouthparts also provide a suitably challenging dissection.

Plant material can be used providing the task is suitably complex. An example is to make a leaf scrape of a grass leaf to isolate an epidermal layer for viewing under the light microscope. A suitable procedure for this is described below:

1. Lie a blade of grass flat on a microscope slide.

2. Irrigate the slide with water using a drop pipette.

3. Using a safety blade (single edge blade with a reinforced back) vertically, gently sweep the blade along the top of the grass removing tissue from along its length.

4. Repeat with the blade always coming from the same direction and adding water as necessary to reduce friction.

5. When enough layers of the leaf have been removed, the green colouring will disappear, as only the epidermal layer is left.

6. Examine the epidermal layer under a microscope. You should be able to see epidermal cells, stomata and possibly leaf hairs.

Note 1: This activity works well if the razor is swept evenly and gently but relatively quickly across the leaf blade. Try not to be too 'exact'. It is also better if only small amounts are removed during each 'sweep'.

Note 2: If parts of the leaf appear colourless and other parts green, this is because in some parts not all of the mesophyll has been removed (as this contains chlorophyll).

Exam question

1. (a) The distribution of two plant groups, mosses and flowering plants, was investigated along a 50 metre transect from grassland to the edge of a pond. At 5 metre intervals, the percentage cover of mosses and flowering plants was determined. The soil moisture level was also measured at each sampling point. The results are shown graphically below.

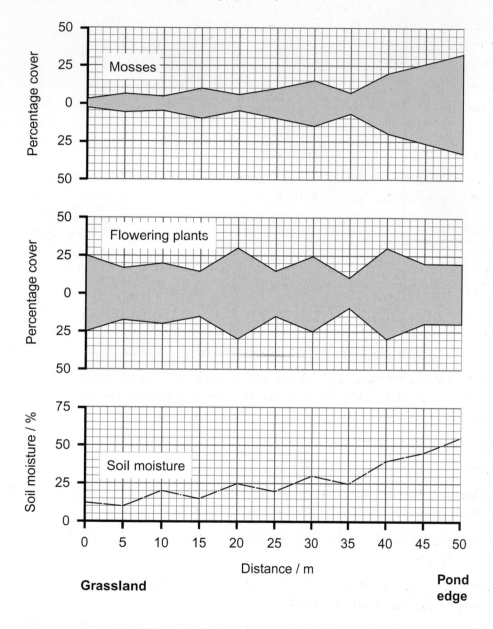

(i) Describe the relationship between the distribution of each plant group and soil moisture levels. [2]

(ii) With reference to the ability of mosses and flowering plants to regulate water loss, suggest explanations for the distribution shown. [3]

(b) Ethanol production in three of the species of moss identified (A, B and C) at the pond edge was investigated. A number of ethanol readings was taken from the soil water in the immediate vicinity of each moss species and the mean was calculated for each species.

Mean ethanol production (with 95% confidence limits) by the three species of mosses is shown in the bar chart below.

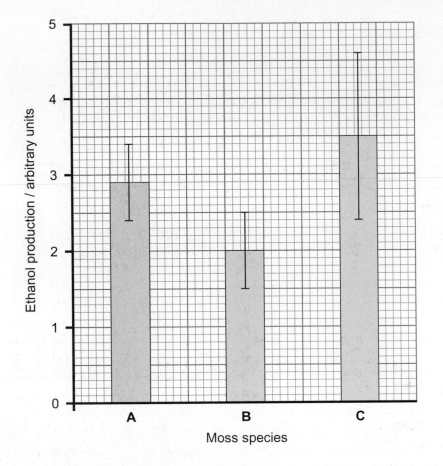

(i) Explain why the mosses produced ethanol. [2]

(ii) The mean levels of ethanol produced by the three species may not be significantly different. Give evidence from the graph which supports this statement. [1]

(iii) Based on the data provided, it is not possible to indicate if the difference in ethanol production between species has a genetic origin.

Suggest how you could experimentally confirm if the difference in ethanol production among the three species has a genetic basis, rather than a purely environmental basis. [2]

Question taken from CCEA's Biology Assessment Unit A2 2, Biochemistry, Genetics and Evolutionary Trends, June 2014, © CCEA 2017

Chapter 15 – Statistics

It is important that students following the A2 course are able to use and interpret a range of statistical tools and tests. These include estimates of the standard deviation of the mean, confidence limits, the Student's test (*t*-test) and the chi-square test.

Statistical analysis is an important part of biology. It enables data to be analysed or compared in an **objective** way (as opposed to a subjective way) and therefore removes bias.

Biological data tends to be very variable and, due to this variation, it is not always easy to identify if differences between two sets of data indicate that real differences exist between the parameters being measured as opposed to the differences being due to random variation – the use of a statistical technique helps us do this.

Compare the information in the following graphs showing data of leaf length in oak. In Graph 1 it is very obvious that the samples A and B are different but this is less obvious in Graph 2.

Why can we be fairly sure that the two sets of data are **significantly different** in Graph 1 but less so in Graph 2?

Note: Significance is a key term in statistics. A significant difference is where the difference between data sets is due to more than random variation alone – ie the data sets are really different.

In Graph 1:

- the **mean** values are further apart.
- there is less **variability** within each sample.
- there is a larger **sample size**.

Not surprisingly, many statistical tests take into account the differences in mean between samples being compared, the variability of each sample and the size of each sample.

Note: A statistical test can tell us whether two samples are significantly different but it will not tell us the reason for the difference.

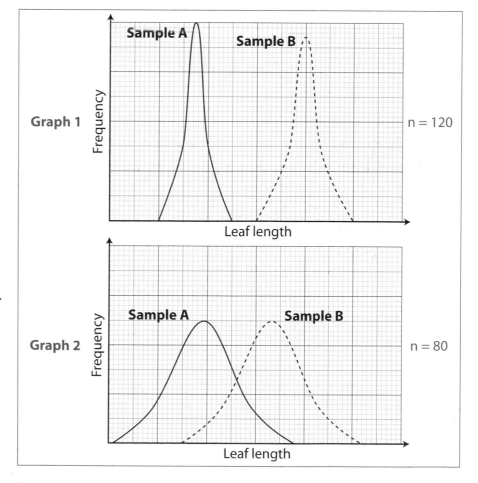

Note: The data in Graphs 1 and 2 (page 275) are **normally distributed**. This means that most individuals are close to the average or mean with relatively few having extreme values for the parameter being measured.

When planning a statistical investigation it is normal to establish a **null hypothesis (H_0)**. In the examples in Graphs 1 and 2 this could be written as:

The difference between mean leaf length in sample A and sample B is due to random variation and is not significant.

Note: When establishing a null hypothesis, the starting assumption is that there is no significant difference between the two sets of data being compared.

Some key terms and formulae

Sample mean (symbol $\bar{x}$) – The average or mean value of the sample under consideration.

Note: Although the mean is the parameter most used, and most useful, as a measure of central tendency, other measures include the mode (the most common value, for example, the tallest bar in a histogram) and the median (the value that is exactly midway between the highest value and the lowest, for example, the sixth highest of 11 measurements of height).

Standard deviation – A measure of the variability (spread) of the data. The standard deviation in a normally distributed sample is the value either side of the mean, between which 68% of all the values of the sample are trapped. If there is a lot of variability the standard deviation will be large, whereas if most values are grouped tightly around the mean, the standard deviation will be small.

If a data set has a mean of 14 and a standard deviation of 3, this means that 68% of the sample values lie between 11–17.

Note 1: Standard deviation ($\hat{\sigma}$) gives an indication of the data spread in a group of values (for example, a sample). If the standard deviation is based on a population sample, it does provide useful statistical information about the actual mean of the whole population.

Note 2: Variance ($\hat{\sigma}^2$) is another indicator of variability or spread in a group of values.

Samples and populations

It is important not to get confused between the **sample mean** (for example, the mean length of 30 leaves if that is what is being measured) and the **population mean** (for example, the mean length of all the leaves in that particular population of plants).

Quite often in biological investigations, we obtain a sample on the premise that it will be a reliable indicator of the entire population. The sample mean ($\bar{x}$) may or may not be close to the true population mean (μ) and it is important we get some indication of how close it is likely to be when using samples to compare populations.

The **standard deviation of the mean** (also called the **standard error**) with the symbol $\hat{\sigma}_{\bar{x}}$ can be calculated using the formula:

$$\hat{\sigma}_{\bar{x}} = \sqrt{\frac{\hat{\sigma}^2}{n}}$$

Note: $\hat{\sigma}^2$ is the best estimate of population variance and is calculated using the formula:

$$\hat{\sigma}^2 = \frac{\Sigma(x - \bar{x})^2}{n - 1}$$

The standard deviation of the mean gives a measure of how much, on average, the sample mean differs from the mean of the population as a whole. If the sample mean is truly representative of the population as a whole, the difference between the two values (the sample and population means) should be small. If the difference is small then, for statistical purposes, the mean of the sample is **reliable**. In effect, comparing the samples is a reliable way of comparing the populations.

Note 1: In a biological context, the term **reliable** means that if the data were collected again (or an experiment was repeated) the outcome would be similar.

Note 2: Not surprisingly, the formula for the standard deviation of the mean (page 276) takes into account both variability of data and the sample size.

95% confidence limits

The **standard deviation of the mean** gives us an indication of how close the sample mean and the population mean are likely to be. However, it is possible to use the standard deviation of the mean to give us another statistic that gives us the limits within which the true mean of the population almost certainly lies. It is not absolutely certain that the true population mean lies within these limits, but we can be 95% sure (ie 95 times out of 100 we will be correct).

95% confidence limits are provided by the formula: $\bar{x} \pm t(\hat{\sigma}_{\bar{x}})$

where t is determined from a table of t values at $p = 0.05$ and $n - 1$ degrees of freedom (n = sample size).

Statistical tables use probability levels, for example, between $p = 0.1$ (10% probability) and 0.001 (99.9% probability) rather than percentage probability. 95% probability is the $p = 0.05$ value. The table below summarises the different ways in which probability can be interpreted when comparing two samples.

Note: Confidence limits can be worked out for any level of probability but it is biological convention that 95% confidence limits are an appropriate statistical indicator in most investigations. If we are 95% sure that two data sets are different we can regard the difference as being significant.

p value	$p = 0.1$	0.05	0.02	0.01	0.002	0.001
Probability that result (for example, difference between means) is due to chance (ie random variation) only	10%	5%	2%	1%	0.2%	0.1%
Probability that result shows significant difference (for example, difference between means is significant)	90%	95%	98%	99%	99.8%	99.9%

Note: The critical probability values are highlighted in blue.

95% limits can be used in tables (often as a column immediately to the right of the mean values) but are particularly useful in graphs. The graph on the right shows the mean total leaf areas of wild garlic plants throughout the growing season in more open woodland (A) compared to those in a woodland with lower light levels (B) (due to shading by rhododendron).

As can be seen from the graph, the 95% limits of the samples taken during the growing season from the two populations (A and B) do not overlap. This strongly *suggests* that the two samples are significantly different. In general, if the 95% confidence limits of two (or more) samples do not overlap, we can be reasonably sure (but not certain – even at the 95% level of probability) that the samples are significantly (statistically) different.

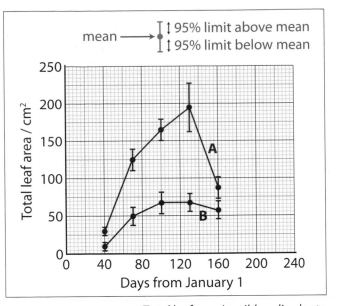

Total leaf area in wild garlic plants in different growing conditions

Note 1: As can be seen from the graph above, the 95% confidence limits are drawn both above and below the sample mean. This is because the 95% limit gives us information about how close the sample and population means are likely to be. It does not tell us whether the real population mean is likely to be higher or lower in value than the sample mean.

Note 2: 95% confidence limits are particularly valuable when comparing a number of sample means and determining which (if any) are likely to be statistically different from the others; for example, if we had been comparing a number of garlic populations with several samples taken at each time.

Worked example (95% confidence limits)

The mean leaf length of a **sample** of 20 ash leaves was 60 mm. The standard deviation (error) of the mean was calculated as being 1.433.

1. As the sample size was 20, the degrees of freedom (d.f.) is 19

2. The tabulated *t* value, at $p = 0.05$ and d.f. 19 = 2.093

3. 95% confidence limits = 2.093 × 1.433 = 3

4. We can conclude, at the 95% level of probability, that the mean of the **population** falls between 57–63 mm

    Note: In an exam question, if you are being expected to calculate 95% confidence limits you are likely to be given the standard deviation (error) of the mean, or an equivalent stage.

The *t*-test (Student's *t*-test)

The *t*-test is a more robust statistical procedure for comparing two sample means – it is a statistical test designed for that purpose. Sample means will invariably be different but the *t*-test allows you to determine if the difference is down to random chance or is significant (ie due to real differences between the two samples).

The formula for the t-test is: $\quad t = \dfrac{\bar{x}_1 - \bar{x}_2}{\sqrt{\hat{\sigma}_{\bar{x}_1}^2 + \hat{\sigma}_{\bar{x}_2}^2}}$

Note: In effect this is the difference between the sample means, divided by the square root of the sum of the squares of the standard deviation of the mean for each sample.

Once you obtain the value for the t-test it is important to determine if this value indicates that the difference between the means is significant. To do this there are a number of steps you must carry out:

- Work out the number of degrees of freedom. It is $(n_1 + n_2 - 2)$ where n_1 is the sample size in one sample and n_2 is the sample size in the other.

- Use a table of t values (Student's t values) to check where your calculated value for t is placed in terms of probability in the appropriate degrees of freedom row.

- Your value will almost always fit between two values in the appropriate row. The p values at the top of the table for the two rows, either side of the tabulated value, are the p values within which your value lies.

- Remember that $p = 0.05$ is the statistically significant cut off point in most biological experiments. A value of $p = 0.05$ means that there is a 5% chance that the difference between the means is down to random variation. More than 5% suggests that there is a reasonable chance that the variation is random. Less than 5% suggests that the possibility of the differences being down to random variation are so low that it is safe to conclude that the two samples are significantly different.

- If $p > 0.05$ (falls to the left of the p > 0.05 column in the table), the null hypothesis is accepted; if $p < 0.05$ (falls to the right of the 0.05 column), the null hypothesis is rejected.

p value (probability value)	Significance value	Explanation
$p > 0.05$ (greater than 0.05)	No evidence of significant difference between samples.	There is more than a 5% chance of the variation between the two samples being due to chance (random variation) – too high to suggest that the differences are significant.
$p < 0.05$	The samples are significantly different at the 95% level of significance.	There is less than a 5% chance of the variation between the two samples being due to chance (random variation) – a low enough value to suggest that the two samples are significantly different.

- Although the $p < 0.05$ is normally the cut off in determining if differences are significant in biological investigations, a greater degree of significance is often required in biological or medical research before drawing conclusions that two samples (or treatments) are actually different. The following table summarises the outcomes for different probability values.

p value (probability value)	Significance value	Explanation
$p > 0.05$ (greater than 0.05)	No evidence of significant difference between samples.	There is more than a 5% chance of the variation between the two samples being due to random variation – too high to suggest that the differences are significant.
$0.05 > p > 0.01$	The samples are significantly different at the 95% level of probability ($p = 0.05$) but not significantly different at the 99% level of probability ($p = 0.01$).	There is between a 5% and 1% chance of the variation between the two samples being due to random variation – a low enough value to suggest that the two samples are **significantly different**.
$0.01 > p > 0.001$	The samples are significantly different at the 99% level of probability ($p = 0.01$) but not significantly different at the 99.9% level of probability ($p = 0.001$).	There is between a 1% and 0.1% chance of the variation between the two samples being due to random variation – a low enough value to suggest that the two samples are **highly significantly different**.
$p < 0.001$	The samples are significantly different at the 99.9% level of probability ($p = 0.001$).	There is less than a 0.1% chance of the variation between the two samples being due to random variation – a low enough value to suggest that the two samples are **very highly significantly different**.

Note 1: It is convention to indicate significant difference at the 95% level of probability with an asterisk*; a highly significant difference as ** and a very highly significant difference as ***.

Note 2: A t-test will provide information as to whether two samples are statistically different or not. It will not tell you what has caused the difference if there is one.

Worked example (t-test)

The table below represents data concerning egg production per toad for two populations of toads in different rivers.

	Populations	
	A	B
Sample size (number of toads)	30	35
Mean (number of eggs per toad)	141	97
Standard deviation (error) of the mean	12.7	9.8

1. Formula: $t = \dfrac{\bar{x}_2 - \bar{x}_2}{\sqrt{\hat{\sigma}_{\bar{x}_1}^2 + \hat{\sigma}_{\bar{x}_2}^2}}$

2. $t = \dfrac{141 - 97}{\sqrt{12.7^2 + 9.8^2}}$

3. $t = \dfrac{44}{16.04}$

4. $t = 2.743$

5. $0.01 > p > 0.002$ (at 60 d.f. – closest value to 63)

6. The two samples are highly significantly different**.
   There is a (highly) significant difference between the mean number of eggs produced per toad in the two populations.

Note: In an exam question, it is usually enough to work out that the two samples are significantly different (or not).

The chi-square (x^2) test

In some investigations, it is not the issue of determining if the difference in samples (and populations) is significantly different but if the data fits an expected ratio. The chi-square test is an appropriate test to confirm if offspring ratios in genetic crosses fit an expected ratio.

You will be familiar with the common genetic ratios (for example, 3 : 1 and 9 : 3 : 3 : 1) but actual offspring ratios very seldom match the ratios exactly in reality. The chi-square can provide information as to whether any deviation from the expected numbers is significant (at a given, invariably 95%, level of probability).

In the chi-square it is important to work out the expected frequencies, based on the data presented and then carry out a series of calculations based on the expected and the observed data. It is normal to construct a table as shown on page 283 in the worked example.

Once the calculated x^2 value is worked out, it is then necessary to refer to the appropriate statistical table (x^2) using the appropriate degrees of freedom (number of classes minus 1; for example when carrying out a test on a 9 : 3 : 3 : 1 ratio there would be 3 degrees of freedom as there are 4 categories).

As with the t-test, check where the calculated x^2 value fits between two tabulated values in the table columns. The two probability values at the top of the table show the probability range within which the tabulated value lies. If the calculated value lies to the right of the 0.05 level this means that there is more than a 95% chance that the observed data does not fit the expected ratio, ie the deviation from the expected data is too great (to confirm the expected ratio). However, if the calculated value lies to the left of the 0.05 column ($p > 0.05$), then the difference between the observed and expected values is not significant and the predicted ratio holds based on the data available.

Worked example (chi-square test)

The photograph below shows a maize (corn) cob. Each kernel (seed-like structure), represents a single fruit, each of which contains a single seed. The photograph shows that in this particular cob, the fruits (seeds) differ both in terms of colour (purple or white) and shape (smooth or wrinkled).

Individual fruits (seeds)

Maize (corn) cob

Each seed is a consequence of a single fertilisation event. Consequently each seed on the cob is equivalent to a single offspring in terms of working out genetic offspring ratios.

The photograph below shows a close up of the same cob with a section of the cobs highlighted.

White and smooth   Purple and wrinkled

White and wrinkled   Purple and smooth

Close up of maize (corn) cob

When working out offspring ratios in maize, it is probably not practical to count all the kernels so a section should be sampled at random, for example, the kernels within the yellow outline in the photograph.

The kernels within the sample identified can be (approximately) grouped as:

purple and smooth	53
purple and wrinkled	20
white and smooth	19
white and wrinkled	4
Total	**96**

Based on this data it is logical to conclude that the kernels sampled represent a dihybrid ratio of **9 : 3 : 3 : 1**, the consequence of a cross between two maize plants each heterozygous for both kernel colour and shape.

The **null hypothesis** is that there is no significant difference between the observed and expected offspring numbers, ie the results are a good fit to a 9 : 3 : 3 : 1 ratio.

Category	O	E	(O–E)	(O–E)²	$\frac{(O-E)^2}{E}$
purple colour smooth coat	53	54	–1	1	0.02
purple colour wrinkled coat	20	18	2	4	0.22
white colour smooth coat	19	18	1	1	0.06
white colour wrinkled coat	4	6	–2	4	0.67

$$x^2 = 0.97$$

As there are 4 categories (classes), there are **3** degrees of freedom.

Using the table of x^2 values and 3 d.f. a value of 0.97 gives a probability of
0.9 > p > 0.5

This means that there is more than a 5% chance (based on tabulated values somewhere between 90% and 50%) that the deviation between the expected and the observed results is due to chance (random variation). Therefore, the 9 : 3 : 3 : 1 ratio stands and the null hypothesis is accepted.

The chi-square statistical test can also be used in a non-genetics setting. For example, if investigating the percentage germination in three varieties of seed, the assumption can be made that percentage germination will be the same for each variety – the expected column will therefore be the mean percentage germination across the three varieties. The observed will be the data in terms of percentage germination in the three varieties.

The **null hypothesis** could be that there is no significant difference in percentage germination among the three varieties.

Exam questions

Questions testing statistics have been incorporated into the relevant A2 2 chapters.

Copyright

Copyright has been acknowledged to the best of our ability. If there are any inadvertent errors or omissions, we shall be happy to correct them in any future editions.

Acknowledgements

Questions from CCEA Biology Past Papers, 2011–16 are included with the permission of the Northern Ireland Council for the Curriculum, Examinations and Assessment, © CCEA 2017.

Credits